JET
The Story of a Pioneer

Sir Frank Whittle
K.B.E., C.B., F.R.S.

JET

Published by Sapere Books.
24 Trafalgar Road, Ilkley, LS29 8HH
United Kingdom

saperebooks.com

First published by Frederick Muller Ltd, 1953.

ISBN: 978-1-80055-709-3.

TABLE OF CONTENTS

PREFACE

This book is not an autobiography. It is primarily the history of my association with the development of the turbo-jet engine in Great Britain. I have included a very brief account of my life prior to my practical work on the turbo-jet engine, in order that the reader may have some idea of the nature of the soil in which the seed of an idea took root and flourished. I have been unable to resist the temptation to include a certain amount of "There I was, upside down, nothing on the clock, and still climbing" sort of thing, partly because I hope it will help to lighten a somewhat heavy theme, and partly because I do not like people to forget that at one time I had some skill as a pilot. This material is not entirely irrelevant, because I have always held that my experiences as a pilot contributed immensely to my work on the jet engine.

This is not a technical book — or at least it is not intended to be — and I hope that it will be reasonably comprehensible to the lay reader. The nature of the subject, of course, makes it necessary to include a small amount of technical matter, but I have done my best to keep this down to an absolute minimum, yet I still feel a little uneasy lest it should fall between two stools — too non-technical for the engineer and scientist and a little too technical for the lay reader. I have been too close to the technicalities of my work for too long for it to be possible for me to see the book from the lay readers' point of view. My attempt to keep the book non-technical has another disadvantage — our long and bitter struggles with engineering problems receive far less prominence in the narrative than would be appropriate in a balanced history, and the reader may well get the impression that I spent far more time arguing, and writing controversial letters than working on the engine development itself. This, of course, is quite wrong — the truth is that by far the greater proportion of my time was concerned with engine design, manufacture, testing, analysis of test results, and many other engineering aspects of the development. Perhaps some day it may be possible to write a detailed technical history to supplement the present record. Those who would like to know more of that part of the story now are referred to the First James Clayton Lecture which I delivered to the Institution of Mechanical Engineers on October 5th, 1945, entitled "The Early History of the Whittle Jet Propulsion Gas Turbine."[1]

The writing of this book serves many purposes. Firstly, I hope that the act of writing it will serve to free me from the painful emotions which recollection of much of what I now place on record still evokes. Another object is to correct a number of incorrect statements which have appeared in the Press and elsewhere from time to time. A third and very important object is to put on record the major contributions to Britain's present lead in the turbo-jet engine field of such men as R. Dudley Williams and J. C. B. Tinling and others whose valuable work has been too much overlooked hitherto.

Apart from these special reasons for writing the book, I think it is in the public interest that this history should be published, because it concerns the expenditure of large sums of public money and records many things (including many mistakes) which may provide useful lessons for the future.

It has not been easy for me to place on record facts which suggest that mistakes were made by certain individuals for whom I retain a considerable liking and respect. This is particularly true of Lord Tedder and Sir Henry Tizard. I hope these distinguished gentlemen will forgive me, and will understand that at no time did I ever question the sincerity of their motives or under-value their always friendly attitude towards myself. In any case, I have made it clear that they were primarily responsible for the important decisions favourable to the continuation of work on the jet engine at a time when many of their advisers were still sceptical, and this factor alone should more than counter-balance the less favourable parts of the record. I would not wish to detract from their justifiably great reputations, and I do not think this is likely if readers bear in mind that the turbo-jet development was but a small section of their many and heavy responsibilities at a time of great urgency. I feel sure that they would now agree with much of what I say. In this connection I recall a small but significant incident when the then Minister of Supply, the Rt. Hon. G. R. Strauss, was presenting the W.1 engine to the Science Museum, South Kensington. Lord Tedder was sitting in the front row of the audience, while I was on the platform behind the Minister. When, during his speech, the Minister implied that the development owed much to the generous help and wise policies of the Ministries concerned, Lord Tedder gave me a very meaning wink which seemed to say far more plainly than words "You and I could tell a very different story". I was hard put to it to maintain the gravity which the occasion demanded.

The foregoing remarks apply to a lesser extent to a number of other individuals.

I have been extremely careful to ensure that I can substantiate fully every allegation I make, and that where I have made, or implied, criticisms, I have done so confident in the belief that it is in the public interest to do so.

The main history really ends with my resignation from the Board of Power Jets (R. & D.) Limited and the break-up of the pioneer team early in 1946, but I feel that many people would be disappointed if I did not give some account of certain important events which took place after that date. I have therefore included these in a short epilogue.

I have relied very little on memory except in that part of the record which relates to my life up to the year 1936, but even there I have had the assistance of my flying logbook and a few diaries. After 1936 I kept very careful diaries, notes of telephone conversations, copies of letters and many other records and it is on these that the greater part of this history is based.

I have been working on this book at intervals over a number of years. The original text of over 250,000 words was far too long. I cut it down to about 180,000 words by the sacrifice of much biographical material, including some of my favourite anecdotes — originally inserted to give the reader what I hoped would be a little light refreshment now and then. When I was advised that the book was still far too long, and that it should be cut down to less than 110,000 words if possible, a further drastic pruning and much re-writing were necessary. This involved the deletion of much material not directly concerned with the main course of development at Power Jets. It has to be remembered, therefore, that this record is now an account of that section of jet development in Great Britain with which the writer was most intimately connected, and does not claim to be a balanced history of all the British effort in this sphere. Indeed, certain important aspects of Power Jets' work have not been described where they had no influence on the development of the simple jet engine. Thus, for example, no reference is made to the considerable volume of work by Power Jets on the "ducted fan" form of aircraft gas turbine, though this may well come to be a widely-used type of power plant in the future.

I have never made any claim to literary skill, and I hope that I shall be forgiven for many shortcomings in style. For me, writing is always a very laborious business and I sincerely hope that this is not too obvious in the narrative.

August, 1953.

CHAPTER 1

When the first official announcement about British and American work on jet propulsion was made in January, 1944, one of the national newspapers published a photograph of myself as a child of four holding a toy aeroplane. That photograph now seems to have been far more symbolic of the future than my father could possibly have realised when he took it. The toy was one of my presents for Christmas 1911, and it is one of the few things of that time of my life that I can remember fairly clearly.

Whether that toy was the starting point of my interest in aircraft or whether it was given to me because I was already interested I don't remember, but it is linked in my mind with memories of occasional flights over Coventry at about that time by one or two early aviators. Flying, of course, was then still in its infancy. Only eight years had then elapsed since the Wright Brothers made their historic flights at Kitty Hawk N. Carolina (December, 1903).

My parents had been brought up in the typical Lancashire working-class background of those days — a very hard life by modern standards. After their marriage they moved to Coventry where I, their first child, was born on June 1st, 1907. Our home was one of a row of working-class houses in the Earlsdon district.

There is no doubt that such engineering and inventive abilities as I possess were inherited from my father, who was a very prolific inventor and skilful mechanic. I grew up in an atmosphere of invention. On Sundays, especially, my father would usually be at work on some new idea and I was soon familiar with the drawing-board, T-square and other implements of the draughtsman.

Unfortunately for him, my father, who had to go to work in the cotton mills at the age of eleven, never had the advantages which later educational reforms made possible for me, otherwise he might well have become a distinguished engineer.

In 1916 the family moved to Leamington Spa because my father had — by dint of saving and borrowing — purchased a small engineering business known as the Leamington Valve and Piston Ring Company. The little factory was far less imposing than its name, and for a time my father worked in it practically on his own. It was while helping him that I first acquired practical experience of certain manufacturing processes, when I was only about ten years old. At first I was given such simple jobs to do as the drilling of valve stems, but later graduated to lathe work. For this help I received small sums on a piecework basis.

My first six years of school life were spent at council schools in Coventry and Leamington, but at the age of eleven I succeeded in gaining a scholarship to a secondary school which later became Leamington College. Nobody could have been more surprised than I was at this achievement.

The first year at my new school was extraordinarily inconsistent. At the end of the first term I was bottom of Form IIIA and was "demoted" to IIIB. This disgrace provoked me out of a natural laziness and I succeeded in getting back to IIIA by being top of the form at the end of the second term. At the end of the year I gained another scholarship which earned me a money grant of £10 a year. Thereafter I relaxed and settled down to four years undistinguished by any form of scholastic achievement, chiefly because of an extreme dislike of homework.

My attitude towards the work in the school curriculum was one of trying to scrape through with the least possible effort, but this was not characteristic of my attitude towards learning in general. In school the only subject in which I took any real interest was chemistry, but outside school I was a voracious reader of popular science books and often spent many hours in the Leamington Spa reference library reading up such subjects as astronomy, physiology, engineering (particularly aircraft engineering) and exploring many other fields of knowledge not catered for in school.

Had the headmaster and his colleagues realised what a useful amount of knowledge I was acquiring out of school, they might have been more tolerant towards the results of my official studies.

In the light of subsequent history, it is of significance that it was during my school days that I first became interested in turbines. But elementary textbooks on the theory of flight and practical flying were the chief subjects of my private study — so much so that I remember feeling quite sure that I knew enough about the subject to fly an aeroplane without going through the formality of being taught.

But when I attempted to join the Royal Air Force as an aircraft apprentice at Halton at the end of 1922 I met with a setback. I passed the written examination with flying colours, but failed the medical examination because, being only five feet tall, I was considered to be under-sized.

I was bitterly disappointed and also very surprised, because I had always been a very active child and had something of a reputation amongst my companions for rather dangerous activities — such as running along bridge parapets and emulating my simian ancestors up trees — which would not have been possible without a combination of wiriness, strong nerve and a good sense of balance.

Before being sent back home, I made several unsuccessful attempts to have my case reconsidered. My persistence, however, was not entirely wasted. A physical training instructor, Sergeant Holmes, took pity on me and gave me a list of exercises and showed me how to do them. He also wrote out a diet sheet.

During the next few months I carried out Sergeant Holmes's instructions to the letter and the treatment was effective. In six months I added three inches to my height and three inches to my chest measurement.

But for a time it seemed as though my efforts were to be in vain. When I applied to take the medical examination again, I was told that I could not be allowed a second chance. It appeared that it was a case of "once rejected, always rejected".

After further unsuccessful attempts to have my case reconsidered, I hit upon the ruse of starting all over again as though I had never previously applied. I got away with it, and this time was successful in both the written and the medical examinations, and so found myself in the Royal Air Force at last, having got in under false pretences in a sense.

I became one of about 600 apprentices of the September, 1923, Entry at Cranwell.

CHAPTER 2

I cannot pretend that I enjoyed my three years as an aircraft apprentice, but I undoubtedly received a very fine training as an aircraft mechanic. I was trained as a rigger for metal aircraft — at that time a new trade, because aircraft with metal structure were a comparatively recent innovation. Our time was largely divided between workshops and school, but several hours a week were also devoted to drills and physical training.

My dislike of the strict discipline and barrack-room life was tempered by my association with the Model Aircraft Society to which I devoted hundreds of hours, often when I should have been elsewhere.

It would be difficult to over-emphasise the importance of the Model Aircraft Society on my subsequent career, partly because of the absorption of the large amount of aircraft engineering knowledge which went with it, and partly because my abilities in model making compensated in the eyes of authority for certain shortcomings in other directions. There is little doubt that my model work had much to do with the fact that I was one of the five apprentices to be awarded cadetships at the R.A.F. College (also at Cranwell) at the end of my three years' apprenticeship.

The highlight in connection with my model work was the making of a large model of ten feet six inches wingspan powered by a two-stroke petrol engine. I headed the small team which worked on this ambitious project and was responsible for the design of the airframe, the drawings, wooden jigs for the construction of the delicate wing ribs and other parts of the structure, and the fabric covering. The engine was made by a laboratory assistant who was a very skilful mechanic. Only the miniature sparking plugs, of which we purchased two, were not made by us.

The model was completed about two or three weeks before the passing out was due, and it was an exciting moment when we assembled it outside the workshop and gave the engine its first run mounted in the model. The big question was: would it fly? Alas, we never found out, because when we were towing it to the aerodrome to give it its first (and perhaps only) flight test, our route took us past the C.O.'s office. The C.O. — Wing Commander R. J. F. Barton — came out and asked us to postpone the first flight until passing-out day, when the Under Secretary of State for Air, Sir Philip Sassoon, would be present to see it fly. Unfortunately, when the day arrived, the two sparking plugs let us down badly. The first one failed during an engine test early in the morning, and the second failed when we were running up the engine in preparation for the first flight and in the presence of a very distinguished audience, and so no flight was possible. Possibly my strong prejudice against piston engines dates from this event.

No further opportunity to fly the model ever occurred because on the day following we all went on leave. We were bitterly disappointed, especially Westbury, the maker of the engine, who expressed his feelings by removing the engine and taking it home.

Though the model never flew, it was by no means a wasted effort so far as I was concerned, because I believe it had much to do with the fact that I was recommended for a cadetship.

My cadetship was very nearly a near miss, because five were to be awarded and I passed out sixth. Unfortunately for him, but fortunately for me, the apprentice who had passed out top failed his medical examination and so I just scraped in.

It is not for me to comment on the quality of Robert Barton's judgment, beyond stating the fact that four of the five he selected passed out in the first seven from the R.A.F. College, and all, except one, who was killed in a flying accident, have since attained high rank.

No words of mine would be adequate to convey my delight at my good fortune. The future looked very bright. Commissioned rank was in sight, but above all, I was to become a pilot. On many successive Saturday mornings I had stood in the ranks of the Apprentices' Wing at the West Camp Colour Hoisting Parade and had watched the Cadet Wing marching on to parade with envious eyes. To me there was nothing more desirable than to become one of their number. In my mind's eye I often see the Cadet Wing as I saw them then, marching with guard-like precision, setting a standard of smartness which was an example to everybody else on parade.

The magnitude of the "step up" associated with the award of a cadetship was, perhaps, best illustrated by a small incident a few hours before I went on leave for the last time from the Apprentices' Wing. I encountered the Squadron Sergeant Major who was convinced that I had a long record of undetected crime and who had tried to catch me out many times. He gave me a look which would be hard to describe, and growled "I suppose next time I see you I shall have to stand to attention and say 'Sir'." I deemed it wise to make no comment and just responded with a happy grin. Fortunately, such a situation, which would have been mutually embarrassing, never arose.

CHAPTER 3

Today the R.A.F. College is housed in a splendid block of buildings at the western end of the R.A.F. Station, Cranwell, but during my time as a Flight Cadet[2] we were housed in a series of temporary huts which had been erected during the First World War.

The Cadet Wing was divided into two squadrons, "A" and "B" — I was a member of "B" Squadron.

As the Course lasted for two years and there were entries every six months there were four "terms", each about thirty strong and equally divided between the two squadrons.

Young as it was in 1926 the R.A.F. College had evolved a number of deeply-rooted customs. Members of each term tended to keep very much to themselves, and the gap in status between the members of the different terms was remarkably wide. First termers were, of course, the lowest of the low, and the slightest breach of etiquette could bring down fearful retribution from the members of the senior terms.

For the first two weeks of term, pending the completion of uniforms, the prescribed dress for first termers was dark lounge suits and bowler hats. During this period the Cadet Wing always looked a little odd marching on parade with one quarter of their number dressed thus. The bowler hats were natural targets for the members of the senior terms, and it was not unusual to see the somewhat ludicrous sight of the first term marching heads up, swinging their arms, chest out, and so on, but with battered bowler hats, some with their crowns almost detached and flopping up and down in rhythm with the step. We were naturally very thankful when the time came to discard these emblems of our very junior status.

We were paid seven shillings a day, and for those who were reasonably careful this was ample to live on.

The training syllabus of the Cadet College was directed towards turning out General Duties Officers, and so the curriculum included a very wide range of subjects of which, in our eyes, flying instruction was by far the most important.

A substantial part of our time was spent in school. As in the Apprentices' Wing, school subjects were broadly divided into two groups — humanistics, comprising English literature and history; and science subjects, comprising physics, mathematics, mechanics and theory of flight.

In the workshops we received courses in every branch of workshop practice associated with the repair and maintenance of aircraft. The range covered was much wider than for an apprentice, but it was of necessity much more superficial. Nevertheless, it was very valuable training.

Apart from school and workshops, many other forms of Service knowledge were imparted in lecture courses on navigation, signals, meteorology, Air Force Law, armament, organisation and so on.

It was a very full life. Apart from the wide range of training already outlined, there was drill instruction, physical training, rifle practice and compulsory games.

Often the day's programme would take us up to dinnertime — dinner itself was a parade. This often meant a fearful scramble, especially when, as often happened, there was very little time to bathe and change into mess kit before the dinner roll call.

As a flight cadet I made one or two half-hearted attempts to continue my interest in model aircraft, but the very full programme gave very little time for hobbies. Also, and more important, model-making had been an outlet for my interest in flying and such an outlet was no longer necessary. It paled into insignificance compared with the real thing.

Fencing was the means by which I satisfied the compulsory games requirement. I enjoyed this sport and became moderately proficient with the foil, sabre and épée, but though several times selected as a member of the College team, I did not succeed in gaining my colours, chiefly I think because in matches I failed to perform in accordance with my usual standard. As soon as it became important to win, it had an inhibiting effect and I was afflicted with a kind of stage fright which caused me to become self-conscious and over-anxious.

In connection with our instruction in scientific subjects, we had to write a thesis each term. During my fourth term I chose as my subject "Future Developments in Aircraft Design". This task was really the starting point of my subsequent work on jet propulsion. In the course of its preparation I came to the conclusion that if very high speeds were to be combined with long range, it would be necessary to fly at very great heights where the low air density would greatly reduce resistance in proportion to speed. I was thinking in terms of speeds of 500 miles per hour at heights where the air density was less than one quarter of its sea level value. The top speed of R.A.F. fighters in those days was about 150 m.p.h.

It seemed to me unlikely that the conventional piston engine and propeller combination would meet the power plant needs of the kind of high-speed, high-altitude aircraft I had in mind, and so, in my discussion of power plant, I cast my net very wide and discussed the possibilities of rocket propulsion and of gas turbines driving propellers, but it did not then occur to me to use the gas turbine for jet propulsion.

The periods allotted for flying instruction were comparatively few and were often a "washout" due to weather, and so it was not until my second term that I first flew solo after a total of eight hours' dual instruction on the Avro 504K. The rest of my flying training at Cranwell was spread over the Avro 504N, Bristol Fighter, the D.H.9A and the Armstrong Whitworth Siskin. (The Siskin was a single-seater fighter.)

Most of us who learned to fly in the Avro 504K have affectionate memories of that old stager. It had a Monosoupape rotary engine (i.e. the whole engine rotated round a fixed crank shaft), and for this reason was generally known as the Mono-Avro. One marked characteristic was the strong smell of the castor oil which was ejected with the exhaust from the rotating cylinders. The engine was not controlled by a throttle in the normal sense, but by a device known as a "fine adjustment". In effect, it had only two speeds — "Stop" and "Go". To cut down the power, one had to cut the ignition in and out at short intervals with a thumb switch on top of the control column (the "blip" switch). It quite often happened that one forgot to take one's thumb off the "blip" switch in time to catch the engine before it stopped entirely and then, unless one were high enough to start it again by diving (thus forcing the propeller to "windmill"), it meant a rather hurried forced landing.

Occasionally the Mono engine would throw a cylinder off entirely; at other times the engine would catch fire in the air, but despite these hazards, serious accidents due to the nature of the engine were comparatively rare.

My early solo flights were marked by one or two incidents. After three and a half hours solo I had engine failure, but being within easy range of the aerodrome I was able to land safely. A few weeks later I was less fortunate. I got lost in conditions of poor visibility and landed to find out where I was. On taking off again, I struck a tree on the boundary of the field, and the aeroplane was totally wrecked. However, I escaped without injury. Many of my fellows took some convincing that I had not wrecked the aeroplane to avoid the annual cross-country run — a very unpopular event with everybody.

A curious thing about my flying training was that while learning to fly the Bristol fighter I became afflicted with a sudden loss of confidence, possibly because I was over-sensitive to the bad language and intemperate criticism of a short-tempered instructor. However, after some aptitude tests and wise counsel from a medical officer I swung to the other extreme, so much so that I was disqualified for dangerous flying in the competition for the flying prize at the end of the two years. This last no doubt influenced the final entry in my logbook as a Cadet. Under the heading "Any special faults in flying that must be watched" there was an entry in red ink reading: "Over-confidence. This is most marked. He gives aerobatics too much value and has neglected accuracy. Must learn to discipline his flying. Inclined to perform to gallery and flies too low." My proficiency on Siskins was assessed as "Exceptional to above average".

It has been often wrongly stated that I was the first pilot in the R.A.F. to perform the manoeuvre known as a "bunt", i.e. the first half of an outside loop. The most I can claim is that I was the first cadet to do it, and may possibly have been the first to do it in other than a training type of aircraft. I believe it was bunting in a Siskin from a height of 1,500 feet that caused the judges to disqualify me in the flying prize competition, yet, in my own defence, I must add that this was in accordance with a programme agreed with my Squadron Commander.

My two years as a Flight Cadet ended in July, 1928. I passed out second and received the Abdy Gerrard Fellowes Memorial Prize for Aeronautical Sciences. My flying time amounted to 80 hours and 10 minutes.

CHAPTER 4

In due course I received notification of my posting to 111 Fighter Squadron at Hornchurch, and reported there as a brand-new Pilot Officer on the 27th August, 1928.

The Squadron was equipped with Siskin IIIAs.

By then, though still only twenty-one years old, I had become engaged to Dorothy Mary Lee, whom I had known since I was eighteen and whose home was in Coventry.

My fifteen months in 111 Squadron was, perhaps, the most carefree period of my whole life, and a very pleasant contrast with the preceding five years. The intimate atmosphere of the small officers' mess appealed to me (there were only about fifteen officers — a few of whom were married and lived in married quarters).

It was possible to go on weekend leave every other weekend unless one were orderly officer. It was also possible to get annual leave up to sixty-one days a year. Added to this, the working hours were short and so life passed pleasantly by.

In those days the present Fighter Command was a much smaller formation known as Fighting Area, which formed part of what was known as the Air Defence of Great Britain. Squadron training was based on a systematic pattern which culminated in the annual A.D.G.B. exercises. During the first part of the training programme the emphasis was on individual training. This was followed by practice in flying in flight formation, etc., after which the emphasis was transferred to the training of the whole squadron as a single fighting unit. Accompanying the various phases of flying practice was a ground-training programme, all of which helped to supplement the fairly extensive training I had already received.

Towards the end of 1929 I was attached to the Central Flying School at Wittering, as a pupil of the 30th Flying Instructors' Course. My total flying time was then 333 hours, mostly on Siskins.

Flying instruction was supplemented by lectures and so, in general, this course added a further three months' valuable training to my experience.

During the eighteen months which had elapsed since leaving Cranwell, I had continued my quest for a suitable type of power plant for a very high altitude high-speed aeroplane.

I had given much thought to a jet propulsion arrangement in which the propelling jet was generated by a low-pressure fan driven by a conventional piston engine, both the fan and its driving engine being situated within a hollow nacelle or fuselage. The proposal included provision for extra heating of the air compressed by the fan by the burning of additional fuel before expulsion from the propelling nozzle. However, I eventually came to the conclusion that this arrangement offered no real advantage over the piston engine-propeller combination, and so continued my search for something better.

I later found that the basic concept underlying this scheme had been patented by a Dr. Harris of Esher in 1917. This type of power plant was later put into practice by the Italians in the Caproni Campini aeroplane which first flew in 1940. After the expenditure of considerable effort the Italians also came to the conclusion that it was not worth while.

While I was at Wittering, it suddenly occurred to me to substitute a turbine for the piston engine. This change meant that the compressor would have to have a much higher pressure ratio than the one I had visualised for the piston-engined scheme. In short, I was back to the gas turbine, but this time of a type which produced a propelling jet instead of driving a propeller. Once this idea had taken shape, it seemed rather odd that I had taken so long to arrive at a concept which had become very obvious and of extraordinary simplicity. My calculations satisfied me that it was far superior to my earlier proposals.

I discussed the scheme with one of the C.F.S. instructors, Flying Officer W. E. P. Johnson, whose name will recur many times in this narrative.

Johnson was not an engineer, but, having qualified as a patent agent in civilian life, he had strong technical interests (he was also an excellent pilot, and at that time he had the distinction of being the only officer in the R.A.F. qualified in instrument flying) which were manifested in various ways. For example, he decorated his aeroplane with wool tufts and tapes to make the airflow over the wings "visible" to his pupils. (It is of interest to note that about ten years later, Johnson used the same technique in a transparent model of a jet engine combustion chamber and thereby brought to light some very important facts.)

Johnson was instrumental in arranging that I should explain my jet engine proposal to the Commandant, Group Captain Baldwin (later Air Marshal Sir John Baldwin). So far as I can remember, Johnson and I saw him together and though Baldwin was non-technical, he was quite considerably impressed and promised to bring the matter to the attention of the Air Ministry.

A few days later I was instructed to report to the Air Ministry with my sketches and calculations. I first explained them to W.

L. Tweedie, a technical officer in the Directorate of Scientific Research, and later, in company with Tweedie, to Dr. A. A. Griffith at the Air Ministry's South Kensington Laboratory.

The result was depressing. I learned from Tweedie that the Air Ministry's attitude about the practicability of the gas turbine was in accordance with a very unfavourable report on the subject that had been written some years before. Griffith himself was a believer in the gas turbine as a means of driving a propeller, but he pointed out, quite correctly, that certain of my assumptions were over-optimistic and that I had made one important mistake in my calculations.

I returned to Wittering in rather low spirits, but cheered up somewhat when, in making a careful revision of my calculations, I discovered another important mistake which largely had the effect of neutralising the first one, and so my confidence in my conclusions was restored.

In due course I received a letter from the Air Ministry to the effect that the scheme I proposed was a form of gas turbine, and that as such its successful development was considered to be impracticable, because materials did not then exist capable of withstanding the combination of high stresses and high temperatures which would be necessary if a gas turbine were to have an acceptable efficiency. In fairness to the Air Ministry, I should add that I think that what they said was true. Nevertheless, I feel that they should have foreseen the possibility of big improvements in materials and kept the proposal "on ice" for a later period. I agree that at the end of 1929 it was before its time, but only by very few years.

Despite the official rejection of the scheme, Johnson urged me to take out a patent and offered to assist in drafting it — an offer which I readily accepted.

The Provisional Specification was duly filed on the 16th January, 1930.

In accordance with regulations, the Air Ministry was formally notified of my action, but I was informed that the Ministry had no official interest in the patent. There was thus no suggestion that it should be put on the "secret list". This meant that after the complete specification was filed and accepted, a little over eighteen months later, the invention was published throughout the world.

After qualifying as a flying instructor, I was posted to No. 2 Flying Training School at Digby in Lincolnshire.

Shortly after my arrival at Digby, my promotion to Flying Officer was gazetted. In those days this was automatic after eighteen months as a Pilot Officer, provided one had passed the promotion examination.

Teaching pupils to fly proved to be a much more interesting occupation than I had expected, and was by no means without its excitement. Many a time an instructor is faced at very short notice with the difficult decision as to whether to take over the controls or let the pupil get himself out of a difficulty. If a nervous instructor takes over before he need do, he tends to destroy the confidence of his pupil, but if he leaves it too late he may destroy both his pupil and himself.

One of my first batch of pupils, G. Silyn Roberts (later Air Commodore) was an M.Sc. of Bangor University. He has recently reminded me that I told him all about the jet engine, and admits with amusement that he was a disbeliever especially after he had discussed it with one of the professors of his University, who was also sceptical. He did his best in a tactful way to convince me that I was on a wild-goose chase and was much amused by the persistence with which I held my views.

The R.A.F. Display at Hendon was then an annual event, and one of the regular features of the programme was an exhibition of "Crazy Flying" with two aircraft flown by instructors from one of the Flying Training Schools, who were selected by competition. The late Flying Officer G. E. Campbell and I were chosen as the competitors from No. 2 F.T.S. and were successful in winning the competition.

Campbell had taken part in the Display four times before this, so I had a very experienced partner. In addition to being a brilliant pilot he had a most charming personality, and as we were already very good friends and in the same flight it was appropriate that we should be paired off in this way.

The "crazy flying" turn was a comedy event. The basic idea was to fly as though one had never flown before and do all the wrong things — mostly at a height of two to three feet above the ground. It was a very specialised form of flying in reality, and there were not many pilots in the R.A.F. who were skilled at it.

Campbell and I evolved a carefully synchronised programme with several novel manoeuvres — mock collisions, "crazy" formation, formation "hopping" and so on.

Our first experiments with the formation "hopping" manoeuvre proved expensive. I wrecked my aeroplane while practising it. I was so concentrating on keeping station and synchronising properly, i.e. pulling up when Campbell went down and vice versa that when Campbell went a bit too high, I went a bit too low and struck the ground very heavily. I bounced into the air again and knowing from the "feel" of the aeroplane that it was badly damaged, I made a very gentle circuit and attempted a landing but, unknown to me, the wreckage of my shattered undercarriage was trailing several feet below me and more or less acted as an anchor. Some time before I was expecting it, the aeroplane suddenly decelerated and plunged its nose into the ground. Apart from a severe blow on the shin, I was unhurt. As I could hear the hissing of petrol as it dripped on to the hot engine, I lost no time in getting out of the cockpit. My brother officers said they had never seen anybody get out of an aeroplane so quickly.

A similar thing nearly happened to Campbell, but he got away with nothing worse than a burst tyre.

Two days later I had another mishap. The undercarriage of an aeroplane I had borrowed from another instructor collapsed while doing the flat turn take-off with which we opened our performance. The aeroplane flicked over on to its back just about when it had reached flying speed. Once again I was not hurt, but the aeroplane was very much the worse for wear. I extricated myself from the inverted cockpit and walked disconsolately towards the hangars. I was met by a furious Flight Commander who, his face flushed with rage, sarcastically demanded "Why don't you take all my bloody aeroplanes into the middle of the aerodrome and set fire to them — it's quicker!"

At the Display itself, our performance seemed to go down very well, though I was told afterwards that at least one spectator was not at all impressed. An old lady was heard to comment to an excited small boy "There's nothing to get excited about — they haven't got far to fall!"

A few days after the Display I was very pleased to receive the following letter from the A.O.C. of No. 23 Group (which comprised the Flying Training Schools in Britain):

Dear Whittle,

You will see published in Orders an appreciation by the C.A.S. of the work done by all officers to make the Display a success.

I want to add my personal congratulations on the excellent show put up by you. The crowd appreciated your evolutions very much indeed...
Yours sincerely,
P. B. Joubert.[3]

In the aircraft park at the Display the two Avro 504NS flown by Campbell and myself were lined up with five Fairey Flycatchers of the Fleet Air Arm. It is a strange and tragic fact that of the seven pilots in that line, I am the only survivor. Campbell was killed four years later in a collision while practising formation aerobatics for the 1934 Display; two of the Fleet Air Arm officers were lost when the submarine M.2 foundered; two others were killed in flying accidents; and the sixth lost his life in a road accident.

CHAPTER 5

Throughout my time at Digby I continued to develop my ideas on the turbo-jet engine and kept in touch with W. E. P. Johnson at Wittering on this subject, both in connection with the drafting of the Complete Specification and in connection with attempts to interest commercial firms.

My logbook records that on October 4th, 1930, Johnson and I flew from Wittering to Brooklands. Our purpose was to have a talk with Squadron Leader George Reid of Reid & Sigrist because Johnson thought there was a chance that he might back the invention. (Johnson knew him by virtue of his connection with "blind flying". Reid & Sigrist made the turn indicator which was then coming into use.) Reid took a very sympathetic interest in the scheme and said he thought it was sound, but that the magnitude of the proposal was such that far more money would be required for its development than he could possibly find. He advised us to seek sponsors with much greater resources than those at his command.

I have more reasons than one for remembering that particular flight. We flew over Cardington where the R.101 was riding at its mooring mast. A few hours later this enormous airship was to be a mass of blazing wreckage on a hill near Beauvais in France. This was the tragic end of an attempt to fly to India, and in it the then Secretary of State for Air, Lord Thompson, and several distinguished aviation personalities including Sir Sefton Brancker, lost their lives. Shortly after passing Cardington we ran into some of the weather that was to contribute to the disaster. Low cloud and rain very seriously reduced visibility and had I been on my own I would undoubtedly have turned back, but Johnson, having complete confidence in his blind-flying instruments, carried on. This flight impressed very deeply upon me the value of skill in instrument flying and the great importance of the gyroscopic instruments which made it possible.

Towards the end of the year, I visited the British Thomson-Houston turbine factory in Rugby and discussed my turbo-jet engine with F. Samuelson, Chief Turbine Engineer, and his deputy, R. H. Collingham. Johnson was again primarily responsible for the chain of events which led to this meeting.

Samuelson and Collingham listened to me patiently, but though they did not question my sketches and calculations, they said that an engine of the kind I proposed would cost about £60,000 to develop, and the B.T-H. could not contemplate experimental expenditure of this magnitude at that time (this was the time when the industrial depression was at its worst and the unemployed numbered some three million — it seemed to me that a time when there was so much labour available was just the right moment for ambitious experimental work). Moreover, they indicated that they were fully aware of the difficulties in the way of successful gas turbine development. They also argued that as the engine I was proposing was applicable only to aircraft, it was not really appropriate to their field of activity. In retrospect, I do not in any way condemn them for short-sightedness — if anything, it now surprises me that they should have given such a patient hearing to a young man of twenty-three with no academic qualifications.

Towards the end of 1930 I was notified that I was to be posted to the Marine Aircraft Experimental Establishment as a floatplane test pilot. This was particularly welcome because I had been married since the previous May and the housing problem for young married officers was difficult in the Digby area.

CHAPTER 6

At Felixstowe the nature of my duties was very much to my liking. The work offered plenty of scope for indulging my strong technical interests.

The chief complaint of many of us was the very limited amount of flying we were able to put in. Often it never amounted to more than six hours a month because flying was mostly restricted to specific test work, and often, when the weather was quite suitable for normal flying, it was not good enough for the test work required. Sometimes we could get round this by nominally flying for the purpose of doing "handling trials".

Another factor which had a limiting effect on the amount of flying was the rather laborious launching and beaching procedure necessary with floatplanes. Often when the weather itself was satisfactory for flying, the sea would be too rough for launching and take-off.

In May, 1931, my first son, Francis David, was born. This addition to the family did not ease my financial situation. It was very difficult indeed to make both ends meet on Flying Officers' pay and single allowances.[4] The heavy medical expenses I had to meet then and subsequently meant that we had to live with the greatest economy.

My main task, and by far the most interesting, was catapult test work. I was detailed for this quite soon after my arrival at Felixstowe and was sent down to Farnborough for three practice launches near the end of February, 1931.

The Admiralty and the R.A.E. had been doing experimental work with catapults for many years prior to this, so that though

I was frequently the first pilot to be launched from a new type of catapult, I was by no means the first pilot to be catapult launched (as has occasionally been stated). I understand that one of the earliest living things to be catapulted was a sheep! At this point I cannot do better than quote from an article by Commander Peter Bethell, R.N. (*Engineering*, July 2nd, 1943, Vol. 156). Referring to early work at the R.A.E., Farnborough, he says, *inter alia*:

> ...these experiments on human guinea-pigs were preceded by a series of diverting trials of a sort that would have drawn forth a spate of lurid posters from the anti-vivisectionist bodies.
>
> On the edge of Farnborough aerodrome, that blasted heath which has seen so many strange sights since the debut of 'Cody's Cathedral' and the first Army airships, stood the prototype catapult, arranged to discharge its missile on to a kind of Earl's Court slide. The missile was the battered fuselage of an aeroplane, and strapped into the cockpit, in an intrepid and professional attitude, was a large sheep — because that was the nearest approach to a Naval pilot that the R.A.E. scientists could think of or that the Admiralty would permit — Woosh! — The expression on the sheep's face was something that the writer will never forget, and this was the first and only occasion on which he has been actually physically sick with laughter.

The Farnborough catapult on which I experienced my first launches was mounted in a circular pit of such a depth that the wheels of the aircraft being launched were about six inches above ground level. The length of the stroke was about 50 feet and in this distance the aircraft accelerated to just under 60 m.p.h. This meant a maximum acceleration of about 2½ "g" (i.e. with about 2½ times the force of gravity), so that immediately before the launch it was necessary to have one's head back against the head-rest provided. At first the sensation produced by this tremendous acceleration was very odd, but I found that one very soon got used to it.

I cannot now remember whether the Farnborough catapult received its power from compressed air or cordite, but all catapults with which I was subsequently associated were powered by cordite. In any case, all the catapults were lubricated with glycerine. The earlier use of compressed air as propellant was the reason for the introduction of glycerine as lubricant, though the practice continued after the change-over to cordite had been made. The alleged reason for the use of glycerine is worth recording. Originally the compressed air catapults which were being developed at the R.A.E. were lubricated with ordinary lubricating oil. For the purpose of some of these experiments a human guinea pig was used, namely, one of the R.A.E. test pilots. The "aeroplane" was an ancient amphibian which had no engine and no flying controls connected. Mounted in the centre section where the engine would normally have been was a block of concrete. This arrangement was considered satisfactory because in normal circumstances the aeroplane merely ran along the ground after the launch. But one day the lubricating oil and compressed air inside the ram cylinder exploded with great violence, and the unfortunate "stooge" in the cockpit received at least 6 g instead of the usual 2½|, and in an instant found himself at a height of about 150 feet with no engine, no controls and in an aeroplane which was disintegrating into splinters and fabric as a result of the severe overload it had received. Fortunately, he escaped with nothing worse than a severe shaking. Thereafter the change to glycerine as a lubricant was made. (I do not vouch for the accuracy of my account of this incident, as it is based on hearsay.)

For my catapult test work I used to go to sea in H.M.S. *Ark Royal.*[5] Trials were usually carried out in the Solent between Southsea and the Nab Tower and normally only occupied one or two days, but my fifth and last series of trials in July, 1932, covered a period of a month. It was during this series of trials that there occurred one of the most alarming incidents of my flying career. During the last launch of a series to test the effect of reduced wind speed along the catapult, my passenger, Flight Lieutenant F. Kirk, was thrown out of the rear cockpit and fell on to the tailplane. The component of wind along the catapult was nil and so the launching speed was about three knots below the minimum flying speed of the Fairey IIIF floatplane. At the instant the aeroplane left the catapult, the nose rose sharply. Instinctively, I pushed the control column right forward immediately. After staggering a few hundred yards in a practically stalled attitude I realised, with relief, that the aeroplane was not going to plunge into the sea at once. For a few seconds I did not know why the aeroplane had gone practically out of control. My first thought was that the tailplane had been damaged during the launch, possibly by striking one of the steam hoists (which was feasible if someone had forgotten to swing them out of the way) but on snatching a swift glance over my left shoulder I saw a body lying face downwards on the tailplane, and so my next thought was that in some mysterious way I must have "removed" an airman working on the catapult.

When I was a little more collected I looked round again and for the first time realised that the body on the tailplane belonged to Kirk, my passenger! By this time he had struggled round into a sitting position with his back against the fin-bracing wire, his legs dangling over the leading edge of the tailplane and his right hand holding on to the fin. When he saw me look round he gave me a "thumbs up" signal with his left hand and I saw his mouth frame "O.K." Had I been in a better position to appreciate it, I might have been very amused at what was really rather a funny sight, because Kirk was wearing a borrowed flying helmet which was much too large for him and when he opened his mouth the wind distended his cheeks in a most grotesque manner. He seemed far less alarmed than I felt. My right arm was quivering with the strain of holding the stick right forward. I quickly found that it wasn't going to be easy to descend from my height of about 60 feet. When I tried to throttle back the tail dropped because of the reduced slipstream, so I had to keep the throttle open. I could not turn into wind because Kirk's body was blanking off the rudder completely. Fortunately, there was only a light wind blowing. I found I had just enough control to force the nose down very slightly, and so I slowly lost height. Meantime, a German liner was crossing my path ahead and the question was whether I could get down on to the water before I flew into her side. I succeeded with about 200 yards to spare and alighted with the stick fully forward by easing the throttle slowly back. I still had half engine when my floats touched the water. The German liner gave two blasts on its siren, which in my confused state I supposed was meant to convey "Mind my ship!" but which, as I afterwards realised, was an indication that the ship was turning to port to give me more sea room. (The captain of the *Ark Royal* later said that this was a very generous action on the part of the German captain in view of the risk of running aground at that point.)

Kirk then clambered back into the rear cockpit nearly putting his feet through the after part of the fuselage en route. This was the only damage sustained by the aeroplane during the whole incident. He seemed quite calm and collected, while I was almost in a state of nervous collapse. Weak and trembling with the reaction, I looked round at him and just said "My God!" to which he calmly responded, "What are you worrying about?" We taxied back to the ship. After we were hoisted aboard, pink gins were pressed upon us from all directions by a number of very relieved Naval officers.

All catapult trials were filmed, and so it was possible to see afterwards just what had happened. Prints from the film show that after Kirk lost his grip on the rim of the cockpit (because his gloves were slippery with glycerine) he shot to the rear of the long cockpit and bounced into the air turning as he went. He retained his presence of mind to such an extent that one hand had gripped the fin wire before any part of the rest of him touched the tailplane.

Another highlight of this period was a flotation test of a Fairey Seal landplane. This kind of experiment was known as a "ditching trial". The object was to test emergency flotation gear for carrier-borne aircraft for effectiveness after "ditching" in the sea. Only a few days before this trial a Fleet Air Arm Fairey IIIF which had "ditched" and which was not fitted with flotation gear had sunk within forty-five seconds (the pilot was picked up). Another officer (Wing Commander Grenfell) carried out a similar trial a week before I was due to do mine. He turned right over and was temporarily trapped in the cockpit by his life-jacket. For a minute or two it looked as if there would be a vacancy in the Air Force List, but he eventually struggled out. A few minutes later the aeroplane sank because part of the wreckage had punctured the flotation bags. After witnessing this episode, I did not look forward to my own test one little bit, especially as in those days I could not swim.

I was put ashore to collect the aeroplane from Gosport and took off after receiving a radio signal from the ship giving me the "rendezvous".

There was a strong gusty wind blowing and so the ship had steamed to a position off Sandown in the Isle of Wight, because those responsible deemed it advisable to carry out the experiment in the lee of the island. However, even there there was a considerable sea running, and so, if anything, I was rather glad of the fairly strong wind which would reduce my speed relative to the water.

I brought the aircraft down into the required position and "pancaked" it into the sea from a height of about five feet. As soon as the wheels met the water, the aeroplane buried its nose in the sea and a great sheet of water entered the cockpit. For an instant I thought I had turned right over, but though the fuselage reached a vertical position it fell back. I had no difficulty in inflating and launching the collapsible dinghy which was carried in the rear cockpit. I stepped into this dinghy with an immense feeling of relief and floated away from the aircraft. As I did so I heard a shout of laughter go up from the ship's company. I was told afterwards that this was because I looked like a monkey sitting in the dinghy, but I suspect that it was also their way of expressing a sense of relief. I was collected from the dinghy by the pinnace which was standing by.

Altogether the work of this strenuous and interesting month included forty-seven catapult launches, the ditching experiment just described and sundry other trials of a less exciting nature.

During August, 1932, I received a copy of an extract from a letter from the Commanding Officer of H.M.S. *Ark Royal* addressed to the Vice Admiral Commanding Reserve Fleet which read as follows:

> ...I wish to bring to the notice of Their Lordships the very satisfactory work carried out by Flying Officer F. Whittle, R.A.F... This Officer made a total of 47 catapult launches under varying conditions during the series, and in addition carried out a forced landing flotation test in most realistic conditions and in a praiseworthy manner. His services have been invaluable and his airmanship inspired confidence in all concerned in the trials.
>
> His skill as a pilot, and floatplane handling by making up to nine successive catapult launches in one day enabled conclusive results to be obtained in the minimum time.

For six months of my time at Felixstowe I combined the duties of Station Armament Officer with those of test pilot. This post was normally filled by an officer of the rank of Flight Lieutenant who was an armament specialist. At Felixstowe the duties were even more appropriate to a specialist than was the case at most other stations, because of the experimental work involved. It was thus rather an unusual task and one which added further variety to an already varied life. My most important duty in this capacity was to carry out the armament trials of a new flying-boat which was undergoing tests.

CHAPTER 7

During my eighteen months at Felixstowe I maintained a strong interest in the turbo-jet engine and continued my efforts to interest commercial firms. My two chief attempts in this direction were with a well-known firm which specialised in compressor manufacture, and Armstrong Siddeley. The Managing Director of the first of these firms said that the depression precluded them from embarking on such ambitious schemes and so these discussions very quickly ended, but my exchanges with Armstrong Siddeley were rather more protracted. I visited the firm several times during periods of leave spent in Coventry and had a number of talks with their supercharger specialists. These talks ended when the Chief Engineer wrote to me as follows:

> It seems to me that the whole scheme depends upon obtaining material which will work satisfactorily at a very high temperature. Personally I doubt very much whether such material is available and this, I think, prevents the development of the internal combustion turbine. I fear therefore that I cannot hold out any hopes that this firm will take any serious interest in your proposal.

I was fully aware of the great importance of achieving higher efficiencies for the major components of the engine than had been attained with similar components used in other branches of engineering at that time. In particular I had made proposals for an improved form of centrifugal compressor and had filed a patent application for it at about the same time as for the complete engine. In my talks with the Armstrong Siddeley engineers, in addition to trying to interest them in the jet engine scheme as a whole, I also tried unsuccessfully to convince them that the form of compressor I proposed was an improvement on the type they were then using for supercharging their engines.

The engine was frequently a topic of discussion with the technical and scientific officers of Felixstowe and was something of a joke amongst my brother officers. Leonard Snaith christened it "Whittle's Flaming Touch-hole" and he would often greet me with "Well, how's the old flaming touch-hole getting on?" One officer, however, took it much more seriously, namely, Flying Officer R. Dudley Williams, who was a member of a flying-boat squadron then temporarily stationed at Felixstowe, and whom I knew well because he had been a member of my term at the R.A.F. College (we were in the same hut during our first two terms). Little did we realise then how intimately the Fates were to weave the threads of our two lives. Williams's interest was very real. When he heard that I had only applied for a British patent he made some attempts to raise money from his relatives to obtain American and other foreign patents. However, he was not successful, but as will be seen hereafter, he retained his belief in the proposal and this proved to be a key factor in the subsequent history of the development.

Representatives of aircraft and other firms often visited Felixstowe in connection with the experimental work carried on there, and I tried to convince some of them of the merits of my jet engine, but again without success.

I was forced to realise to an increasing extent that I would need to convince people of the value of my compressor proposals before I could hope to get them to accept the much more comprehensive scheme for a complete engine, and to this end I wrote a paper on superchargers which was accepted for publication in the journal of the R.Ae.S. Another object of this paper was to make a case for using an independent engine for driving the supercharger of the main power plant. This was a scheme for which Flying Officer J. H. McC. Reynolds and I had filed a joint patent application. We tried to induce certain firms to take up this proposal also, but again without success.

The need to convince people of the possible improvement in compressors may be judged from the fact that the turbo-jet engine proposal required a compressor having a pressure ratio of the order of 4:1 and an efficiency of at least 75%, while the best aero-engine supercharger of that time (that of the Rolls-Royce "R" engine which powered the Supermarine S.6 which won the Schneider Trophy in 1931), had a pressure ratio of just under 2:1 and an efficiency of 62%. Unless a very great improvement on these figures could be obtained there was little hope for the success of the turbo-jet engine.

Some time after writing the paper on supercharging, I wrote another paper entitled "The Case for the Gas Turbine," but I made no attempt to get this published. This paper is the earliest of my surviving documents in which the theory of the jet engine is discussed. Its contents foreshadowed my later work to a remarkable degree in view of the fact that I had not then received any advanced engineering training. The paper contained example calculations which showed the big increase in efficiency which could be obtained with the gas turbine at great height due to the beneficial effects of low air temperature. It also contained calculations to demonstrate the degree to which range would depend on height with turbo-jet engined aircraft.

My varied duties at Felixstowe were accompanied by a corresponding variety in inventive ideas. My armament duties inspired me to produce a novel method of representing the field of fire from the various gun positions of a flying-boat on a single diagram, and also to devise an enclosed gun turret. My catapult duties inspired me to produce a scheme for what I considered to be an improved method of loading bombs on to aircraft mounted on catapults (this in conjunction with Kirk), and also to produce a proposal for an entirely new type of catapult.

Other miscellaneous ideas included a single fluke anchor and a scheme for simplifying the handling gear of floatplanes.

None of these proposals was ever officially adopted except the field of fire diagram, for which I received, in due course, an expression of the Air Council's appreciation "of the initiative and ability displayed by him in preparing these diagrams". I have forgotten what happened in the case of the gun turret proposal. I had a wooden "mock-up" made of the hood and special gun mounting, and spent much time in the drawing office preparing drawings. However, except for photographs of the mock-up, all my records on the subject have been destroyed or mislaid.

The bomb hoist for aircraft mounted on catapults was turned down by the Air Ministry on the ground that it was not considered to be an improvement on then existing apparatus.

I submitted my proposals for a catapult, but this proposal was also turned down, but here again, a gap in my memory coincides with a gap in my records. I made some half-hearted attempts to revive the proposal in 1938 or 1939, but by then I was too fully occupied with the jet engine development to give much attention to matters outside this field.

In my annual confidential report for 1932, I was strongly recommended for engineering duties. This report also contained the following:

> A very keen young officer and a useful test pilot. He shows considerable ability in aircraft engineering. He has temporarily carried out the duties of Station Armament Officer with success and benefit to this station. He has been employed as catapult pilot in H.M.S. *Ark Royal* and has twice been specially mentioned by the Commanding Officer. A keen and capable young officer.

Every officer with a permanent commission was expected to take a specialist course after four years of general duties. The choice lay between Engineering, Signals, Armament and Navigation. Naturally, I elected to specialise in engineering, and with the backing of the recommendation in my confidential report I was posted to the Home Aircraft Depot, Henlow, to attend the Officers' Engineering Course in August, 1932.

During the eighteen months at Felixstowe I only added 132 hours to my total flying time — bringing it to 741 hours, but this 132 hours had been crammed with valuable experience. It was distributed over 18 types of floatplanes, flying-boats and amphibians, and I had qualified as first pilot on flying-boats. (I have often thought that flying time is a very unsatisfactory measure of flying experience, thus, for example, the intensive test work in July 1932 only added 11 hours to my flying time, because each time I was launched from the catapult my flying time was only 5–10 minutes.)

CHAPTER 8

In the preliminary examination for new students at Henlow, I surprised myself and my examiners by obtaining an aggregate of 98% in all subjects. I think that this was the first time that I really realised the extent to which my continuous interest in engineering subjects had improved my knowledge.

On the strength of this result, the Air Ministry agreed that I should be allowed to take the course in eighteen months instead of the usual two years. It was arranged that I should be attached to the senior course then beginning their second year, and would then spend six months completing that section of the workshops training normally covered in the first year.

I took my final examinations in written subjects at the end of my first year and obtained distinction in every subject except Mechanical Drawing.

The Air Ministry had, a short time before, discontinued the practice of sending one or two officers selected from the Engineering Course to Cambridge University to take the Mechanical Sciences Tripos. I therefore sent in a formal application that my case should be specially considered. This application was supported by the Officer Commanding the course. The Air Ministry agreed in a letter worded as follows:

> …that in view of this Officer's excellent work on the Specialist 'E' Course they have decided as an exceptional case to allow this Officer to proceed to Cambridge University for the two years' 'E' Course…

I completed my course at the end of 1933 and was not due for posting to Cambridge until July, 1934, so a six-months' gap had to be bridged. I was posted to the Engine Repair Section of the Depot as Officer i/c Aero-engine Test Benches. During this period my promotion to Flight Lieutenant was gazetted.

During my time at Henlow I continued to do paperwork at intervals on my turbo-jet engine scheme, and, though it was often the subject of interesting discussions with the instructors and my fellow students, there was no progress towards turning it into a practical device. Indeed I was beginning to feel that it was long before its time and was giving a certain amount of attention to other schemes. The most important of these was a proposal for a new type of aircraft weapon, which I called "the flying bolas" because of its similarity in principle to the "bolas" used by the South American Indians (which consists of three weights attached to the ends of lengths of rope joined together at their other ends. When the weapon was hurled at an enemy it would, if skilfully directed, wind itself around his body).

This device was duly submitted to the Air Ministry. A short time later I received a copy of a letter which said, *inter alia*:

> with a view to deciding whether this method of attack is practicable the Council will endeavour to arrange for a practical trial to be made in about a year's time when a suitable target aircraft will probably be available for this purpose...
>
> I am to request that an expression of the Air Council's appreciation of the zeal and initiative displayed in connection with this invention may be communicated to Flying Officer Whittle.

Thereafter I heard no more about it and never knew whether the promised test was ever carried out, or whether the matter was completely forgotten. This may have been my own fault, because I did not make any official inquiry as to the fate of the invention.

Notes made in May, 1934, which appear to have been the basis of two official letters to, and one conversation with, the Commanding Officer, Henlow, suggest that I was becoming rather despondent about the fate of inventions by serving officers relating to Service equipment. I had come to the conclusion that when an invention had little or no commercial application outside the Service, it was a waste of money to take out a patent and so, for the future, I had decided that where an invention would find its chief application in the Service I would submit the idea for official consideration, but would not take out a patent unless instructed to do so at Air Ministry expense.

For the course at Cambridge University I was officially attached to Cambridge University Air Squadron.

I was expected to keep in flying practice during the course and for this purpose put in time on the Avro Tutors with which the Squadron was equipped. As at Henlow, the intensive course of study made it difficult to put in more than a very limited amount of flying, and I only managed a total of 23 hours in the rest of 1934 (during my two years at Henlow my total flying time was just over 107 hours).

Being a serving officer with the rank of Flight Lieutenant, my position was rather a curious one. I was twenty-seven years old and was thus several years older than the great majority of my fellow undergraduates. I was never resident in my college (Peterhouse) and, being married, I was not expected to dine in Hall more than once a week. However, in all other respects I was expected to conform to the rules of one in *statu pupillari*, and in theory at least was as much subject to university discipline as any of the undergraduates.

I found that it was, in many ways, a big advantage to have gone to the University after several years of practical experience, because I had acquired a strong desire to know the explanations of many of the phenomena I had encountered during this experience. This, of course, was most marked in those subjects which were closely associated with aeronautical engineering. Many items of knowledge which had great practical significance for me must have seemed relatively academic to those who had gone to university direct from school.

In January, 1935, my 1930 jet engine patent became due for renewal. For this a fee of £5 was required. Shortly before the renewal date I received an official letter from a branch of the Contracts Directorate of the Air Ministry reminding me that the renewal date was near and adding that there was no intention of paying the renewal fee out of official funds.

By then I had virtually given up hope of ever seeing the engine take practical shape. I had become convinced that it was "before its time". I also had a fuller realisation of the cost and effort which would be required for its development (though the event showed I was then still very much underestimating these factors). Moreover, I could ill afford £5 in view of the then recent medical expenses arising out of an illness of my elder son and the birth of my younger one. I therefore decided against renewal and allowed the patent to lapse.

The normal period for the Mechanical Sciences Tripos was three years, but by virtue of my previous course at Henlow I was expected to take it in two years and so omitted the normal first year of studies.

CHAPTER 9

One morning in early May, 1935, while in the offices of the University Air Squadron, the C.O.'s secretary handed me a private letter. This letter was to affect my life probably more than any other document ever has. It did not look at all exciting; in fact, it looked a very ordinary letter. It was from R. Dudley Williams who, as already recorded, had been a fellow Cadet at Cranwell and who had taken some interest in my turbojet idea when we were both stationed at Felixstowe in 1931. Since the Felixstowe days I had heard little of him except that he had retired from the R.A.F. because of ill-health.

Even when I read the letter I did not sense that it was pregnant with fate. It was handwritten and read as follows:

> This is just a hurried note to tell you that I have just met a man who is a bit of a big noise in an engineering concern and to whom I mentioned your invention of an aeroplane, *sans* propeller as it were, and who is very interested. You told me some time ago that Armstrong's had or were taking it up and if they have broken down or you don't like them, he would, I think, like to handle it. I wonder if you would write and let me know.

I read it through quickly, stuffed it into my pocket and gave it no further thought for several hours. On re-reading, my first impulse was to reply that I had been forced to conclude that it was "before its time". On second thoughts, I decided it might be worth while encouraging his interest further in case his "contact" should prove useful in connection with other inventions I then had in mind.

Having allowed the patent to lapse there seemed little hope of raising money to finance the invention. However, I replied to Williams on the 7th May telling him that I had allowed the patent to lapse, and said, *inter alia* (and referring to past efforts) "nobody would touch it on account of the enormous cost of the experimental work and I don't think they were far wrong, though I still have every faith in the invention. However, if anybody were keen on taking it up I think it would pay them." (I did not really believe this.) "There is no doubt in my mind that as things stand at present, it is the only way to high-altitude flying."

I suggested a meeting to talk about it and so, on a Sunday a few days later, Williams and his partner, J. C. B. Tinling, came to my house in Trumpington and we talked all the afternoon about our plans.

I had not met Tinling before. He was also ex-R.A.F. He had been invalided out before the expiry of his five years short-service commission after receiving serious injuries in a flying accident.

Our talk that Sunday afternoon was in quite optimistic vein despite our general disappointment that the master patent was no longer in force. I told them that it was my view that the patent position could be re-established to some extent by patenting a series of improvements to the original scheme. I did not feel the confidence that I was showing. I did not really believe that the time was ripe for an attempt on the turbo-jet engine itself, but I felt that if they were encouraged to believe that it was worth while, something would come of our joint activities. They themselves were not in a position to provide any substantial sums. The idea was that they should come to some business arrangement with a big financier or financial group by which he or they would finance the development in exchange for a share in the rights of the invention. I convinced them that as a result of the thinking I had done since 1930 there were sufficient patentable improvements to provide a bargaining basis.

The net result was that we agreed on an arrangement by which they would cover the expenses of taking out further patents, and any other expenses which might arise in their efforts to raise money, and would act as my agents. In return, they were each to receive a quarter share in our joint commercial rights.

We decided to aim to raise £50,000 which, in our optimism, we supposed would be ample for the development of a complete jet-propelled aeroplane.

I was not particularly optimistic in other ways. For example, I told Williams in a letter dated 26th May that it was not a particularly efficient type of engine, but that there was plenty of scope for development. I said "its virtue lies entirely in its extremely low weight and that it will work at heights where atmospheric density is very low".

In the next few weeks three provisional patent specifications were filed covering improvements to the original scheme.

As I was a serving officer, each patent application became subject to a formal agreement with the Air Ministry. There was a standard form of agreement for all inventions which the Air Ministry did not intend to sponsor themselves. It gave the inventor the commercial rights but retained the right of "Free Crown User". This agreement was a severe handicap if the nature of the invention was such that the Government was likely to be the chief "customer". Recognising that it was likely to prove an obstacle to raising private money, I attempted to get the agreement modified, but the Director of Contracts refused to consider any alteration. It will be seen that my uneasiness on this account was fully justified by events.

During the next few weeks our hopes rose and fell — at one moment Williams and Tinling would report that they had good hopes of finding the money almost immediately; and then our hopes would be dashed. The financier concerned had cooled off or — in one case — had suddenly gone to sea in his yacht and was inaccessible.

At my insistence, we had agreed on one very important thing — that in no circumstances would we take the idea to anyone connected with the aircraft industry. I pointed out that if one of the big aircraft firms took an interest in the invention, the only thing which could stop them from proceeding independently from us, if they wished to do so, was such patent protection as we happened to have at the time, and it might mean a very expensive court action to establish the validity of the patents. (In a then recent patent action the costs had been of the order of £100,000.) We were obviously in no position to risk such an action. I was therefore very worried when I heard that Mr. M. L. Bramson had heard about and was interested in the scheme, because he was very well known in aeronautical circles, both as a pilot and as an engineer and had links with several firms with aeronautical interests. The sequence of events which lead to Bramson's interest was more or less outside the control of Williams and Tinling. However, the three of us agreed that since the damage was done (as we supposed), we had no option but to discuss the proposal with Bramson and hope for the best. Fortunately, my pessimism about his aeronautical contacts proved to be groundless, though it nevertheless remains the fact that our fear of independent action compelled us to a course of events which was not of our own choosing.

After meeting Bramson my uneasiness was greatly diminished — his initial response to the idea was one of enthusiasm and he managed to convey the respect he felt for me as an engineer. I, in turn, at once recognised his considerable abilities. Further, he made no suggestion of an approach to any of the aircraft firms. Instead, he enlisted the interest of a firm of investment bankers, O. T. Falk & Partners, and negotiations were opened between Williams, Tinling and myself on the one hand, and Falk & Partners on the other. In these negotiations Bramson played an important part. Falk & Partners requested him to act as their consultant, and to write a formal report on the project.

Mr. L. L. Whyte, M.C., was the member of the firm of Falk & Partners with whom we had most of our dealings, though quite frequently Sir Maurice Bonham Carter, one of the Directors, also took part in the discussions.

Whyte was a remarkable man. He was a scientist, philosopher and banker — a most unusual combination. He was primarily a physicist having taken a Cambridge degree in Natural Sciences.

Negotiations with Falk & Partners began in the autumn of 1935 and, after many meetings, we reached agreement by the beginning of November. Bramson had then completed his report. It was entirely favourable and this naturally influenced Whyte and his colleagues. (Unfortunately, I have been unable to trace this important document.)

In the meantime, in addition to my normal studies for the final year of the Mechanical Sciences Tripos, I was working on the preliminary design of an experimental engine and also doing aerodynamic research under Professor (later Sir) B. Melvill Jones.

When it appeared that we were nearing agreement, we considered plans for starting practical work and it was decided that we would place a contract for an experimental engine with a suitable engineering firm — preferably turbine manufacturers.

At my suggestion we decided to approach the B.T-H. Company, and so I went to Rugby for a talk with the two senior turbine engineers, F. Samuelson and R. H. Collingham, to whom I had tried to "sell" the idea in 1930. I outlined our aims. They said that the B.T-H. might be willing to accept a contract if it were on a "cost-plus" basis. It was too big a "shot in the dark" for a firm tender.

The Air Ministry insisted on a number of amendments to the draft agreement with Falk & Partners, including the requirement that the President of the Air Council be a party to it. It was then known as "The Four-Party Agreement" and was dated 27th January, 1936. Under its terms a company was to be formed with an authorised capital of not less than £2,000 for the purpose of exploiting the turbo-jet engine. I was to assign all my patent rights to this company, and Falk & Partners were to provide the first £2,000 of capital and had the option to put in a further £18,000 at par within eighteen months. In return for the patent rights, Williams, Tinling and myself were to have a 49% share in the company which was not to be "watered down" before the capital subscribed for in cash had reached £50,000.

An interesting point about the Four-Party Agreement was that under it I was entitled to act as Honorary Chief Engineer and Technical Consultant to the company for a period of five years,

> provided always that the work to be done by the inventor under this clause … shall not conflict with his official duties

> and that the time which the Company shall be entitled to require the inventor to devote to such work and supervision shall not, without the consent of the President of the Air Council, in any one week exceed a total of six hours...

This condition was one insisted on by the Air Ministry and it made it very clear that at that time my work in connection with the engine was to be very much a "spare time job". I believe this clause carried great weight with the Royal Commission on Awards to Inventors, at a much later date, because it made it so obvious that, in the earliest days at least, my work on the engine did not come within the scope of my official duties.

The Company was duly incorporated in March, 1936, with an authorised capital of £10,000 and was called Power Jets Limited. We chose this name as being descriptive of our aims; yet at the same time unlikely to disclose them.

To give effect to the provision of the Four-Party Agreement there were two classes of shares — "A" shares, of which there were 98, allotted to Williams, Tinling and myself in the proportion 21:21:56, and "B" shares, to be subscribed for in cash by investors. The Air Ministry had required me to allot 25% of my commercial interest to the Crown and so 14 of my "A" shares were held in trust for the President of the Air Council. My net holding of 42 thus equalled Williams' and Tinling's joint holding in accordance with the arrangement agreed between us some time before.

The majorities of the "A" and "B" shareholders each had the right to nominate half the board of directors, with the "B" shareholders having the further right to nominate the chairman who had a casting vote. Thus at that time the "B" shareholders controlled the Company.

The Directors were L. L. Whyte and Sir Maurice Bonham Carter representing the "B" shareholders (with Bramson acting as alternate director for Sir Maurice) and Williams and Tinling representing the "A" shareholders. Whyte was appointed Chairman.

CHAPTER 10

We had not waited for the formal incorporation of the Company to get on with the job. Several weeks earlier, Falk & Partners placed a contract with the B.T-H. Company for the design drawings of an experimental engine to my requirements, and from that time on I frequently visited the B.T-H. works for technical conferences.

Bramson and I were in continuous consultation and most of the engineering decisions I took at this time were agreed with him. (He was employed as consultant to Power Jets.) For a time we thought our best course would be to make the individual components of the engine and test them separately. There were strong reasons for this, because we were going beyond all previous engineering experience in many ways, and it thus seemed an appalling gamble to aim for the complete engine in "one go". It soon became clear that the plan for separate component testing would be far too costly. For example, to test the compressor alone would have required a 3,000 h.p. electric motor. (A figure of £27,000 was quoted for compressor test plant.) We therefore decided that we would have to go for the complete engine (at an estimated cost of less than £5,000) and hope for the best.

It was to be purely an experimental engine and was not intended for flight, but the design was based on a flight objective. We estimated the power required for a small 500 m.p.h. mail plane and made that our design target.

The major organs of a turbo-jet engine are: a compressor, a combustion chamber assembly, a turbine, and an exhaust pipe ending in a jet nozzle. Large quantities of air drawn in at a front intake pass through these organs in that order. The flow through the engine is continuous. In the combustion chambers the air compressed by the compressor is heated by the steady combustion of fuel. The compressed and heated gases then pass through the turbine, thus providing the power to drive the compressor to which the turbine is connected by a shaft. They then pass along the exhaust duct and emerge from the jet nozzle as a high-velocity propelling jet.

Our compressor was of the single stage centrifugal type generally similar to, but much larger than, an aero-engine supercharger (or fan unit of a vacuum cleaner). The turbine was also a single stage unit (a turbine may be thought of as a very powerful windmill). Thus the main moving part of the engine — the rotor — was made up of the compressor impeller, the turbine wheel and the shaft connecting the two. It was designed to rotate at 17,750 revolutions per minute which meant a top speed of nearly 1,500 feet per second for the 19 in. diameter impeller and 1,250 feet per second for the 16½ in. diameter turbine.

Our targets of performance for the compressor, combustion chamber assembly and turbine were very ambitious and far beyond anything previously attained with similar components.

The best that had been achieved with a single stage centrifugal compressor was a pressure ratio of 2.5 with an efficiency of 65% (an aero-engine supercharger). Our target was a pressure ratio of 4.0 with an efficiency of 80%.

Our designed airflow of 1,500 lb. per minute was far greater in proportion to size than anything previously attempted (that was one of the reasons why I expected to get high efficiency). For this pressure ratio and airflow the compressor required over 3,000 h.p. to drive it. Power of this order from such a small single stage turbine was well beyond all previous experience. Finally, in the combustion chamber we aimed to burn nearly 200 gallons of fuel per hour in a space of about six cubic feet. This required a combustion intensity many times greater than a boiler furnace.

I felt fully confident (too confident for those days, I am afraid) that we could achieve our targets for the compressor and turbine because I was convinced that the way to get high efficiency with these components was to make them do as much work as possible in proportion to their size. In this belief I have been fully justified by the outcome.

But the combustion problem was another matter. I saw no reason why we should not get the desired combustion intensity, but felt much less sure of my ground and so decided to seek outside help. With this object I went to the British Industries Fair at Castle Bromwich on the 19th February, 1936. I visited the stands of several well-known firms who specialised in burners and combustion equipment for boiler firing and other purposes. Without disclosing the nature of the project, I outlined our combustion chamber problem. For the most part I met with blank astonishment and was told that I was asking for a combustion intensity at least twenty times greater than had ever before been achieved. I was therefore feeling rather discouraged by the time I visited the stand of a small Scottish firm, Laidlaw, Drew & Company. But when I explained our needs to Mr. A. B. S. Laidlaw, a director of the firm, things looked more hopeful. He tried to find out what lay behind my request. I did not tell him, but did my best to convince him that it was a very important project. (Later he told me that from the first he guessed that it was some form of gas turbine.) He said he could see no reason why the combustion intensities we required could not be achieved, but that experiments would be necessary before a combustion chamber could be designed.

I assured him that provided the terms of his firm were reasonable we would give them the contract for making test apparatus for preliminary experiments.

All this time I was based at Cambridge, but, of course, was having to do quite a lot of travelling. There were frequent visits to London for consultations with Bramson, and the others connected with Power Jets; to Rugby for engineering conferences with the B.T-H. turbine engineers; and to Edinburgh to discuss the combustion problem with Laidlaw. I usually flew to Edinburgh and was thus able to combine business with the requirement that I should put in a certain number of flying hours per year.

In addition, I was visiting sundry firms in connection with special problems. I went to the Hoffman Company in Chelmsford to discuss bearings; to Alfred Herberts in Coventry to discuss the special machining problems of the shaft assembly, and so on.

When I visited the B.T-H. works on the 23rd March, 1936, I was shown a tentative assembly drawing. It was a long way from my conception of the engine and I was compelled to reject it. I decided to specify my requirements more closely and sent a preliminary drawing for the general arrangement to the B.T-H. (29th March, 1936). Thereafter things went more in accordance with my wishes and work on detail drawings started in April, 1936.

The Tripos examinations were then looming very near. I had set my heart on obtaining a First, but the work on the engine had seriously interfered with my studies. So for five weeks I concentrated entirely on preparation for the Tripos. Bramson deputised for me in the meantime.

Rather to my own surprise, I obtained my First. Not without some penalty in health. I was unwell throughout the examination, due to the combination of excitement and strain of the preceding few months, aggravated by the tremendous spurt I had had to make at the latter end to make up for lost time.

In the normal course of events, I would then have been posted to engineering duties in the R.A.F. This would have made it very difficult to carry on with work on the engine, particularly if I had been posted overseas. Fortunately, however, my tutor, Mr. Roy Lubbock, M.A., had been taking a great interest in my work on the engine and had brought it to the notice of the Director of Education of the Air Ministry. The latter, influenced by the advice of Lubbock, and by his own interest in the project, succeeded in obtaining Air Ministry[6] approval for a postgraduate year on research work. This meant, in effect, that I would be able to devote the greater part of my time to work on the engine. In this way the Air Ministry made an important contribution to the very early phases.

By July, 1936, the initial stages of manufacture had started; I visited High Duty Alloys at Slough to watch the making of the compressor impeller forging. A few weeks later I visited Firth Vickers in Sheffield to witness the forging of the turbine wheel — not an easy process.

Our combustion experiments started at the beginning of October, 1936, and continued into December.

Laidlaw was present at many of the tests and our various experiments were the result of joint consultation. The apparatus was very crude, but nevertheless we soon satisfied ourselves that the intensity of combustion we required was possible, but we had to make many experiments before we felt we had sufficient data to embark on the design of a combustion chamber for the engine.

The site of the tests was immediately outside the B.T-H. turbine factory and in the open air. Overhead, built out as an extension of the offices, was the turbine factory planning office. This structure gave us some protection from the weather, but its occupants had a lot to put up with when tests were in progress below. The noise was often deafening, particularly on occasions when the combustion process was really a series of high-frequency explosions. In addition to the very considerable noise nuisance, the apparatus often emitted dense clouds of fuel vapour and smoke, much of which found its way into the planning office. Once, when the planning office staff returned from lunch they found that every desk and table had been swept clean. Everything — pens, papers, ink-pots, books, instruments — was on the floor. They thought a practical joker with a very distorted sense of humour had been at work, until we started up another test below them and the violent vibration made everything start "walking" again. One of them asserted that the linoleum on the floor rose and fell in waves when we were at work underneath. On one occasion when the fumes were particularly dense, the female staff retired to the cloakroom and refused to return until somebody had done something about it. The Chief Engineer of the B.T-H. would probably have thrown us out if he had seen some of the things that went on outside. The apparatus was usually anything but leak-proof and large pools of fuel would collect underneath. Sooner or later flaming drops set them alight and we, conducting the tests, would be stepping between the pools of flame like demons in an inferno.

The turbine drawing office was only a few yards away and they also got the benefit of the noise and fumes. It was said that Power Jets' drawings could be recognised by their smell — of fuel oil — because in the intervals of combustion testing, I would disappear into the drawing office to see how things were going on there. (The arrangements between Power Jets and the B.T-H. required that I should give my approval to all the drawings by signing them.)

Despite the attention which these experiments attracted, surprisingly little information leaked out, and only a few of those actually working on the project knew what it was all about. Some people naturally supposed that we were trying to develop a flame-thrower. Others thought we were merely mad!

Nineteen thirty-six ended with most of the detail design work completed and with manufacture of the engine fairly well advanced in spite of many irritating delays. I have not the details of the total expenditure of Power Jets up to that time, but it was probably of the order of £3,000. We were paying for the work as we went along — the B.T-H. were submitting monthly bills.

The availability of materials capable of withstanding the combination of stress and temperature which the design required was a vital factor. It was, in fact, the lack of these materials that had been the chief barrier to the successful development of a gas turbine in the past. To some extent there had been a vicious circle operating. Until suitable materials existed a gas turbine was not a practical possibility. On the other hand, until the gas turbine itself existed, there was not a great demand for the materials. However, certain other engineering needs had tended to break this vicious circle. The increasing demands made on the exhaust valves of aero engines had resulted in steady progress in the development of creep-resisting steels. ("Creep" is the slow extension which a high stress causes in a material at a high temperature.) A steel known as "Stayblade" made by Firth Vickers appeared to have properties adequate for our purpose, and so we used this material for the wheel and blades of the turbine. Materials for the compressor impeller and casing presented a less serious problem, because they were not exposed to very high temperatures. Nevertheless, they had to be of very good quality particularly in the case of the highly stressed impeller. For this we selected an aluminium alloy known as RR.56.[7]

During the first three months of 1937 we made steady progress in manufacture and by the end of March were very nearly ready for the climax for which we had all been so impatiently waiting — the first test run of the engine.

We had heard vague rumours of work in other countries, but the Air Ministry told us that nothing was known of such developments officially. We now know, of course, that the Germans were working almost exactly in parallel with us. While the B.T-H. were building my engine, the aircraft firm of Heinkel were building a turbo-jet engine to the design of a young engineer named von Ohain.

The engine was slightly damaged during mechanical tests in March when, while spinning the rotor with compressed air on the turbine, the compressor impeller fouled its casing at a speed of 9,000 r.p.m. It was an inauspicious start. We could not afford new parts so had to be satisfied with cleaning up the damaged ones.

CHAPTER 11

The Aeronautical Research Committee, the Director of Scientific Research of the Air Ministry and the Engine Section of the R.A.E. were all aware of what we were doing, but so far were not taking more than a benevolent interest. I was keeping them informed of our work from the technical point of view and Whyte was trying to get the Air Ministry to give some financial support.

Dr. D. R. Pye,[8] then the Deputy Director of Scientific Research, in December, 1935, wished me every success in my "bold venture outside the limits of designs which have hitherto been built", but he made it clear in reply to a letter from Bramson that his view was that what we were doing constituted "long-range research".

Our best friend was Sir Henry Tizard, Chairman of the Aeronautical Research Committee, the function of which was to advise the Air Ministry on future research. As far as I know, the first time Tizard heard about our work was when he met members of Power Jets and myself at a Cambridge University Air Squadron Dinner in March, 1936. As a result of what was said then, Whyte sent Tizard a copy of Bramson's report. As time went on Tizard's interest increased. During October, 1936, in a letter to Whyte he said that it was time someone made a bold experiment of this kind, though he thought that Power Jets would have to be prepared for a long series of costly experiments before a tolerable efficiency would be obtained. A few days later I had lunch with him and he hinted to me that the time had come for a more active interest by the Aeronautical Research Committee. As a result of Sir Henry's views (so I believe), the Director of Scientific Research asked Power Jets to submit a "write up" of the engine and said that this would be sent to the R.A.E. for their opinion. At the same time it was hinted that the A.R.C. might take the view that the work of Power Jets might yield information of sufficient value to justify some financial assistance from the Air Ministry towards the cost of research.

At the R.A.E. the people mostly concerned were Dr. A. A. Griffith and Hayne Constant. The former was head of the Engine Section. (As already recorded, I had first discussed my turbo-jet proposals with Griffith at the end of 1929.) Both were very interested in our work though they thought I was over-optimistic in some of my design assumptions. Griffith had been a believer in the gas turbine as a means of driving a propeller for many years. As early as 1926 he had been an advocate of the gas turbine as an aircraft power plant, but had hardly been more successful in influencing the Air Ministry than I, a little over three years later. A limited amount of testing of small-scale components was sanctioned in 1929, but otherwise he received little encouragement in spite of the fact that he had already established a high reputation in the aeronautical world. All direct work on the gas turbine at the R.A.E. ceased from 1930 to 1937.

I received a copy of Griffith's report on the Power Jets' engine early in March, 1937. The final conclusion was:

> ...in its present form the proposed jet propulsion system cannot compete with the conventional power plant in any case where economical flight is demanded (e.g. the transport of the maximum percentage of useful load over given distance). It is of value only for special purposes such as the attainment of high speed or high altitude for a short time in cases where take-off requirements are not stringent.

This report and a paper by Constant, once more setting out the case for the gas turbine driving a propeller as power plant for aircraft, were discussed by the Engine Sub-Committee of the A.R.C. Sir Henry Tizard took a prominent part in the discussions which led to a strong recommendation that the Air Ministry should take up the development of the internal combustion turbine as a matter of urgency. In consequence, the R.A.E. were authorised to go ahead with their proposals for a gas turbine-propeller engine in co-operation with the firm of Metropolitan Vickers. The arrangement between the R.A.E. and Metropolitan Vickers was rather similar to that which existed between Power Jets and the B.T-H.

There was another important difference between the R.A.E.'s project and ours, apart from the use of a propeller. Griffith and Constant favoured the axial flow compressor in preference to the centrifugal type, because they felt that what it promised in greater efficiency and reduction of frontal area more than compensated for the greater mechanical complexity.

CHAPTER 12

We had our first test run on April 12th, 1937.

I recorded it in my diary as follows:

> Pilot jet successfully ignited at 1,000 r.p.m. Speed raised to 2,000 r.p.m. by motor. I requested a further raising of speed to 2,500 r.p.m. and during this process I opened valve 'B' and the unit suddenly ran away. Probably started at about 2,300 and using only about 5 h.p. starting power … noted that return pipe from jet was overheating badly. Flame tube red hot at inner radius; combustion very bad…

Valve "B" referred to was the controlling valve and the "return pipe from jet" was the pipe carrying fuel from the main burner back to the tank. "The unit suddenly ran away" meant that the revolutions of the engine had increased rapidly and out of control, not, as some might suppose, that the whole outfit had gone charging across the turbine factory!

This record was, of course, a far from adequate description of the situation.

The engine mounted on its test truck was situated on a test site on the gallery of the turbine factory. The jet pipe extended into the open air through a window. In addition to the engine the test truck carried the 20 kw. starter motor, the instrument panel and controls, and a hand magneto with leads connected to a high tension sparking plug in the combustion chamber.

A safety "screen" had been erected around the engine consisting of three rectangular sheets of steel plating about one inch thick, two of them standing vertically and the other placed across the top. This was considered to be very necessary because if a turbine over-speeds it is liable to burst, with disastrous results. Pieces may be hurled through the air at speeds of the order of 1,200 ft. per second — that is, almost as fast as a rifle bullet. There had been several occasions in the past when steam turbines had burst with fatal results.

I was at the controls.

When all was ready the fuel pump (driven by a separate electric motor) was switched on and one of the test hands engaged the starter coupling (which was designed to disengage as soon as the main rotor of the engine overran the starting motor). I then gave the signal for starting. When the starter motor had raised the speed about 1,000 r.p.m., I opened the control valve which admitted fuel to a "pilot" burner in the combustion chamber and rapidly turned the handle of the hand magneto to ignite the finely atomised spray of fuel which this burner emitted. An observer peering through a quartz observation window in the combustion chamber gave me a "thumbs up" sign to show that the pilot flame was alight. I signalled for an increase of speed of the starter motor, and as the tachometer indicated 2,000 r.p.m. I gradually opened the main control valve. For a second or two the speed of the engine increased slowly and then, with a rising shriek like an air-raid siren, the speed began to rise rapidly, and large patches of red heat became visible on the combustion chamber casing. The engine was obviously out of control. The B.T-H. personnel, realising what this meant, took to their heels in varying directions, one or two of them into large steam turbine exhaust castings which were standing nearby, and which made useful shelters for such emergencies. I screwed down the control valve at once but this had no immediate effect and the speed continued to rise. Fortunately, the acceleration ceased at about 8,000 r.p.m., and slowly the revs dropped again.

This incident did not do my nervous system any good at all. I have rarely been so frightened.

The next evening, after an alteration to the fuel system which we supposed would improve matters, we tried again. This time things were even more alarming. The engine accelerated out of control from about 1,500 r.p.m. without the main fuel control being opened at all. Though I switched off the fuel pump thereby cutting off all fuel supplies, the speed rose rapidly. In addition sheets of flame belched from the jet pipe, and clouds of fuel vapour jetting from leaking joints were ignited by patches of red heat on the combustion chamber. Flames were leaping and dancing in mid-air above the engine. The B.T-H. personnel, alerted by the earlier experience, disappeared even more rapidly. Fortunately, once more, the uncontrolled acceleration did not take the engine beyond 8,000 r.p.m.

Later that evening Laidlaw, who was staying at the same hotel in Rugby, insisted on my drinking considerable quantities of red wine to calm my nerves after this alarming experience.

There was a simple explanation. Owing to an oversight in the arrangement of the fuel system, it was possible for the main burner to inject fuel into the combustion chamber every time the fuel pump was switched on. Though this injection only happened for a few seconds at a time, fuel pump tests were frequent, and so the amount of the fuel unknowingly injected into the combustion chamber was considerable. The shape of the combustion chamber permitted this fuel to accumulate below the fuel burner. It was this "lake" of fuel which was responsible for the "runaways".

We then arranged to drain the combustion chamber before each attempt to start, but despite this the engine ran away again on the third attempt. This time because a spring which formed part of the burner mechanism was weakened by overheating.

(The burner injected "upstream" and was therefore itself immersed in flame.)

Partly as a result of this experience and partly on Laidlaw's advice we decided to try "downstream" injection of the fuel. We then made our fourth attempt and this time ran under control up to 7,600 r.p.m., but shut down when one of the patches of bright red heat on the combustion chamber walls set fire to the ignition cables.

In further attempts, despite modifications made in efforts to improve the combustion, though the engine would generally run under control, it would not accelerate beyond 8,500 r.p.m. apparently because any further opening of the control meant that the extra fuel injected was burning, not in the combustion chamber, but in the jet pipe after the turbine.

Despite opposition from Laidlaw, who wished to continue with modifications to the downstream injection system, I insisted on an experiment with a system, based on the principle of the primus stove, in which a kerosene boiler in the combustion chamber injected vaporised kerosene upstream.

One morning I gave Collingham a graphic description of what had been happening and how frightened I had been. He was a blunt Yorkshireman and told me that I didn't know what it was to be frightened. "You should have been standing near one of our vertical turbines when it jumped out of its bearings, then you would have known what it was to be frightened," said he, or words to that effect. Samuelson and Collingham were present for the first time when we made our attempt to run with the kerosene boiler. Starting procedure was normal in so far as anything could be described as normal up to this stage. When I opened the main control, the engine accelerated smoothly enough at first and for a moment or two appeared to be under perfect control, then once more it ran away with the usual terrifying crescendo of noise, and a great jet of flame from the propelling nozzle. Again there was a rapid exodus. The story goes that Collingham was out of the turbine factory and into the nearby locomotive shed before anybody else got started. As usual, I remained rooted to the spot, not because I was particularly brave, but because I seemed almost to be paralysed, also I think that deep down I felt fairly confident that it would not run away to a speed which would make the possibility of bursting likely.[9] It did not, in fact, exceed half speed on this occasion. What had happened was that the kerosene boiler hadn't sufficient heating surface and after a few seconds it "primed" and liquid kerosene was injected through the nozzle instead of vapour. This ended our one attempt to run on vaporised kerosene during this series of tests, though we were to revert to it later.

This incident had embarrassing after-effects that evening. Each time I thought of Collingham's rapid exit — associated with his earlier remarks — I was seized with uncontrollable fits of laughter. These attacks would come on me without warning while I was sitting in the lounge or dining-room of the hotel and must have intrigued the other residents more than a little. It was undoubtedly a "hysterical" reaction from acute nervous tension.

Later Collingham told me "I'll admit I was frightened — in fact, I was badly frightened."

This incident made me more willing to accept Laidlaw's recommendations to try downstream injection again. Our experiments along these lines led to some improvement, and after making various alterations we managed to reach higher speeds under control. One of these test runs was stopped — very rapidly — when the compressor impeller seized in its casing at a speed of 12,000 r.p.m. This brought the engine to rest in little more than one second with a piercing shriek. Bramson was present on this occasion and his instinctive reaction was to turn to run, but before he had taken one step the engine had stopped. Walter Smith, the Shop Superintendent, put his hand on Bramson's shoulder and said, with a strong north-country accent, "It's no use runnin', sir, it'll soon catch you if it wants!" This remark was most appreciated by those who knew that Walter Smith himself had disappeared down the factory at high speed on at least three occasions.

The damage due to the seizure, and the temporary overheating that had occurred during the uncontrolled accelerations, though not serious, all contributed to a general deterioration of the engine, but we were far from being able to afford new parts, so had to content ourselves with repairing as best we could.

By the latter end of April it was very clear that we still had a long way to go on the combustion problem, and that the compressor was well below its design efficiency.

We made strenuous efforts to improve the engine by relatively minor modifications, but only with moderate success. By early July I was forced to conclude that a major alteration to the general arrangement would be necessary before we could hope to reach our target. We finally abandoned our attempts to improve matters with the general arrangement as it then was on the 23rd August, 1937.

A further reason for suspending tests at that time was a request from the Chief Engineer of the B.T-H., H. N. Sporborg, that Power Jets should find another site. After observing a test run up to 13,600 r.p.m., he had come to the conclusion that to continue testing in the open factory was too dangerous. Moreover, our testing caused work in other parts of the factory to slow down or stop altogether.

Sporborg eventually agreed to allow Power Jets to rent part of their disused foundry at Lutterworth — the Ladywood Works — for further test work.

CHAPTER 13

The months of May, June and July of 1937 brought with them other anxieties. In June negotiations opened between Power Jets and the Air Ministry to find ways and means by which the Ministry could contribute to the cost of the work.

The need for further financial assistance was becoming acute. Falk & Partners, having raised about £7,000, were saying that they were having difficulty in raising further money. Their option to increase their holding to £20,000 was due to expire on the 27th July. When it became clear that Falk & Partners were not going to take up their option, Williams, Tinling and I told Whyte that if the money were not forthcoming we would exercise our full rights under the Four-Party Agreement and take over control of the Company.

I still find it difficult to understand why those financing the Company should have begun to get "cold feet" just at the moment when there were clear indications that the Air Ministry was going to help financially — even though this help was likely to be well below that which we considered right and proper. Sir Henry Tizard's attitude should have been a further encouragement. A few days after a talk with Whyte he placed his views on record in a letter (dated 22nd June, 1937) as follows:

> You ask for my opinion about Whittle's scheme.
>
> I think there is nothing inherently unsound in his ideas. He may possibly be somewhat optimistic in some of his predictions, but even allowing for that, I think it highly probable that if he has the necessary financial support and encouragement, he will succeed in producing a new type of

power plant for aircraft. I am particularly interested in this work because I think that if we are to provide the high powers which will be necessary for aircraft of the future, we must develop some type of turbine. Further, the fact that such an engine would use heavy oil is of great importance from the point of view of defence and of commerce.

I have a very high opinion of Flight Lieutenant Whittle. He has the ability and the energy and the enthusiasm for work of this nature. He has also an intimate knowledge of practical conditions — this combination of qualities is rare and deserves the utmost encouragement. I sincerely hope he will get the necessary finance because I think you will have to make up your mind that a large expenditure will be necessary before final success is reached. My general opinion of the importance of this work leads me to express the hope that the money will be raised privately so that the knowledge that it is going on will not be widespread.

P.S. — Of course, I do not mean to imply that success is certain. All new schemes of this kind must be regarded as 'gambles' in the initial stages. I do think, however, that this is a better gamble than many I know of on which money has been spent.

This was a very valuable letter to have "on the record", coming as it did from the Chairman of the Aeronautical Research Committee.

In addition to these encouraging signs, the B.T-H. were reacting more favourably than hitherto to the suggestion that they should take shares. (Though it was nearly six months before they did so.)

Internal tension increased. Falk & Partners asked for an extension of the option. Williams, Tinling and I held a "council of war" and decided that we would not agree to any extension of the option but that we would give them time to find the money. There was a complete deadlock, which developed into a major crisis on the 8th July when Whyte told Williams that the method of finance up to then must stop, but that to carry the Company over the next few days, O. T. Falk & Partners would lend a small sum to the Company.

The option duly expired on the 27th July. Falk & Partners continued to finance Power Jets by loan.

This financial crisis was long drawn out and it was not until the beginning of November, 1937, that new agreements were signed. Nevertheless, it must be said to the credit of Falk & Partners that there was no actual cessation of work through the stopping of finance.

These internal difficulties had an adverse effect, I believe, on the negotiations with the Air Ministry. Early in July the Air Ministry had proposed a contract worth £10,000 altogether. There was also a hint that we could hope for a further research contract on satisfactory completion of the one then proposed.

Whyte and I agreed that this offer was reasonably satisfactory, but about a month later there was a sinister hint that the Contracts Directorate would require to be assured of the financial standing of the Company before giving the contract.

Matters proceeded very slowly.

Towards the end of September the prospective contract was reduced to £5,000. Even at this figure it was not signed until the following March.

The B.T-H. were also blowing hot and cold about subscribing money.

Sporborg had given Whyte the impression that the B.T-H. were willing to put money into Power Jets. The sum mentioned was £2,500. But towards the end of July both Sporborg and Samuelson were saying that there was little value in Power Jets' published patents. I pointed out that what had been published by no means represented the whole of the patent position. A factor influencing them on the other side was their knowledge that Power Jets were likely to receive an Air Ministry contract. All the same it was not until January, 1938, that they actually put in their £2,500.

The supplementary agreement which modified the Four-Party Agreement was dated 1st November, 1937. Falk & Partners undertook to find a further £3,000 within fourteen days, and the "A" shareholders agreed not to deprive the "B" shareholders of their voting rights, or of their right to nominate half the Board. But the right to appoint the Chairman passed to the majority of the "A" shareholders (i.e. myself); thus, the control of the Company passed into the hands of Williams, Tinling and myself.

We agreed that we would allow Whyte to remain Chairman. This was not so strange as it may sound. We had a high opinion of his integrity and ability and he had convinced us that he had an intense interest in the development and believed it to be extremely important in the national interest. We felt confident that once this particular crisis was behind us he would continue to further the interests of Power Jets to the best of his ability.

CHAPTER 14

In the meantime my postgraduate year at Cambridge had expired (about July) but D.S.R. had been successful in getting the Air Member for Personnel's approval and Treasury sanction for me to be posted to the Special Duty List to continue work on the engine, thus this work became my official full-time employment. The family therefore moved to Rugby early in October. This made things very much easier for me because of the big reduction in travelling time.

After the family moved to Rugby I was, apart from visits to sub-contracting firms and to London for sundry meetings, spending most of my time in the B.T-H. works. I had managed to insinuate myself into an unusually privileged position. Samuelson had, earlier in 1937, agreed to let me share an office with one of the senior engineers working on our project. Nobody questioned my frequent incursions into the factory or the drawing office, and to all intents and purposes, I and the B.T-H. engineers and draughtsmen working on the job were operating as a single team.

My chief preoccupation at the latter end of 1937 was with the design and manufacture of the new parts for the reconstruction of the engine, and with modifications to those of the original parts which we still proposed to use. We were, of course, using as much of the original engine as possible in order to keep down the cost. Much of the design work was governed by this requirement. We were using the same rotor except for new turbine blades; the same compressor casing, though greatly modified, and so on. The major changes were to the sheet metal components.

During December I was spending a fair amount of time writing a detailed report on the first series of tests in anticipation of the Air Ministry research contract, under which this report would be required.

The monthly bills from the B.T-H. were beginning to rise. For the most part they had been of the order of from £100 to £200, but the figure for November was almost £400, which caused some concern in Power Jets.[10] The B.T-H. readily agreed that I should be allowed to check the costs in detail every month, and so this task became part of my activities from December 1937 onwards. I learned a great deal from the process and was also able to achieve some minor savings. I had noted that there were usually a few additional test fitters standing around when tests were in progress; I naturally thought they were "keen types" — until I discovered that they had been booking their time to the job. The Cost Accountant was not, of course, to know who were needed and who were not. Once I was aware of these things I was able to guard against them.

In October, 1937, we started more combustion tests. We had come to realise that though we would have no great difficulty in achieving the intensity of combustion we required, there were still many problems to be solved. We had to avoid an excessive loss of pressure; we had to get an even temperature distribution in the combustion chamber discharge; soot formation had to be avoided; there must be no distortion of combustion chamber parts due to local over-heating, and so on. This new series of tests began on October 22nd and continued until well into December, on the same site as before. Once more Laidlaw and I collaborated closely. We tried many experiments, but most of the effort went into the development of a suitable arrangement for the injection of vaporised kerosene, with which we found it was possible to get very short flames.

I had feared that my appointment to the Special Duty List would prejudice my Service career, but my anxiety on this score proved to be groundless when my promotion to Squadron Leader was gazetted on 6th December, 1937.

CHAPTER 15

During the early weeks of 1938 work started on the relatively minor alterations necessary to prepare our section of the Ladywood Works for engine testing. Williams relieved me of much of the detail in connection with this. I also had the assistance of Mr. Victor Crompton who had joined Power Jets as their first employee in the new year.

The economy with which we were preparing the premises for use may be judged from the fact that we spent about £200 on the job.

As already indicated, the Ladywood Works had been the B.T-H. foundry many years before, but at this time, except for a part used for storage by the B.T-H., the low buildings were derelict and dilapidated. There was foundry sand everywhere.

The mysterious comings and goings of Crompton and myself intrigued the Lutterworth police. Those were days in which there were a number of I.R.A. bomb outrages and I understand that one theory was that we were I.R.A. terrorists using the deserted premises to make bombs. Crompton showed one suspicious policeman round the parts we were proposing to use, but of course did not disclose what we were doing. The engine was still under reconstruction at the B.T-H. and so there was nothing to see which, if anything, made the police more suspicious than ever. Maybe they also heard the occasional shot from my .22 rifle when I tried to pot a rabbit in a nearby field from my office window.

While the reconstruction of the engine was in progress, I was keeping a closer eye on the detail design than hitherto. Amongst other things, this led to the discovery that, according to me, the turbine blades of the engine as tested between the previous April and August had been incorrectly designed, and that there was a sharp divergence of view between the B.T-H. engineers and myself about the principles of turbine blade design.

There had been a number of technical controversies before this, but usually discussion had led to a satisfactory compromise. There had been no argument about the turbine blade design, because I had assumed that the B.T-H. engineers were far more competent in such matters than I was, and so I had left it entirely to them.

At this point, it is necessary to be a little technical to explain the nature of the controversy.

Everybody has seen the vortex or whirlpool which often forms when water runs out of a bath or washbasin and most people will have noticed that the water spins more rapidly as it spirals towards the centre. Also that as the water goes towards the centre it goes "downhill" i.e. the velocity increases as the pressure decreases. In an ideal vortex of this kind the product of the whirl velocity and radial distance from the centre remains constant. This is the characteristic of a free circular vortex. The pressure rise from the inside to the outside is caused by the centrifugal force of the whirling fluid.

I had taken it for granted that the flow of hot gases or steam from a ring of turbine nozzle blades would have the characteristics of a vortex and had supposed that steam turbine engineers designed accordingly.

I discovered that there was a fundamental difference of view on this point early in December, 1937.

My diary for the 4th December recorded:

> Am roped into a heated argument which is going on between Collingham, Cheshire, Randles[11] and one of Cheshire's

> colleagues. The position is that the new nozzle and blade design involves an end thrust on the bearing of 1,500 lb. as against the original 180 lb. Collingham and I say that the bearing could not possibly stand this and the net result is that Cheshire is instructed to return to an impulse section.

I was a very puzzled man when I left the meeting to which this entry referred, and so spent a few days revising my turbine theory and trying to account for so large a difference in end thrust for two designs of turbine blades intended for the same job. I could not reconcile the figures at all, and so set about trying to find out what the engineers in the blade design office had done without betraying what, I supposed, was my own ignorance. I found the answer when I casually asked Cheshire one morning what their figure was for the pressure difference from the inside to the outside of the annular ring of gases leaving the nozzle ring. He was very surprised by the question and told me that they assumed that the pressure was constant. I pointed out that according to me, in the case of our engine at least, there was a very considerable difference of pressure due to centrifugal force. I showed him my calculations and conclusions. Cheshire was rapidly "converted" and inferred, much to my surprise, that I had made a fundamental discovery in turbine design.

According to my theory, the change of angle or "twist" from root to tip of the turbine blades ought to be twice as great as that provided in the B.T-H. design. Also it led to a quite different result for the end thrust on the bearing. Indeed, according to me the end thrust was negligibly small.

It may seem a very strange thing that specialists on turbine design had overlooked a phenomenon which I had more or less taken for granted. I heard somebody once define a practical man as "one who puts into practice the errors of his forefathers". This blade business was a good example of it and of how, if habits of thought become deeply rooted, errors may persist from generation to generation. Turbines had slowly evolved from the primitive form in which a few steam jets (often four only) spaced evenly, impinged on the blades or "buckets" of a single wheel. In such cases it had been reasonable to assume that the velocity and pressure in the blast from each jet was uniform and to design the blades accordingly. It had seemingly occurred to no one that as jets were made more numerous and placed closer together until "full peripheral" admission was achieved, there would be a fundamental change in the nature of the flow.

Randles also was quickly converted to my view and said that there was no doubt that it was a matter of fundamental importance, and, as far as he knew, quite a new concept in turbine engineering. Apart from Cheshire and Randles, however, my theories met with the strongest opposition and a certain amount of resentment. This last was understandable. No one who has been a specialist in some particular field for years is likely to feel pleased when some young "amateur" tells him that he has been wrong from the start.

I had a sheet metal nozzle ring made up and used it for tests, using the same compressed air supply as we used for combustion tests. These experiments largely verified my predictions, but even these demonstrations left many of the B.T-H. engineers unconvinced.

There was another important piece of evidence in support of my theory. A B.T-H. turbine which had been operated for some time by the purchaser had provided clear evidence that the end thrust was in the opposite direction from that allowed for in the design. This was easily explained by "vortex theory" but some preferred to believe that there must be some other explanation.

When the controversy was at its height, some wag in the blade design office composed the following piece of doggerel:

Some steam, as it passed through a nozzle one day,
Was heard, as it turned round the corner, to say,
"Here we go gathering nuts and may,
Here we go into a vortex."

But the poor old steam, it whirled and swirled,
And left the buckets all twisted and twirled,
All because someone had plained and not purled,
And had not allowed for the vortex.

And so at a vortex you must not sneeze
Or muck about with the vortices,
Because, if you want high efficiencies
You must design for a vortex.

The immediate result so far as the engine was concerned was that, at my insistence, Collingham agreed to make the turbine blades of the reconstructed engine in accordance with angles specified by me.

When I reported the matter to my colleagues in Power Jets they, Bramson in particular, were very excited about it and insisted that a patent specification be filed at once, and so this was done. When the B. T-H. were notified of this, it did nothing to reduce the resentment already aroused, and the affair more or less left a permanent scar on the relationship between Power Jets and the B.T-H.

Later I discovered that others were waking up to vortex flow. Griffith of the R.A.E. told me that he had used the same theory in R.A.E. designs and that others were at least aware of the phenomenon. Later still when evidence began to accumulate that I might be right, Samuelson gave instructions to re-blade one of their experimental steam turbines to test the theory. Some months later, these tests were made in circumstances which increased my resentment about the B.T-H. attitude towards the business. In my eyes I had done them a great service, but some of the seniors acted as though I had done them an injury. Though I had helped in the design of the blades of this experimental turbine, it reached my ears that instructions had been given to carry out the tests at a time when I was not in the factory. When I protested emphatically about this, he persisted in his refusal to allow me to be present at the test, but somewhat reluctantly agreed that I should see the results. These fell short of my expectations, but nevertheless, showed a distinct improvement on the best obtained with blading designed by conventional methods.

CHAPTER 16

During the first few months of 1938 the financial position of Power Jets continued to be precarious — every penny had to be watched and all contributions were gratefully received. Amongst those who backed their faith in me by putting in small sums were Randles, two of the B.T-H. draughtsmen engaged on our work — Atkinson and Richardson — and a few of my personal friends who had only the vaguest notion of what it was all about.

The Air Ministry was still hesitating about risking public money on the venture. Dr. Pye had become the Director of Scientific Research and his deputy was W. S. Farren.[12] There were times when it seemed that they did not trust me personally. After a talk with Farren on the 28th March I recorded in my diary:

> He says that my general policy has been such that they have not felt that they could give me their confidence. He seems to have several erroneous impressions. He thinks I was connected with the delay in signing the contract. I told him I had refused to take part in discussions on the subject. I left still in the dark as to why there should be a misinterpretation of my motives and feeling rather depressed that this should have happened. I gave him as strong an assurance as I could that I put my duty as a Serving Officer before any commercial interests.

The reference to the delay in signing the contract suggests — correctly — that Power Jets were partly responsible for the delay at this time. Whyte tried to get a more favourable one than the one proposed. My own view was that the Company should accept the contract offered because I was convinced that we would do well enough to induce more favourable contracts later. I believe that D.S.R. and members of his staff were still hesitant about going on with Power Jets at all, because of the work the R.A.E. were doing. (The R.A.E. had been authorised to go ahead with the design of their propeller gas turbine project a few days after the beginning of our first series of engine tests.) Another factor which seemed to antagonise D.S.R. was that Bramson and myself were impatient to have work started on an experimental aeroplane. D.S.R., of course, felt that we were trying to run before we could walk and that we should confine all our energies to making the engine work.

The usual series of hold-ups inevitable with experimental work delayed the completion of the engine and it was not until almost exactly a year after the first test in April, 1937, that we resumed test running.

We had purchased a 10 h.p. B.S.A. car engine, second-hand, to use as a starter motor and this, being very much lighter than the 20 kw electric motor previously used, made it possible to use the truck complete with its wheels, and, in fact, the engine mounted on its truck was towed the seven miles from the B.T-H. factory to the Ladywood Works.

Crompton was still the only Power Jets' employee and so I asked Samuelson to allow B.T-H. fitters and test hands to work at Lutterworth as and when required. He agreed, and so over the Easter weekend Bentley, Berry and Bailey,[13] Crompton and I were busy preparing the engine for tests. We had our first run with the new arrangement on the 16th April, but then and during the next day or two we could only run at very low speeds because of fuel system troubles which were causing severe speed fluctuations. These troubles — fuel pump failures, swarf in the pipe lines and so on — prevented us from running for more than a few minutes at a time until the 29th April when we ran for over an hour up to the very modest speed of 8,200 r.p.m. This test was brought to an end when a large cleaning rag, which Crompton was using to mop up oil, was whisked out of his hand and drawn into the engine. I saw it go and shut down immediately, but not in time to save a certain amount of minor damage.

I still retain a vivid picture of Crompton (with Whyte in the background) standing frozen with a mingled look of horror and blank surprise.

We did not get very much test running with this edition of the engine, because on the 6th May, when running at 13,000 r.p.m., there was a disastrous failure of the turbine.

The engine had been running for 1 hour 45 minutes, when the failure occurred — much the longest run up to then. Inspection showed that the turbine nozzle assembly had been in contact with the turbine wheel and the intense rubbing at such a high speed had caused very severe overheating, as a result of which nine turbine blades had failed. There was, of course, much secondary damage; partly due to the detached blades and partly due to the severe "out of balance" caused by the failure.

However, this particular run was significant in that we at last succeeded in getting a few thrust readings. The thrust at 13,000 r.p.m. was 480 lb. as compared with an expected figure of about 550 lb. (It was rather a hazardous business getting a thrust reading, because it was necessary to go past the engine and note the reading of the spring balance which linked the test truck to a post embedded in the test room floor.)

I was greatly depressed by the breakdown, more particularly as I reproached myself for the weak feature in the design which was responsible for it. It also seemed at first as though very little of the engine could be saved.

To add to my depression, Power Jets was again in a low financial state. I had reason to think that Whyte and his colleagues were losing confidence both in the engine and in me, and I supposed that this disaster would destroy their faith entirely. I thought the effect on the Air Ministry and the B.T-H. would be the same, but in this at least I was wrong. Only a few days later Collingham remarked that having got so far, if it were their job, they would not stop even if they had to spend a further £60,000. D.D.S.R. (Farren) did not seem to be at all depressed by the failure and so my spirits recovered somewhat, in spite of many signs of strain (I was beginning to suffer from very severe headaches and other disturbances).

I soon decided that another major reconstruction would be necessary.

I abandoned the idea of trying to make a satisfactory arrangement with a single combustion chamber and produced a layout with ten small combustion chambers (to conform with the then existing ten discharge ducts from the compressor). This made a much more compact and lighter engine. I had avoided multiple combustion chambers hitherto because of the elaborate ignition arrangements seemingly required to ensure that all combustion chambers lit up properly. However, I hit upon the idea of "inter-connecting tubes" by means of which each combustion chamber would light up from its neighbour, so that it would only be necessary to provide initial ignition in one. (In practice, initial ignition is usually provided in two as an additional safeguard against a starting failure.)

The new arrangement received the general approval of Bramson, the B.T-H. engineers, Constant and D.S.R. Constant, like myself, was a little uneasy about the ten combustion chambers, but thought that we were following a promising line, and felt that our work was deserving of increased financial support from the Air Ministry. It may thus be seen that he was not allowing the R.A.E. work, in which he was directly interested, to influence his judgment where Power Jets was concerned.

Fortunately, inspection revealed that, with a little ingenuity, much more of the engine was usable than had seemed likely immediately after the breakdown.

To test whether the inter-connecting tube arrangement would work, we made a combustion chamber similar to the design intended for the engine, and with it we were able to satisfy ourselves that ignition would spread from one combustion chamber to another in the desired manner. For once a combustion test was not misleading, and inter-connecting tubes have remained a key feature in the design of engines with multiple combustion chambers from that day to this. We did not realise it at the time, but the apparatus we used was very similar to the successful combustion system which was developed much later after many heart-breaking disappointments. This was not the first time that we had been near the design which was ultimately to prove successful without realising it, because even in the very first series of combustion tests at the end of 1936 one of the systems tried (and designed by Laidlaw) had many of the characteristic features of the later successful combustion chambers. At the time it seemed hopeless, but, in the light of subsequent experience, it seems that some slight adjustment might have made all the difference and might have saved at least three years.

The financial situation of Power Jets, already difficult, was getting worse. Whyte hinted that Falk & Partners "had the position of several of their companies under review". I was getting tired of the continual worry about the precarious financial position and wanted to see the Company running on a less hand-to-mouth basis, and was pressing for the raising of more capital.

At the end of June, 1938, we had only about £1,200 in hand.

I told Whyte and the others that my time on the Special Duty List was time lost on normal R.A.F. duties and I would not think it worth while risking this damage to my career if the future of the Company was not put on a more certain basis.

Whyte argued that it was almost impossible to raise money in the circumstances. Since the Company had accepted an Air Ministry contract, the work had become subject to the Official Secrets Act and thus it was not possible to tell anybody enough about the work to induce them to risk their money.

Williams, Tinling and I were very disturbed by the very strong indication we had received that Falk & Partners were losing interest. Between ourselves we agreed that Power Jets' liabilities must not be allowed to exceed the available cash and that unless further capital were forthcoming within the next two weeks or so, work at the B.T-H. would have to stop until it was clear that we could pay for it. Williams told Whyte of our views and, in order to bring pressure to bear, told him that we felt we should report this position to the Air Ministry. This caused considerable tension. Whether or not it was because this threat was effective I don't know, but I then received a letter from Whyte intended to set my mind at rest about the financial position. He said he was taking immediate steps to improve matters and gave me an assurance that Falk & Partners would not let the Company get into difficulties.

Whyte's letter reassured me somewhat, but, so that there should be no misunderstanding, I warned him, a few days later, that if the Company got into debt and that the price of getting it out of debt was a modification of the rights of the "A" shareholders, then rather than agree to such modification we would allow the Company to go into liquidation. (In which event the patent rights would have reverted to Williams, Tinling and myself, and theoretically at least, we would have been in a position to negotiate for the formation of another Company.)

My uneasiness about the position as a whole had reached the ears of D.S.R. and his staff. When I had a talk with D.S.R. at the Air Ministry, Dr. Pye said that he was disturbed by suggestions that I was losing confidence in the engine. I told him that my confidence in the ultimate success of the engine was as strong as ever, but I had come to realise that it was going to be a much longer job than I had previously supposed. I explained that the mechanical troubles we had been having were disheartening in themselves, but on top of this I had the worry of the financial situation. In these circumstances my Service career was more important to me than the engine, and I was not prepared to go on unless I had a clear indication that the Air Ministry believed that it was in the best interests of the Service that I should do so. D.S.R. then said that it had been virtually decided that I was to remain on the Special Duty List for another year, and asked whether that was in accordance with my wishes. I said I was quite happy to go on if the Ministry considered that that was where my duty lay. Farren, who was present, said that it would only be their wish if they were satisfied that I still strongly wished to go on, because their whole interest in the job rested on their confidence in me and on my confidence in the eventual success of the work. If I gave up, then so far as they were concerned the work could stop; they would not consider appointing a successor.

It may be seen that I was seeking to get the Ministry to recognise that my work was important to the Service, and that it should be acknowledged as consistent with my duty as a serving officer.

I made further attempts to get the B.T-H. to put in more money, but though Collingham had expressed the opinion that having got so far, "it would be a crime to stop", Sporborg said that the B.T-H. were not prepared to put in any more money at that time. He thought the Air Ministry ought to be giving much more support than they were doing.

There was some indication that the Air Ministry would do more. Whyte received a strong hint from Tizard in September that there might be a substantial increase in financial assistance from the Air Ministry. I passed this on to Sporborg, and repeated Tizard's comment that "a few thousands would be a small insurance for the B.T-H. to pay to be in on the ground floor of what might prove to be a new industry".

It was evident that the B.T-H. were sceptical of the value of Power Jets' patents, and no doubt they (rightly) argued to themselves that they were getting a great deal of valuable experience from the job for nothing.

At Whyte's request, Bramson summarised the technical position as it stood on the 19th July, 1938, as follows:

(*a*) The work done to date constitutes a quantitative experimental verification of the principle underlying the Whittle system of jet propulsion.

(*b*) At 73.3% of the design speed, quantitative verification of the jet engine has been obtained and there is a strong probability of obtaining it shortly at full speed.

(*c*) Experimental evidence already makes it practically certain that the thermal efficiency of the unit (which it has not yet been possible to measure) cannot be so far below estimate as to nullify the positive results.

(*d*) The feasibility of jet propulsion for aircraft has been, for the first time, experimentally established.

By the 30th June, 1938, private capital subscribed had reached the sum of just under £13,500 of which about 25% had been found by Williams and friends of us three "A" shareholders. Of the remainder, about half was from the B.T-H. and J. & G. Weir Ltd. The direct expenditure on the engine totalled just under £9,000.

CHAPTER 17

Serious testing of the engine in its third form began on the 26th October, 1938.

The test running was covered by a new Air Ministry contract. The old one had been terminated after a total payment of £1,900 — £1,000 for a report on the first series of tests and £900 for proportion of running which had been done in the second series. Under the new contract the Air Ministry agreed to pay for the greater part of the cost of the second reconstruction, and for twenty hours' experimental running at the rate of £200 per hour. The total sum involved was about £6,000.

For the first few tests a kerosene boiler mounted in the jet pipe supplied fuel vapour to each of the ten combustion chambers. We soon found that this arrangement was unsatisfactory because the boiler proved to be too big an obstruction to the flow of the high-speed gases in the jet pipe, so I decided to change to individual vaporisers in each combustion chamber. This meant a temporary suspension of engine tests while Crompton and I made a further series of combustion tests to evolve a suitable arrangement. When it seemed that we had succeeded, we resumed engine testing in December 1938.

Power Jets' staff had then been augmented by the addition of two night-watchmen, an office boy (Hancock), and my secretary, Mary Phillips, making five employees altogether. Hitherto I had shared the typing with Crompton and it was a great relief to have secretarial assistance. Amongst other things, it became possible to make much more detailed records of test work.

A later addition to our strength was Sandy, the watchdog (price: ten shillings from the Battersea Dogs' Home). For a watchdog he had a highly nervous disposition. Whenever I fired my .22 rifle from my office window in a vain attempt to get a rabbit, Sandy would vanish at high speed and have to be collected from about five miles away by Hancock.

Our office furnishings were few and mostly purchased by Crompton from second-hand dealers in Lutterworth, piece by piece as the necessity arose. We still had bare floorboards, and the walls were whitewashed, unplastered brick. My office was at the head of a flight of stairs and was on the corner of the building with the window overlooking the railway. Its situation made telephone conversations rather difficult at times. It seemed to me that the engine-drivers always chose to stop and blow off steam a few feet from my window. The more obliging drivers would shut off when I leaned out of the window and waved the telephone receiver at them.

Our progress in the early months of 1939 was slow. At first we were impeded by troubles in the fuel system, and it was not until the 20th February that we were able to raise the speed above 8,000 r.p.m.

Our difficulties at this stage had an adverse effect on D.S.R. and his staff. I was given to understand that they felt that we were not making as much progress as we should. It felt that way to me as well, but it did not help to know that they were becoming pessimistic.

On the 22nd February, (1939) Farren told me that my position would come up for review in a comparatively short time, and that he would have some difficulty in making a case to the other Service departments to secure the retention of my appointment. He said that it was most important, both from my point of view and his own, that we should produce much more in the way of results than we had done up till then. He pointed out that if I were a civilian there would be no particular problem, but because I was a serving officer he found himself in a difficulty because he had made promises to the other Service departments based, in turn, on our promises which, in effect, were not being kept.

I do not think that this was said to put undue pressure on me, but it had the effect that, when I was faced with the choice between an immediate improvisation or a month or two's delay for a more extensive modification, I chose the former because of the feeling that any suggestion of delay at that time would have meant the withdrawal of all official support. I was forced into a policy of "more haste, less speed".

This was, perhaps, the most critical moment in the whole history of the development. Had the Air Ministry lost interest in the job, it would almost certainly have meant closing down altogether. Fortunately, our improvisations began to produce results and the intensity and speed of running increased. During March we were able to raise the maximum speed to the neighbourhood of 14,000 r.p.m. Severe combustion troubles prevented the attainment of higher speed at that time.

A two months' delay was forced upon us by the failure of the compressor impeller by cracking at the blade tips. We attempted to carry on after the first crack appeared by cutting off the tip of that particular blade (and of the opposite one to preserve balance), but within a short time another blade tip failed and a piece of it passed right through the engine, fortunately without doing much additional damage.

A spare impeller forging had been ordered some months before, and so the delay pending the manufacture of a new impeller was not as great as it might have been.

Testing with the new impeller[14] was resumed on the 17th June, 1939. Progress was then more rapid than it had been at any time hitherto. On the 23rd June we reached a speed of 14,700. The next day we went to 15,700 and then on the 26th we ran up to 16,000. We made several runs up to this speed on succeeding days, but never for very long. Combustion continued to be the chief problem, and so our efforts on the engine were supplemented by combustion tests on the usual site at the B.T-H. Time after time we would get good results on the combustion test rig, but when we modified the ten combustion chambers of the engine accordingly, the result was always disappointing. One or more of the vaporisers would become blocked with carbon or would be burnt by local over-heating. We had achieved a compact flame, but we could not make the combustion chamber components last for any length of time.

We were still borrowing fitters and other skilled workmen from the B.T-H. as required. Sometimes the modifications to the engine would be done at Lutterworth, but for the most part, Crompton and I were shuttling to and fro between Lutterworth and Rugby with combustion chamber components and B.T-H. personnel. Quite often we would gain a few hours by getting one of the watchmen to do some of the dismantling of the engine during the night.

As the amount of running at higher speeds increased, there were clear indications that the material we were using for the turbine blades was not good enough for the conditions to which it was subjected. Had we been free of combustion troubles, and had the turbine and compressor been as efficient as had been assumed in the design, then theoretically at least, the Stayblade steel from which the turbine blades were made had properties good enough for the purpose. As it was, the temperatures of the gases impinging on the turbine were well above those allowed for in the design. Added to this, one of the so far unsolved elements of the combustion problem was bad temperature distribution, which unfortunately was usually such that the hottest gases impinged on the turbine blades near their roots where the stress was highest.

My efforts to find better materials included an approach to Dr. Colin Smithells (then Managing Director of Lodge Plugs Limited) to discuss the possibility of using ceramics either alone or in combination with metal. Smithells advised me to get in touch with Dr. Pfeil of Messrs. Henry Wiggins' because he thought there was a good chance of a nickel-chrome alloy (similar to the "Inconnel" used in elements for electric fires) having creep-resisting properties good enough for our purpose. Accordingly, I phoned Dr. Pfeil and outlined our needs, but at that time he said he did not think they could help us. This was unfortunate. Had Dr. Pfeil and his colleagues started on the work then, that was to prove so valuable later, at least a year might have been saved. Looking back, I am much impressed by Smithells' accurate forecast of the future where turbine blade materials were concerned.

During 1938, in the course of one of my frequent visits to the R.A.E., Constant had told me of another material — Firth Vickers' Rex 78 — but at that time his view was that it was too experimental to use, but as our need for something better than Stayblade was becoming urgent, we ordered a quantity of Rex 78 bar in April, 1939, from which the turbine blades of a spare rotor for the experimental engine were to be made. Rex 78 was a high nickel-chrome alloy steel generally similar in constitution to Stayblade, but having very much better creep-resisting properties.

We were still gravely impeded by finance. At least half the engine ought to have been scrapped because of general deterioration. It must have happened many times that the beneficial effects of a modification were masked by the effects of deterioration, but it was almost impossible to determine to what extent this was so. Later experience strongly suggested that our progress might have been much more rapid had we been able to afford to replace parts which had been damaged and distorted in the course of testing.

The anxieties aroused, by the Air Ministry's attitude and by the Company's financial position, added to the more direct strain of the immediate engineering problems, affected my health quite seriously. Ear trouble which had started a year earlier became chronic and I also suffered from frequent severe headaches and indigestion. I was almost continuously under treatment. It is possible that these things affected my judgment.

Crompton, who had also been working extremely hard, showed signs of breaking down under the heavy load, but he refused to take a rest and in the end I had to order him away for a holiday.

Fortunately for us, the R.A.E. were getting more enthusiastic about our work. Hitherto their attitude had been that though it could supply valuable information and experience in connection with gas turbines in general, the turbo-jet engine itself would not become a successful aero-engine, but in April, 1939, Constant told me that he was coming to believe that we had, after all, got the basis of a practical aero-engine. He said that the effort should be intensified and that we ought to be developing several engines simultaneously, otherwise at the rate of work to which we were then limited we would take about fifteen years and it would make a nice little hobby for me in my retirement.

Sir Henry Tizard also remained a good friend. Early in May, 1939, he told Whyte he was willing to back any further requests for help from the Air Ministry and that he would use his influence to prevent me from being taken away from the work. D.S.R. was then still pessimistic about my position, so much so that on the 12th May, Whyte had felt it necessary to protest strongly against the suggestion that I might be posted. Whyte was told that my Service career might be damaged if I remained. He had replied that he was certain that I was prepared to take the risk rather than give up my work on the engine. When Whyte told me of this, I assured him that he had correctly reported my attitude.

Apart from the matter of my position, Whyte reported that the pessimism of only a few weeks earlier had been largely dissipated and that Pye and Farren were more favourable to the engine than ever before, though he still thought them very grudging. He said that there had been a sinister hint that if the Air Ministry came to regard the work as of real national importance, another firm might be asked to take over the job.

On the 30th June, 1939, D.S.R. paid us a visit and witnessed a test run of 20 minutes' duration up to a maximum speed of 16,000 r.p.m. He also studied performance figures previously obtained. These showed that though the performance of the engine was fairly well below prediction at the lower speeds, the discrepancy between actual and expected results was decreasing as speed was increased.[15]

My appointment nominally ended that day, but Dr. Pye was not able to tell me what was going to happen to me. He had, however, requested an extension of my appointment on the ground that the work could not go on satisfactorily without me. He said there were two sources of criticism he had to meet — one from the Treasury, who objected to the cost of my appointment, and the other from the Service side because of the shortage of Squadron Leaders. He asked me if I was prepared to face the possible damage to my Service career. I told him I would take the risk.

This visit marked a dramatic change in D.S.R.'s attitude. Pye was so impressed with what he had seen that he became a complete convert, and said that he now believed we had the basis of an aero-engine. He agreed that the time had come for an important expansion of the effort, and promised his support for the placing of contracts for an experimental aeroplane and an engine for flight test. He also agreed that the Air Ministry should buy the experimental engine and leave it in Power Jets' hands for continued development. One of the big advantages of this arrangement was that the Ministry would pay for the cost of spares and modifications.

Later that day, when I drove Pye to Rugby station, I had the curious experience of having him recite to me all the advantages of the engine. His manner of doing so was almost as though he were trying to convert a sceptic. I was tactful enough not to point out that he was preaching to the first of all converts. It was a measure of the degree to which he was carried away by his enthusiasm.

A week or two later, Power Jets received the contract for the flight engine, and the B.T-H. accepted a sub-contract for its manufacture — on a "cost-plus" basis as before.

We had hoped that the contract for the experimental aeroplane (for which we had already prepared tentative layouts and shown them to Pye) would be placed through us. Instead, the Ministry placed a direct contract with the Gloster Aircraft Company. Power Jets were very satisfied with the Ministry's choice of Gloster's because this was in accordance with our recommendation. I had already met and had had talks with George Carter, Gloster's Chief Designer, P. E. G. Sayer, their Chief Test Pilot, and others of their senior personnel. In these contacts my old friend, Wing Commander J. H. McC. Reynolds, had acted as intermediary. He was then Air Ministry Overseer at the Gloster works. Power Jets and Gloster's found themselves in good general agreement in a very short time.

Early in July, 1939, I was working on the design of the flight engine. At the wish of D.S.R. and his staff, who did not desire the introduction of any radical changes, it was decided that the design of the flight engine should be generally similar to that of the experimental engine, except for changes to achieve a very considerable weight saving. The flight engine was designated the "W.1".

At this time there were other signs that things were going to be a little easier financially. The B.T-H. increased their investment in Power Jets by £2,000, and the firm of J. & G. Weir Ltd., who had earlier subscribed £3,000 through Falk & Partners, also increased their holding by £2,000. These were small sums from the point of view of the firms concerned, but very welcome to Power Jets in the light of their needs.

Combustion troubles on the experimental engine continued. Nevertheless, we managed to reach a speed of 16,650 r.p.m. by the middle of July. The Air Ministry contract required us to run up to 17,000 r.p.m., but as the engine was the cardinal piece of equipment in the solution of the combustion problem, and as it was now clear that this was the key factor in the development, D.S.R. agreed to my request that this requirement should be relaxed so as to enable us to concentrate on getting the combustion right at lower speeds. Accordingly, the test running contract was regarded as having been completed.

Towards the end of August, 1939, D.S.R. told Whyte that my appointment with Power Jets was to continue, and that the Air Ministry would wish the work to go on if war broke out.

It may thus be seen that the Air Ministry's attitude towards Power Jets had greatly altered, and though test running was temporarily not covered by contract, we had no need to feel nervous on this account.

CHAPTER 18

After the outbreak of war, Whyte, Williams and Tinling gave up their other interests and devoted the whole of their time to the affairs of Power Jets. This was a great relief to me because it left me much freer to concentrate on purely engineering problems.

There were certain other small but valuable additions to our strength during the rest of 1939. The B.T-H. agreed to allow L. J. Cheshire to join us on loan. This was one of the many important things which must be credited to the B.T-H. contribution to the work. A further important addition to our engineering strength was D. N. Walker — a very able mechanical engineer. We also began to build up a drawing office and a small workshop, but these were as yet on a very modest scale indeed. The "workshop" was equipped with a few small sheet-metal working tools which enabled us to carry out modifications to the combustion equipment of the engine.

The combustion problem continued to be the main obstacle to development on the engine, and so the Air Ministry authorised us to install combustion test apparatus at the Ladywood Works to supplement the work we were continuing to do at the B.T-H.

We received further Air Ministry contracts to cover spares for the experimental engine and for the W.1 flight engine, but the most important of the new contracts was for a new and more powerful engine designated the W.2.

It may be seen that despite the fact that the Air Ministry had agreed to the continuation of the work after the outbreak of war, there was seemingly as yet no sense of urgency on the part of the officials concerned. The conditions under which we were working had made it virtually impossible to raise money from private sources and we had become entirely dependent on the Air Ministry for finance. In other words, the degree of expansion of the effort was entirely governed by what the Air Ministry would sanction.

I can only guess at the factors which underlay the Air Ministry's caution during the first few months after the outbreak of war. Perhaps it was because certain officials who had an influence on policy did not yet believe in the soundness of our proposals. Perhaps it was because those who did believe that the development was important felt that Power Jets were the wrong people to handle it, and that it would be better to hand it over to a long-established engineering firm. Others may have felt that the work which had been started by the R.A.E. in co-operation with Metropolitan Vickers was more likely to yield fruitful results.

There were also indications that personal antagonisms towards Whyte and myself were affecting the situation. So far as Whyte was concerned, this was probably a legacy from the protracted negotiations for the early contracts. It seemed to me that the Civil Servants concerned were misinterpreting Whyte's motives and more than once I found it necessary to defend Whyte, because I knew that he quite sincerely believed, as I did myself, that the nature of the work was such that it was more appropriate that it should be financed out of public funds than by private capital. D.S.R. and others, however, had always insisted that the greater part of the finance should be found privately and seemed reluctant to recognise that this had been made virtually impossible by the requirements of the Official Secrets Act. I had the impression that in their eyes, Whyte was fighting to get the State to make payments which would result in large profits going into private pockets (as though this had not been happening for years with the aircraft industry). So Whyte was in the rather difficult position that, on the one hand, the Air Ministry thought that he was trying to go too fast and, on the other, I thought he was not willing to go fast enough. While Whyte was not unconscious of his responsibilities to those who had risked their money in the venture, there is no doubt at all that he was motivated more by what he believed to be necessary in the national interest than by anything else. He had right on his side, but like so many others throughout history, he had to suffer for it. The feeling spread from one official to another that Whyte was difficult to deal with. As happened with me later, influential individuals, who had as yet had no opportunity to judge for themselves, became prejudiced against him before meeting him.

Meanwhile, the preliminary design of the experimental aeroplane was crystallising. The Air Ministry's specification was numbered E.28/39 ("E" for experimental) and hence the aeroplane came to be known as the Gloster-Whittle E.28/39.

In the original specification Gloster's were required to design with a view to its ultimate conversion to an interceptor fighter, but later it was decided that it was to be purely a flying test bed for the W.1 engine. It was to be quite a small aeroplane of all-up weight of about 2,800 lb. The general arrangement was the result of joint discussions between Power Jets, Gloster's, and the aerodynamic section of the R.A.E.

Naturally, there were frequent exchanges of visits between Lutterworth and Gloucester. Our most frequent visitor from Gloster's was R. W. Walker — George Carter's chief assistant on the project. He was usually accompanied by Messrs. James and Lobley.

On one occasion when Walker from Gloster's entered my office, he found a group of us on our knees studying a blueprint on the floor. This amused him considerably and he mentioned that their people had come to refer to Power Jets as "The Cherry Orchard". I asked "Why Cherry Orchard?" He explained that the atmosphere at Power Jets reminded them of the play by Chekhov in which various characters would appear on the stage, say something quite irrelevant and then disappear again. (Not having seen the play I didn't know to what extent this was a true misrepresentation of it.) I asked him why he thought Power Jets was like that, so he said that in the first place, Power Jets was quite different from any other engineering concern he had ever seen, and then went on somewhat as follows: "A small boy comes through one door carrying a cup of tea; then you jump up, pick up a rifle and fire it through the window. Next, one of your directors appears, to ask whether he can afford to have a three-inch gas pipe put in; then the same small boy comes through another door with another cup of tea —" While he was still speaking one of the two doors of my office was thrown open by Cheshire who appeared, poised, with a blotting-pad held aloft and announced "Rocking Blotters!" This was to apprise us of the fact that a "luxury" item for which he and others had been agitating had at last been supplied. This incident did nothing to diminish our "Cherry Orchard" reputation. (Somebody else likened the Ladywood Works to "the typical wicked professor's hideout".)

Another incident in keeping with this atmosphere occurred about that time. Crompton came into my office with a very worried expression and said, in low dramatic tones, "You would not be sitting there, sir, if you knew what was going on underneath." "What's that?" I asked. He replied in an even more sinister tone, "Voysey's boiling cordite." Then feeling he had done his duty, he disappeared rapidly. This statement was a slight exaggeration, but not without foundation. Immediately below my office was a small cubicle which we were using as a kind of laboratory. Voysey was making experiments with the object of evolving a starter motor (for the engine) operated by cordite. When Crompton accused him of boiling cordite, he was, in fact, merely melting it in a flask over a Bunsen burner.

I should explain that R. G. Voysey was a young engineer who joined us in January, 1940. He was one of four very important additions to our engineering strength during that month. The other three were Wing Commander George Lees, O.B.E., on loan from the Education Branch of the R.A.F., W. M. Ogston and R. D. van Millingen.

George Lees became my deputy. I had known him for many years because he had been one of my instructors both in the Apprentices' Wing and on the Officers' Engineering Course. He was several years older than I was, but his amiable nature and his very flattering respect for me were such that I felt no embarrassment in having my former instructor as my deputy. We applied for him to be posted to the Special Duty List for work with us after a visit in which he had expressed a very strong wish to work on the job.

We chose our recruits with great care and our subsequent work owed much to this fact. Walker, for example, was the only successful candidate out of 140 replies to an advertisement.

Apart from Lees, Walker and Cheshire, our engineering recruits were very young and relatively inexperienced, but they had high academic qualifications. In my eyes, their limited practical experience was not a disadvantage. Indeed, I tended to regard it as an advantage, after some of the difficulties I had had with people who had become inflexible through years of experience. I was sure that young engineers with the right combination of initiative, intelligence and engineering training would more readily conform to the needs of this new field of engineering. I think I can claim that I was not mistaken.

Applicants for engineering posts in Power Jets were interviewed by Whyte and myself. I would give them a very intensive "oral examination". I was in the habit of putting many questions which I did not expect them to be able to answer, chiefly to test their intellectual honesty. I rejected many applicants because they attempted to bluff their way through instead of having the honesty to say they did not know. Ogston's interview was one I remember better than most. He had taken First Class Honours in engineering at Oxford, yet he seemed to try to convince us that he was not good enough for our purposes. Puzzled by his self-deprecation, I said, "Well, you obtained First Class Honours, didn't you?" He replied, "Yes, but I had to work far harder than anybody else to do it." Fortunately, Whyte and I had a very much higher opinion of him than he seemed to have of himself, and he duly became one of the most valuable members of the team.

By the end of January, 1940, the total strength of the Company was about 25, including the three full-time directors and personnel on loan. There were then four draughtsmen headed by R. H. Rout.

In our modest plans for further extension, we were hoping to obtain sanction to spend approximately £10,000 on workshop equipment. Discussions on this subject led to a certain amount of internal tension. I wanted a much greater expansion than Whyte was willing to contemplate for the time being. This tended to reopen the wounds in our relationship caused by the financial controversies of 1937 and 1938. Unfortunately, this breach was to widen as time went on.

CHAPTER 19

Towards the end of January, 1940, we had two important visitors on separate occasions — Sir Henry Tizard and Air Vice-Marshal (later Lord) Tedder. Both saw demonstration runs on the experimental engine and were duly impressed.

Tizard commented, dryly, "A demonstration which does not break down in my presence is a production job." He also said that we had got much further with the combustion problem than he had been led to believe. He told me that if he had been responsible for the engine he would have felt very proud of himself indeed.

Tedder drove up from London in company with Whyte and a member of his staff. At the time it was bitterly cold and most of the roads in the Rugby district (and throughout Britain) were impassable with snow, and so we were more than a little surprised when Tedder arrived in the evening, having made most of the journey in the dark. Fortunately, we were able to run the engine — I say "fortunately" because just at that time the bitter cold had interfered with test running because of freezing of the pipes carrying the cooling water (the turbine wheel was cooled by water jackets on each side). Though I do not actually remember it, it is probable that on that particular day we had to work hard to get a cooling water supply.

Tedder told me that he had been very thrilled by the engine for some time and asked what I wanted to speed up development. I told him that our chief need was for more extensive test apparatus; in particular we needed test equipment adequate to enable us to do individual tests of the major components, i.e. of the compressor, turbine, etc., independently of each other. Tedder thought that test apparatus on this scale could not be made and installed in time to make any useful contribution to the war. Nevertheless, he promised to do all he could to help on the development.

After this visit, Tedder wrote to me:

> Just a note to say how glad I was to have an opportunity of seeing your 'child' in action. It really is a fascinating and impressive job and, having seen it, I shall certainly feel even more than before that it is up to me to do all I can to help it forward.
>
> All the best...

Though we were agreeably surprised by Tizard's views of the progress we had made on the combustion problem, we knew we were still far from our objective. It would be hard to convey an adequate picture of the intensity of our effort in this direction. At the time of Tedder's visit we had experimented with no less than 31 different types of vaporiser, not counting many of the modifications to some of the types tested, but we were still in trouble with "coking" up of vaporiser tubes, local over-heating and distortion and bad temperature distribution at the outlets from the combustion chambers.

Our troubles were not limited to the combustion problem. For example, we had two main bearing failures, but though these caused substantial delays, they were only in the nature of teething troubles. They were almost certainly due to the unfavourable conditions in which we had to do our testing. The building, having been a foundry for many years, had foundry sand even in the crevices of the roof, and when the engine was running, there was usually a fine "rain" of this sand. It is probable that the bearing failures were due to it. The second of the two failures occurred at a speed of 17,000 r.p.m., which was the highest speed reached up till then. The thrust recorded was about 1,000 lb., which was only a little below the design figure for the speed.

By January, 1940, the design of the W.1 flight engine was well advanced and we were working on the preliminary design of the W.2 for which the design target was a maximum thrust of 1,600 lb. as compared with 1,240 lb. for the W.1.

The general arrangement of the W.2 was basically similar to that of the W.1 but there were a number of important differences. These included the substitution of air cooling for water cooling for the turbine wheel (the need to avoid water-cooling jackets was underlined by the freezing troubles we had had).

Despite the fact that the B.T-H. were both contractors to, and shareholders in, Power Jets, there was a growing antagonism between the two firms. This seemed to be mainly due to two things — B.T-H. resentment about Power Jets' patent policy in connection with vortex design turbine blading, and the increasing frequency of technical disagreements between certain of the engineers and myself.

We never could understand the B.T-H. attitude about vortex blading. It seemed to us that if a valid patent could be secured then it would be very much to the advantage of the B.T-H., partly because they were shareholders and partly because we were ready to acknowledge their right to a specially favoured position in the matter.

The tension caused by technical disagreements only affected the higher levels. It was, perhaps, aggravated by the fact that Cheshire, Randles and many others in more junior positions were "on my side". These and others, including factory personnel working on the job, were "enthusiasts" and exhibited a strong loyalty to me personally. It may be guessed, therefore, that there were times when my position was distinctly uncomfortable.

Technical disagreements mostly had their origin in the very different background of the B.T-H. engineers and myself. I was an aeronautical engineer trained to think in terms of very low weight and great precision. My experience had given me a clear picture of the special problems peculiar to an aircraft power plant, such as the need for rapid starting, quick response to control, and ability to cope with a range of operating conditions as wide as from take-off conditions in the tropics to high-speed manoeuvring at very great heights where air temperatures would be 50° C. below freezing point. I saw these things through the eyes of a pilot as well as through the eyes of an engineer. The B.T-H. engineers were steeped in an entirely different tradition. Their outlook was appropriate to the manufacture of large stationary electric power generators for power stations and the like, largely constructed from massive castings and forgings weighing many tons and installed on heavy, rigid foundations. To save on manufacturing costs was far more important than to save on weight. Many of them had been twenty to thirty years or more in their profession and had had little or no connection with modern aerodynamic theory. I had the advantage of coming, more or less, fresh from the University with the added qualification of having worked under Professor B. Melvill Jones on aerodynamics research.

Though the device we were working on was primarily a turbine, it was, nevertheless, a field of engineering a long way removed from that to which the B.T-H. engineers were accustomed.

Machine tools in the turbine factory were correspondingly unsuited to the work as I learned by experience as time went on. The factory was not temperature controlled and this is an important condition where great precision is required. Many of the factory personnel were so accustomed to dealing with far heavier components that, skilled though they were, they found it difficult to adjust their methods to relatively delicate work. For example, I required the combustion chambers of the W.1 to be fabricated from stainless steel only $^1/_{64}$ in. thick. In those days the welding of stainless steel presented difficulties in any case, and I was told it could not be done, so I had a word with one of their most skilful welders and more or less challenged him to do something which had not been done before. After a little practice he succeeded.

It is remarkable in retrospect that the work was done as well as it was in view of the unsuitable circumstances. It was a bit like expecting the makers of Big Ben to make a good job of a ladies' wristwatch. I am afraid I was rather intolerant at times. I naturally tended to be so, because it was not important to the B.T-H. when a component was scrapped in manufacture, but it was a serious matter to Power Jets and myself both in cost and loss of time.

My obvious impatience about these things no doubt caused a good deal of irritation and probably provoked certain of the senior members of the B.T-H. staff into looking upon Power Jets' work as a nuisance. Also some were still far from believing that the job was of real importance. At least one of the B.T-H. engineers had proved to his own satisfaction that the jet engine could not compete with conventional power plant for aircraft.

I also felt rather sore about the fact that there seemed to be little or no appreciation of the degree to which their work for

Power Jets, and their association with me, had given them knowledge and experience of value in turbine engineering generally.

In these circumstances, I was very dissatisfied with our state of dependence on the B.T-H. My desire was that Power Jets should ultimately become equipped to do most of the work, but however fast the firm expanded, it could not hope to recruit personnel and equipment sufficient to make a material difference within a few months. We therefore began to look for another sub-contractor. An added inducement to do this was our belief that certain Ministry officials thought the time had arrived to hand the whole job over to one of the established aero-engine firms. In this connection, W. L. Tweedie had specifically mentioned Armstrong Siddeley. I made it clear that I was very strongly opposed to any such course.

It happened that Tinling's wife was a close friend of the wife of Maurice Wilks, Chief Engineer of the Rover Company. This link led to a meeting between Maurice Wilks and myself towards the end of January, 1940, at which I suggested that Power Jets should place contracts with the Rover Company. Wilks promised to discuss the matter with his brother, S. B. Wilks, the Managing Director, and indicated that the latter would probably be willing that the Rover Company should fulfil the function we proposed. He also suggested that they might be interested in a financial share in the venture.

After later talks along the same lines, Major G. P. Bulman, Director of Engine Development at the Air Ministry (to whom S. B. Wilks had, with our permission, mentioned the matter), intervened and in a letter to the Rover Co. inferred that those firms who already had an interest in Power Jets Limited should have no difficulty in providing any necessary further finance.

The same letter virtually refused permission for M. C. Wilks to see the engine and advised the Rover Co. "to tread warily".

Thus it was that the Ministry, which had hitherto been charging Power Jets with not doing enough in the way of raising private money, started to undermine one of our most important steps in this direction.

What then happened behind the scenes I don't know. Though the negotiations with the Rover Co. continued for a time, they took a very unpromising turn.

Early in February, 1940, I went to Harrogate for a long talk with Tedder (a part of the Air Ministry had been moved to Harrogate after the outbreak of war). My objects were twofold — to discuss our equipment needs and to find out what lay behind Bulman's letter to the Rover Co. In this latter connection, Tedder told me that the Air Ministry intended to take a much greater interest in the affairs of Power Jets than hitherto and wanted to ensure that any arrangements made were the best possible. He said the purpose of Bulman's letter was to prevent any hasty action before the Ministry had had time to consider whether it was a good thing. He mentioned that certain other firms might be more suitable. When I remarked that I wanted to be sure that there would be no danger of some large firm trying to squeeze out Power Jets, Tedder assured me that the Air Ministry would not allow that to happen. As he put it — he would "not allow the parents to be robbed of their child".

I left this interview with the impression that the various officials advising Tedder were by no means of one mind about the best course of action.

In referring to a Government Department, it is, of course, misleading to say that the Air Ministry thought this or thought that, especially in a case like ours, where the officials concerned seemed to differ widely in their views. In conversation, it was sometimes difficult to tell whether an official was giving his personal views or expressing the official policy with which, privately, he may have disagreed.

As Director-General of Research and Development, Tedder was responsible to Air Marshal Sir Wilfred Freeman, Air Member for Development and Production, who was taking a keen personal interest in our work. Below Tedder and responsible to him were Bulman and Pye, Directors of Engine Development and Scientific Research respectively. Others who had a large say in Power Jets' affairs were W. S. Farren, W. L. Tweedie and certain officials of the Contracts Directorate. As time went on, it appeared that Tedder was the only barrier to the desire of the others to hand over the development to another firm.

After a conference at the R.A.E., I sat next to Farren at lunch. He made a series of comments about the position of Power Jets which disturbed and depressed me profoundly. Though this was an informal conversation, it seemed to me a clear indication of the way the wind was blowing, and in an effort to scotch what seemed the probable course of events, I wrote to Farren on the 16th February, 1940, as follows:

> During our conversation at lunch yesterday you made various remarks, some of which were to the following effect:
>
> 1. People who had put their money in Power Jets were an unselfish crowd of people who had done a very good job of work, and that there was no hope of them ever getting any return on their money, and that in fact they would be very lucky indeed if they ever made good their loss.
>
> 2. The Air Ministry would not allow Power Jets to become a manufacturing organisation and intended to keep it as a small organisation, and that for manufacture some existing firm would be used.

3. That nobody would make anything out of this engine because it belonged wholly to the Air Ministry and the Department would see that nobody made anything out of it. There would only be the normal legitimate manufacturing profit (from which Power Jets was excluded).

4. That the Air Ministry did not like Mr. Whyte's suggestion of an organisation to handle manufacture in which Power Jets would be part owners.

5. That it was not healthy for an organisation such as ours to depend so much on Air Ministry money; that it should get private money as well, but that it was of little use anybody putting money into Power Jets because if they did so they would lose it, there being no way by which they would get a normal return, Power Jets having no patent position by virtue of the fact that the Air Ministry controlled the situation in this respect, and no manufacturing rights.

6. That the Air Ministry would not place orders with Power Jets for other than experimental engines, and definitely would not place orders for other engines through Power Jets.

It is fortunate that I regard the above as expressions of your own opinion, and not as those of the Department, as otherwise I would be most upset, since it would seem to me grossly unfair that the Air Ministry should allow Power Jets to ripen the fruit and others to pluck it. I am not after big dividends myself, but at the same time it would weigh heavily on me if I thought that many individuals who had put their money in largely because of their faith in me were not to see a just return on that money in the future. In any case I regard Power Jets' organisation as almost as much my creation as the engine itself, and for that reason I want to see it expand. It is in a sense my only 'command' and I believe that Power Jets as such could handle this job in its future stages better than some existing aero-engine firm, who would probably rather kill it than get on with it.

> We have plenty of evidence that the wolves are gathering round the door, and I have a very depressing feeling that your sympathies lie with the wolves.

I sent a copy of this letter to Tedder and he replied telling me not to worry about what Farren might have said.

A few days later, Farren spoke to me on the phone and said that I had misunderstood him and that his own feelings towards Power Jets were all that they should be. He went on to say that what he had tried to do was to point out the kind of undesirable things that might happen. He assured me that he agreed with everybody else that Power Jets had done a marvellous job of work and that he felt, as others did, that it would be unjust if they did not reap some benefit from it.

Nevertheless, it will be seen that my recorded impression of the sense of Farren's remarks proved to be a fairly accurate forecast of the official policy which was put into effect in March and April, 1940, and after.

CHAPTER 20

The main lines of this policy were defined at a meeting at Harrogate on the 25th March, 1940.

I understand that an important part of the background of this meeting was that Freeman and Tedder had decided that the jet engine was to be included in a list of potential "war winning devices", and that the work was to be given a corresponding priority. Tedder presided over the conference. The other Ministry representatives were Pye, Tweedie, and an official of the Contracts Directorate. Whyte and I represented Power Jets, and the Wilks Brothers represented the Rover Company. Sporborg of the B.T-H. had been invited, but had excused himself and was to meet Tedder in London the next day.

Tedder said the purpose of the meeting was to reach conclusions which would enable development work to proceed as fast as possible. He was not expecting production plant to be laid down yet, but development and design work should be done with production in view. To the great dismay of Whyte and myself, he went on to say that the Ministry proposed to give direct contracts for development engines to the Rover Co. Power Jets would be maintained as a research and development organisation and would be expected to co-operate intimately with the Rover Co.

In the course of discussion as to what form the co-operation between Power Jets and Rover's should take, Tweedie stressed the fact that *the Crown had free use of Power Jets' patents*[16] *and therefore he did not see that they had anything to offer in return for finance.* S. B. Wilks commented that the Air Ministry appeared to hold all the cards. Tedder agreed, and, waving his hand in my direction, added "including the Joker".

As the discussion proceeded, it was made clear that Power Jets were not to be allowed to contemplate manufacture of engine parts themselves. Tweedie was even opposed to placing any further contracts for development engines with Power Jets. In vain, Whyte and I argued that much quicker development would be assured if the contracts were given to Power Jets, who would then sub-contract them to the Rover Co. Tedder said this was not satisfactory because it would mean that Power Jets were proceeding with the design without having experienced production people on the job. He seemed a little concerned about the size of Power Jets, and suggested that we were expanding too rapidly. I told him that every member of the staff was, nevertheless, overworked (at this time our total strength was about 39).

This meeting was the forerunner of worse to come.

At another meeting at Harrogate (12th April, 1940), we were told that it had been decided that the B.T-H. and Rover's were to share the production of jet engines. Direct contracts were to be placed with both firms. Power Jets would be maintained as a research organisation only and would not receive contracts for further development engines beyond those already placed.[17] Power Jets were to make available to the other two firms all their accumulated experience and to give them every assistance in their power. Tedder emphasised that he would expect the closest possible collaboration between the three firms.

Tweedie was opposed to any important further extension of Power Jets' test facilities; but Tedder ruled that we should be equipped to carry out our research work efficiently, but any further equipment authorised would remain the property of the Ministry.

At this point we still hoped that Power Jets would continue to dominate the design and development of the engines which the other two firms were to make, but this hope faded later in the same month when it was ruled that they would be responsible for their own drawings and development.

In parallel with these decisions, and associated with them, the Gloster Aircraft Company were instructed to proceed with the design of a twin-engined interceptor fighter, and to prepare plans for its production.[18]

Thus, the Rover Company, in effect, received a free pass into a new industry and were to be subsidised with Government contracts, and test equipment at Government expense into the bargain. All this stemmed from the fact that we had invited them to become our sub-contractors a little over two months earlier.

The position of Power Jets, of course, had been gravely weakened and Whyte naturally sought safeguards. At the meeting on the 12th April he requested that all patents relating to jet engine work applied for by either the B.T-H. or Rover's should be assigned to Power Jets, the particular firm concerned retaining a non-exclusive licence. E. L. Pickles, of the Contracts Directorate, said that it would be very difficult to make any such requirement. Tweedie argued that the firms would be justified in taking out patents as the normal result of their development work. At this I pointed out, with considerable indignation, that any patentable matter could only arise out of the information supplied by Power Jets. Unless some such arrangement were made, none of the parties would be able to be completely frank with the others. The true origin of any invention was difficult to determine when, as often happened, the solution of a particular problem resulted from an engineers' conference. Tedder said that he appreciated the force of this argument and that as he required complete frankness between engineers, some arrangement would have to be made so that there were no barriers.

The atmosphere could scarcely have been less favourable to the degree of co-operation required by Tedder. Commercial negotiations between Power Jets and the Rover Company had broken down several weeks earlier, in circumstances which had thoroughly poisoned the relationship between the two firms. This breakdown had become inevitable after the Harrogate meeting of the 25th March when Power Jets' bargaining position had been completely undermined, partly by the promise of direct contracts to the Rover Co., and partly by the remarks that Tweedie and others had made to the effect that since the Crown had free use of Power Jets' patents, the Company had nothing to offer in return for finance.

There was also a crisis in our relations with the B.T-H. There had been a very unfriendly meeting on the 22nd February at which Sporborg, knowing of and resenting our efforts to find alternative sources of manufacture, had said that the B.T-H. would do no further work on the W.2, pending a decision as to where further orders were to be placed. There was an angry exchange between Sporborg and Whyte because they disagreed completely about what had been said at a meeting a few days earlier.

Though, as a result of the Ministry's policy decisions, the B.T-H. agreed to resume work on the W.2, the atmosphere remained far from cordial.

Whyte's further and perfectly reasonable attempts to obtain safeguards did not help matters. If his proposals were considered satisfactory by the Air Ministry, then either the B.T-H. or the Rover Co., rejected them. Tedder became annoyed at Whyte's persistence because, I believe, he felt that an assurance he had given, that the Ministry had a "moral obligation" to protect Power Jets, should be sufficient. So it might have been if we had not felt that certain of the Civil Servants concerned were seeking an opportunity to have Power Jets closed down altogether, and that Tedder's departure from the Ministry (and, since he was a serving officer, this was inevitable sooner or later) would be the signal for this.

The Contracts Directorate attempted to solve the problem of safeguards by proposing that during the life of any of Power Jets' patents, the other firms were not to make or sell, other than for services of the Crown, apparatus wholly or in part in accordance with drawings supplied by Power Jets, or in accordance with Power Jets' patents except under terms of licences agreed with Power Jets.

Neither the B.T-H. nor Rover's would accept this proposal. They argued that this would put them at a disadvantage relative to any other firm who had not similarly bound themselves. Power Jets were quite willing to accept the Ministry's proposal, and naturally felt that the others' refusal to accept it was unreasonable, to say the least of it. To us, the alleged disadvantage was trivial and greatly outweighed by their free access to all Power Jets' technology.

The problem was never solved, and several months later it was ruled that the matter should be left to arbitration after the war.

It is still a profound mystery to me why the Air Ministry did not insist on the acceptance of provisions giving reasonable protection for Power Jets as a condition of placing the contracts. Power Jets were made to "toe the line" every time, but the other firms could and did say "no", and mostly got away with it.

I was extremely depressed. Everything possible was going wrong. It seemed that we were going to have to struggle even to maintain our position as a research and development organisation. Our efforts to get extra sub-contract capacity had failed miserably. Indeed, we were worse off than ever before, because it was clear that any work the B.T-H. did on their direct contracts would absorb capacity which might otherwise have been available for our sub-contracts. Moreover, I could clearly foresee that there was going to be competition for the then very limited supply of special materials. It seemed that only one thing could save Power Jets from complete extinction — superior technical competence.

Had I believed that either the Rover Co. or the B.T-H. were capable of making a better job of the project than Power Jets, my attitude would have been very different. As it was, what was likely to happen was clear. If the work were successful, the other firms would get the credit. If things went wrong, Power Jets would get the blame.

On the 9th May we received a letter from Tedder saying, in effect, that because of the ill-feeling which existed, the desired co-operation between Power Jets and Rover's was not possible, and that from then on the two firms would act independently. The next day I went to see him at Harrogate, because it seemed to me then that independent action by the Rover Co. would be even worse than the earlier policy. My purpose was to have the decision reversed. I succeeded, after talks with both Tedder and Freeman, but I think now that perhaps it might have been better if I had not succeeded.

I first had a talk with Tedder alone. He said he had been very worried about the way things were going. I said I had been very worried also, and had given up trying to understand recent events. He suggested that a good deal of this worry was unnecessary and that the root of the trouble was Whyte's unreasonable attempts to obtain watertight safeguards on all points, because he did not trust the Ministry's undertaking (the "moral obligation"). I told him he was misunderstanding Whyte completely, and that though I did not get on with Whyte too well myself, I felt bound to say that if he really understood Whyte's motives, he would find they were all he wished them to be. Whyte was acting in what he undoubtedly believed to be the best interests of the nation.

Tedder considered that he had put Power Jets in a very strong position, but they did not seem able to see that this was so. He said he had made up his mind very definitely some time before that in no circumstances would he allow a small company to be swallowed up by two large ones. He added that this was still his attitude in spite of severe provocation.

I told him that though I disagreed profoundly with the Ministry policy, we were handing over all drawings and information we had been asked for, and a large proportion of our staff was engaged on work to provide further information requested by Rover's.

I then repeated my arguments against the Ministry's policy.

We then had a talk with Sir Wilfrid Freeman. He had never met Whyte, but he also inferred that he was the chief difficulty. I defended Whyte as before, and added that Whyte had very good reason to be uneasy about patents. We had had one unfortunate experience in that one of the parties associated with the work had applied for a patent arising out of their connection with it (neither the Rover Co. nor the B.T-H.). We then discussed whether or not we could co-operate with Rover's. I said I thought we could in spite of past difficulties. Certainly I did not see how the policy of non-co-operation could possibly work.

Sir Wilfrid said that his view of my functions was that they should be broader than they had been hitherto. He suggested I was attending too much to detail. I replied that there were still many design points which I felt I could not entrust to others as yet, though I was doing my best to train other engineers. I put it to them that the broader functions that Sir Wilfrid seemed to have in mind would be best fulfilled if I were formally made the Chief Engineer of the whole project, but both Tedder and Freeman were non-committal on this point.

I hinted at my dissatisfaction that most of the Ministry's decisions had been taken without giving me a hearing beforehand, and commented that I did not think the Ministry officials concerned had any comprehension of the enormous amount of work Power Jets had to do.

Sir Wilfrid turned to Tedder and asked him if I was a difficult fellow to get on with, adding: "he seems to be a reasonable enough being in this office." Tedder smiled and said I was a little difficult at times (in our earlier talk, Tedder had remarked that I had to be regarded somewhat as a "prima donna" — very important, but needing to be handled gently). I said to Freeman that I hoped that time would show that I was not as difficult as Tedder implied.

In a short further talk with Tedder alone, after assuring me that he would reverse his decision that Rover's and Power Jets should act independently, he remarked that he had been very glad to have had a personal talk and said he wished that talks with other people had been of the same kind, adding "you and I speak the same language".[19]

A few days later George Lees and I visited the Rover Works with the specific intention of trying to clear up difficulties. We had quite a friendly meeting with the two Wilks Brothers, and there was a mutual exchange of assurances of full co-operation.

The whole tone of our talks was easy and pleasant, and left me with the feeling that we could count on an improved state of affairs thereafter. Amongst other things, I invited them to attach one of their engineers to Power Jets on loan, to serve the double purpose of helping us and of acquiring experience useful to the Rover Co. I also suggested that a similar arrangement might be extended to cover test hands both from Rover's and Joseph Lucas Ltd. (who were to co-operate with Rover's on combustion development and other special problems).

On the 18th May, 1940, I wrote to Tedder saying, *inter alia*,

> I think our present relations with the Rover Co. are all that you hope them to be and I will do my best to see that they stay like that.

Though I was quite sincere in my intentions where the Rover Co. were concerned, I had no real belief that the Ministry's policy could be made to work. Events were to prove how correctly we had foreseen the consequences of the unfortunate decisions of those days.

CHAPTER 21

Meanwhile, events on the Continent took a disastrous turn.

The Germans overran almost the whole of Europe and the plight of Britain became desperate. Chamberlain was replaced by Churchill as Prime Minister.

The Ministry of Aircraft Production was created with Lord Beaverbrook as Minister. The Technical Departments of the Air Ministry were transferred to the new Ministry.

One of the consequences of the formation of the M.A.P. was the appointment of Dr. (later Sir) Harold Roxbee Cox as an additional Deputy Director of Scientific Research. He was given the special responsibility for work on jet engines. He was not entirely new to it because he had formerly been at the R.A.E., and had been present at conferences relating to the E.28 and other aspects of our work. He was assisted by D. G. Tobin who became the channel for most of our dealings with the Ministry. Tobin had been appointed as a kind of "contact" man during April, to keep an eye on the liaison between Power Jets, the B.T-H. and the Rover Company.

When Roxbee Cox first visited Power Jets (12th June, 1940), I gave him my views on Ministry policy. I had high hopes that the moment had arrived for a complete revision, but Roxbee Cox said he could not hold out hopes of any important changes. Nevertheless, he implied that Power Jets could expect more lenient treatment in the provision of equipment to carry out their research functions. A few days later we were told that new test houses would be sanctioned, and that Power Jets would receive contracts for certain items of research equipment.

I missed what might have been an excellent opportunity to get the policy changed when, on the 9th July, I was summoned for a talk with Lord Beaverbrook. I saw him for about three minutes. He fired a series of questions at me, the first of which was "What have you got tucked away?" I replied, "A very good engine, sir." I did my best to answer the rapid bombardment of questions to which I was subjected, without knowing what lay behind them.

"The Beaver" asked me what I thought of Ministry policy. I felt that this was too complex a subject for a very short interview, so I replied that the decisions had been too recent for it to be possible to judge how they were going to work.

After the interview I was still ignorant of the reason for the summons. It was not until a long time afterwards that I heard that knowledge of our work had been withheld from him because it was feared that he might consider it to be an interference with immediately urgent requirements, and that having heard of it indirectly, he sent for me to find out what *was* going on. However, the axe did not fall, and indeed Lord Beaverbrook's parting words to me were to the effect that as soon as we were ready for a prototype fighter to take the engine we should have it.

The outlook for the "close collaboration" desired by Tedder was not promising. The B.T-H. showed little signs of wanting Power Jets' co-operation on their direct contract. We heard they were working on the design of the engine and that they were putting up test houses, but we did not hear about these things "officially". Cheshire told me that he might have to ask to be withdrawn from Power Jets because of the difficulties of his position. He said he was being accused of acting as the channel through which Power Jets were finding out what the B.T-H. were doing.

Not only were the other two firms becoming increasingly secretive towards Power Jets about their work, but Tobin found out and told us that they had been getting together and had already had two or three meetings. Tobin had been told that these meetings had been to discuss such matters as the production of turbine blades. We naturally felt very sore that there had been no invitation to us to send a representative. It sounded to us as though there were moves in the direction of a B.T-H.–Rover *entente* which boded ill for Power Jets.

One evening in August, 1940, I had dinner with Roxbee Cox and Tobin after they had visited the B.T-H. and Rover for the specific purpose of trying to improve matters.

Roxbee Cox said he made it very clear to both firms that all parties had to work together in the closest possible co-operation. He said that he had stressed that if either of them thought it was possible to dispense with Power Jets they were wrong. There was to be no withholding of information by any of the parties concerned. I assured him that Power Jets were doing their part (it had apparently been represented to him that we were not), and that we were doing our best to make the Ministry policy work, even though I no longer believed that the change of atmosphere necessary for co-operation was then possible. I told him that I thought there was still time to stop the downhill slide and make quite different arrangements. I argued once more that everything should be channelled through Power Jets, who, after all, were the only people who had achieved anything at all. I failed to convince him that any major change of policy was desirable, but he did hint that Power Jets also might be given contracts for further experimental engines — the first sign that the pioneer firm might, after all, be allowed to carry on with the work it had started.

It was evident that at this time he gave some weight to the views of those who tended to describe Power Jets as "gifted amateurs" who did not know how to design for production.

Roxbee Cox, having been closely concerned with the job only for a very short time, could, perhaps, scarcely be blamed at this stage for believing much of what he was told by the B.T-H. and Rover Co. Technical points were the chief sources of dispute, and so he probably tended to weigh the background of engineering experience of these two firms against the limited experience of a relatively junior R.A.F. officer. (I had been promoted to temporary Wing Commander on 1st June, 1940.)

Moreover, he thought that both firms would mend their ways after his visits of that day. I was sceptical and said so; I went so far as to hint that unless there were an important change of policy I would ask to be relieved of my appointment.

The Ministry's desire for a frank and complete interchange of information between the three firms was emphasised in a letter signed by Tedder dated 21st August, 1940.

A few days later Tedder, Roxbee Cox and Tobin had a meeting at the B.T-H. with B.T-H. and Rover representatives. They then visited Power Jets.

Tedder told us that he had done some straight talking, and the B.T-H. and Rover Co. could now be in no doubt as to what his intentions were. He said he could see no reason why all the parties could not work smoothly together and get on with the job. He felt that the main obstacles were psychological ones and that something had to be done to increase the mutual trust of all parties.

I tried to convince him that however good the B.T-H. and Rover engineers might be in their particular spheres of experience, this did not necessarily mean they were fitted to deal with the special problems of this new field of engineering.

So far as I knew, the Rover Co. had no previous experience of turbine-type machinery whatever, while the B.T-H. had no experience with anything approaching an aero-engine.

I once more attempted to get a modification of the policy and have the design centred in Power Jets. Tedder would not agree to this, but he did confirm that Power Jets would be given contracts for further experimental engines, though he made it clear that we could not hope for much in the way of machine tools and we would have to sub-contract most of the work.

After Tedder had left, Tobin told me that during the meeting at the B.T-H. one of the reasons given for withholding information from Power Jets was that the latter were liable to put in patents on the basis of information supplied. I was horrified that such a charge had been made in front of my superior officer. Fortunately for Power Jets and myself, they had cited a specific instance, and I was able to prove to Tobin there and then that not only had Power Jets not applied for a patent for the device mentioned (a spring nut on the rotor shaft) but that it was not even referred to in the descriptive matter of any of the patents applied for.

Another example of the kind of thing we were up against occurred at about that time. Roxbee Cox told me that Rover's had complained that there was something wrong with one of the W.2 patterns which we had supplied. Fortunately, there was a casting made from this particular pattern in the B.T-H. works and when it was checked it was found to be correct, so that this charge was also proved to be without foundation. The complaint, of course, should have been made to us in any case. It seemed that no opportunity of discrediting Power Jets was to be allowed to pass. It was obvious that the atmosphere was going to be completely impossible if, every time something small went wrong, one of the parties immediately took it to a high level in the Ministry.

Another characteristic incident occurred when an expensive tool was broken by a sub-contractor making one of the W.2 components for the Rover Co. The latter wrote to us blaming us for the occurrence because one of our drawings had an error. It was true that there was a small error on one of the drawings which had been sent to the Rover Co., but they had fought hard for, and had obtained, the ruling that they were to be responsible for the manufacturing drawings, yet as soon as something went wrong which was due to a mistake in a drawing, Power Jets were to blame. Later we found that though the Rover Co. had insisted to the Ministry that the drawings would have to be made in accordance with their own manufacturing methods and so on, and had persuaded the Ministry to accept their view, they were at this time nevertheless using some of Power Jets' drawings without alteration. This particular incident was one example of this, but further confirmation was received when we requested prints of their drawings of the W.2 compressor casing. When we received them we were astounded to see the names of our own draughtsmen in the bottom right-hand corner. *They were photostat copies of Power Jets drawings with all reference to Power Jets removed* and no acknowledgment of the origin of the drawing.

As time went on, my conviction that we at Power Jets were the only ones competent to control the design was strengthened. This was the chief thing motivating my attempts to get the policy altered. I also wanted to ensure the survival of Power Jets as an entity. From this point of view our position was precarious. To the other two firms, the turbo-jet engine was only a minor part of their total activities, whereas it was Power Jets' sole *raison d'être*. We depended entirely on it, and since we were wholly financed by the Ministry at this stage, our survival as a team hung on a very delicate thread. The Power Jets' team was now a very real thing, and I believe that it was only its high quality and its continuing record of achievement that saved it from extinction at an early stage.

Had I been merely concerned with my own reputation and the survival of Power Jets, then, since I was convinced that neither of the other firms was competent to do the work, my course would have been clear — give them enough rope and they would hang themselves. But such a course of action was not going to provide jet-propelled aircraft by the time we supposed they were going to be needed. I, for one, thought that sooner or later Britain would be attacked by very high-altitude bombers and that the only effective defence would be jet fighters. Though such attacks never occurred, our belief that they would strongly governed our actions.

Since we were the most vulnerable to charges of non-cooperation, being the only one of the parties with an engine in being, we went to considerable lengths to make sure that no such charges could be brought. As I have already told, we had invited the Rover Co. to send personnel on loan, and in consequence, one of their engineers (Mr. Swayne) was working most of his time at Lutterworth from the 17th August, 1940, onwards. *They thus had a representative right inside the organisation.* He was allowed to see everything we were doing and gain experience on many aspects of the development. Co-operation could scarcely go further than that. The B.T-H. were in a similar position through Cheshire, who was now spending part of his time on design work in connection with the B.T-H. Ministry contracts. Cheshire was under no restraint from us in the matter of disclosing information on our work to the B.T-H. In addition to these things, W. E. P. Johnson had been given the special responsibility for liaison, and he kept a careful record of all correspondence and ensured that copies of all letters supplying drawings and other information to the other firms were sent to the M.A.P.

I do not see how we could possibly have done more than we did to fulfil the Ministry's policy in spite of our violent dislike of it.

CHAPTER 22

W. E. P. Johnson, whose early connection (1929–1932) with my work has already been described, joined us in April, 1940, on loan from the R.A.F. to which he had been recalled at the outbreak of war. Later he was released and became a member of the staff with a very wide range of functions. (He had, in fact, resumed his associations with the project in 1935 when, as a patent agent in civil life, he assisted us in patent matters.)

At this time (April–July, 1940), the additions to our staff were small in quantity but high in quality. They included G. B. R. Fielden, a brilliant young engineer with a remarkable combination of knowledge and initiative, and Dr. T. A. Taylor, a very able metallurgist.

After the formation of the M.A.P., and certain indications that Power Jets would be a little more generously treated in the matter of research equipment than hitherto, expansion was a little more rapid. By the 1st September[20] the total strength was about seventy including the full-time directors and personnel on loan.

The size of the Company now justified a fairly well-defined organisation. Wing Commander Lees was my deputy and also responsible for the drawing office of nine draughtsmen and three tracers. Directly responsible to me on design work were Cheshire, Shapiro, Ogston, Voysey, Gott and Bone. Van Millingen was in charge of the small experimental workshop staffed by eighteen skilled workmen, mostly sheet-metal workers. Dr. Hawthorne was head of the combustion test section, the personnel of which included Fielden, Meeson, Darling, Noble and Bennett-Powell. D. N. Walker was responsible for engine testing. Crompton had become specialised on inspection. We also had a small buying department under Arnott, and the small general office staff of about seven was administered by the accountant, Mr. Truan.

Of the above-mentioned individuals, Dr. W. R. Hawthorne, R. F. Darling, J. B. Bennett-Powell and Flight Lieutenant G. W. Bone were all on loan from the R.A.E. This had come about after I had made urgent requests to the Ministry for additional assistance on the combustion problem. The loan of these people was a very valuable acquisition to our strength. Their ability was in keeping with the high standard I was building up in my engineering team. Hawthorne, Bone, Fielden, and I were all First Class Honours men of Cambridge (Hawthorne had also taken his doctor's degree at the Massachusetts Institute of Technology, so he had quite exceptional academic qualifications) and several of the others had equally high qualifications. I think I can fairly claim that the quality of this team in proportion to its size was without its match within the whole of the United Kingdom.

We had outgrown our small allocation of space at Ladywood and people were falling over each other, almost literally, because at one time some engineers were obliged to sit and work on the stairs leading up to my office. A temporary slight alleviation was obtained by hiring a railway coach. This stood on a siding just outside the Ladywood Works and became the office of the combustion engineers. But this by no means met our needs and other steps had to be taken. One of these was the renting of a few rooms in Brownsover Hall, an old country house on the Rugby–Lutterworth road about three miles from Rugby, into which I moved with the design staff.

Brownsover Hall was almost ideal for this kind of work. The former dining-room made an excellent, though somewhat small, drawing office.

Brownsover Hall proved a satisfactory accommodation for the design staff, but the pressure on space continued to grow at Ladywood. Our more urgent needs were met by the erection of temporary wooden huts.

Two test houses were also sanctioned.[21] (Though we were still the only people with an engine on test we were running a very bad third in the provision of equipment — test houses for Rover's and the B.T-H. had been authorised some time before.)

In August, 1940, we had only one machine tool — a lathe, but during the following months we obtained sanction for a few extra tools. This meant an urgent need for more workshop space, and so we tried to get the whole of the Ladywood Works allocated. This became the subject of another battle. The B.T-H. were dispersing their magneto production, and wanted to use the whole of the Ladywood Works. The net result was a compromise; the Minister himself ruled that the space should be shared, so eventually we occupied about half the premises.

About the end of August, 1940, the figure authorised for Power Jets' requirements in equipment and buildings was £27,000 — about the price of three engines.

With the exception of the internals of the combustion chambers, we were still entirely dependent on the B.T-H. for manufacture. Our efforts to get additional sub-contract capacity had largely been frustrated, so there was every indication that our only hope of getting any reasonable speed up was to take on a fair proportion of the work ourselves, but the Ministry was slow to accept this situation, and only after continuous agitation did we succeed in getting piecemeal sanction to build up a workshop capable of making engine components.

During September (1940) Mr. G. Peasgood joined us to take charge of our small workshop, releasing van Millingen for return to experimental work.

Our chief difficulty in engine testing was correct "diagnosis". The engine was a combination of a very experimental compressor, a very experimental turbine and a very experimental set of combustion chambers. The major difficulty was to sort out the behaviour of one component from another. If the turbine appeared to be down in efficiency, was this because part of the combustion was taking place in the exhaust pipe after the turbine, or was the turbine really down in efficiency? In other words, readings which suggested low turbine efficiency might mean what they said or they might mean that combustion was not satisfactory. Similarly, the combustion process and the turbine behaviour reacted back on the compressor. The behaviour of a compressor is quite sensitive to small variations in the quantity of air it is dealing with. If we had a low compressor efficiency, was it because bad combustion or low turbine efficiency (or both) was causing the airflow to be less than it should have been? — we couldn't tell — the behaviour of the components was so absolutely inter-dependent. For correct "matching" of components, it was obvious that these should be separately tested, but my repeated appeals for the necessary apparatus fell on deaf ears. Had we then foreseen the troubles which lay ahead, I would have been even more emphatic on this subject than I was. Later events were to show that matching difficulties could be much more severe than was indicated from our experience with the experimental engine.

Our need for our own manufacturing capacity continued to grow. As I had foreseen, the B.T-H. started to make parts for the Rover Co. This inevitably reduced the capacity available for Power Jets. Not only that, but in one case, turbine blade material which had been ordered by the B.T-H. for a Power Jets' contract was used on a Rover order.

One of the factors which limited us for a time was that our M.A.P. contracts particularly specified the B.T-H. as our sub-contractor, but in October, 1940, Tedder agreed that this restriction should be removed.

CHAPTER 23

The experimental engine, still the only "engine in being", though progressively deteriorating, was continuing to prove most useful. To all intents and purposes, we were using it for combustion development, but though making small advances, we were still in trouble with unreliability of the combustion chamber components.

A tantalising thing was that seemingly good results on the test rigs could not be reproduced in the engine. This happened time after time. It seemed probable that this was due to the difference in the pressure conditions. (In the test rigs the air supply was only a little above atmospheric pressure.) Eventually a large compressor which formed part of the plant used in the construction of the Dartford Tunnel (on which work had been suspended) was made available for high-pressure combustion tests. This was not a very satisfactory arrangement, because no modifications could be made on the spot, and so the engineers concerned had to make frequent journeys between Dartford and Lutterworth. Nevertheless, some useful work was done on the site, but the answers were mostly negative. We found that the vaporising system we were using in the engine, and which frequently would become either choked with carbon or overheated in a very short time, would stand endurance running in the Dartford compressor rig, so it appeared that the pressure conditions did not, after all, account for the differences in behaviour between the rigs and the engine.

The chief reason for these differences was discovered by Johnson when he made a full-scale model of a combustion chamber with transparent plastic material with which, with the aid of wool tufts and smoke, we were able to observe the air flow. This simple but valuable piece of apparatus taught us a lot. It became obvious that the differences which had puzzled us were mainly due to the differences in the pattern of the air flow entering the combustion chamber.

However, a much more significant development occurred in July, 1940.

I. Lubbock of the Shell Petroleum Co., who had been advising us for some time past on combustion and fuel problems, invited us to see a combustion chamber of approximately the same size and form as that used in the engine, and with which Shell engineers were experimenting in their Fulham Laboratory. The fuel was injected in a fine mist of liquid droplets through a controllable atomising burner.

Walker and Johnson went, saw and were conquered. They brought it back in their car, and had it rigged up at Lutterworth the same evening for me to see the next day. Thereafter we concentrated our effort on the "Shell" combustion chamber. We started our work on it on the 19th July, and within a week we were able to report to the Ministry that tests were sufficiently promising to justify the making of a set of similar combustion chambers for the engine.

At this time we had four combustion test rigs in operation altogether, including the one at Dartford.

Despite a series of initial troubles when adapted to the engine, *the introduction of the Shell system may be said to mark the point where combustion ceased to be an obstacle to development.*

In order to feed both the engine and the combustion test rigs with apparatus, it had been necessary to build up our own sheet-metal working section, and by September, 1940, our capacity in this connection was sufficient to enable us to become independent of the B.T-H. for internal components of combustion chambers. (Later, we were able to make combustion parts for the B.T-H. and others.)

Much other useful work was done on the experimental engine during 1940. We improved the fuel system, particularly in respect of starting characteristics. On starting devices, several lines were tried. We experimented with cartridge starters, a small hydraulic motor (this work was done at the B.T-H.), and a small two-stroke petrol engine. Eventually we found we were able to start up with the electric starter motor from the B.S.A. car engine which had formerly been used for starting, i.e. we were able to start up with the starter motor of the original starter motor — but it had taken us a long time to find it out!

Much miscellaneous apparatus was developed, but as it is desired to keep this narrative as non-technical as possible, these things will not be described.

About the middle of 1940 it was decided that, by using a spare rotor which was being made for the experimental engine and certain components originally made for the W.1 (which were considered to be below standard for an engine which had to be airworthy), we could construct an experimental version of the W.1. This "composite" engine was designated the W.1.X.

The W.1.X. proved to be a very valuable engine indeed. Before it was actually completed, it was sent to Gloster's and used as a "mock-up" for the installation of the W.1 in the E.28. This proved an excellent test of the close liaison between ourselves and Gloster's, because the W.1.X. was installed in the aeroplane almost without a hitch.

Both the W.1.X. and the W.1 embodied modifications dictated by experience with the experimental engine.

We felt that it was very desirable to test out certain of the special features of the W.2 in advance if possible, and so, in February, 1940, we produced a design which was really a compromise between the W.1 and the W.2. This was designated the W.1.A. Its stated purpose was to test out such special features of the W.2 as the air cooling of the turbine wheel and the novel compressor intake arrangement. The Ministry eventually gave Power Jets a contract for a W.1.A. and this was also sub-contracted to the B.T-H.

Shortly before this, it had been decided that there were to be two E.28 prototypes, and the second one was to have a different (high speed) wing section from the first. The second aeroplane was to be powered by the W.1.A.

Most of the design work on the W.1.A. was done by Power Jets, but some of the details were left to the B.T-H.

The W.2 being made by the B.T-H. on Power Jets' contract, was (after a certain amount of argument) being made to Power Jets' design, but the W.2, being made by the Rover Co. on direct contract from the M.A.P., differed from Power Jets' design in a number of ways, chiefly in such features as bearings, auxiliary drives, etc., but for the main components, namely, the compressor, the turbine and combustion chambers, they were conforming to Power Jets' design.

I had done the design calculations for the W.2 but, owing to pressure of work, I had limited myself to calculations for the full speed condition. The increase of engineering staff made it possible to do performance calculations in greater detail. The results made me very uneasy indeed about the design. They revealed that if our assumptions proved to be over-optimistic there would be a severe penalty. I reported this fact to the Ministry and we started on a complete revision of the design — the W.2.B.

By the end of 1940 practically the whole of our design effort was devoted to the W.2.B. By then it had been decided that the W.2.B. was to be the power plant for the twin-engined interceptor fighter, the Gloster F9/40 (the Meteor).

The B.T-H. also called the engine they were making on their direct contract a W.2.B. This was rather confusing because it differed in many ways from the Power Jets' W.2.B., though of the same general arrangement. The only direct contributions Power Jets made to it were the supply of initial design figures and the design of the combustion equipment.

The design target for our W.2.B. was a static thrust of 1,800 lb., though it was agreed with the R.A.E. that for purposes of aircraft performance and so on, it would be assumed that at full (engine) speed it would deliver 1,600 lb.

A feature of both the W.2. and W.2.B. was the very simple engine mounting. We intended from the first that engine changing should be a very swift operation, and in this we were undoubtedly successful. (The time to change an engine in the Meteor was about thirty minutes.) This was one of the many ways in which the strong Service associations of many of the Power Jets' personnel was reflected in the design. Williams, Tinling, Lees, Johnson, Crompton, Bone and myself either were, or had been, in the R.A.F. (And by the end of 1940, we had Flight Sergeant King and other airmen on attachment.)

CHAPTER 24

My continued efforts to bring about changes in policy led to some changes in Power Jets' favour, but these still fell far short of what I felt to be necessary.

When Air Chief Marshal Sir Wilfrid Freeman and Roxbee Cox visited us (18th October, 1940), we were told that the Rover Co. had accepted the proposal that their first W.2.B. should be made to Power Jets' design except for the most minor modifications. Roxbee Cox said it was proposed that the B.T-H. should do the same.

Whyte made a strong appeal to Sir Wilfrid to put me in control of the whole of the engineering side of the work, but Sir Wilfrid would not agree for the reasons previously given by Tedder, namely, that it would be distasteful to Rover and the B.T-H.

On 22nd October, 1940, Tedder wrote formally to Power Jets and the other two firms, saying that as the co-operation between the three firms had not been proceeding satisfactorily, it had been decided that Power Jets should supply to the other two firms, *inter alia*, a complete design for the W.2.B., intended for the twin-engined F9/40 fighter aircraft, and that, though it was expected that modifications would be necessary to ensure rapid production, or for technical reasons arising out of the experience of the production firms, these were to be as few as possible and subject to the approval of a committee to be established.

The policy as laid down in this letter represented some improvement from our point of view. It was a step in the direction of engineering control by Power Jets — had it been implemented, but it never was.

On the 1st November, Tobin told us that neither the B.T-H. nor Rover would agree to the conditions laid down in Tedder's letter.

At this time there had been some improvement in Power Jets'–Rover relations, partly because they had accepted the proposal that the commercial position should be subject to arbitration after the war, and partly because they were showing some willingness to work more closely to Power Jets' designs than hitherto. The B.T-H., on the other hand, refused to accept the arbitration proposal and to work to Power Jets' designs (on their direct contract), so that our relations with them had further deteriorated seriously.

It is beyond my understanding why it was that the Ministry was almost brutal in the way in which they forced Power Jets to toe the line, but seemed completely weak and powerless where the other two firms were concerned. We dare not say "no", but the other firms could and did say "no" repeatedly. Nearly every time they did so, the Ministry gave way. Because the B.T-H. refused to accept the position laid down in Tedder's letter, it virtually lapsed, though it was never formally cancelled.

On the occasion of a visit by Tizard and Tedder (9th November, 1940), Tizard arrived first. I told him I was very depressed about the way everything was going, and pointed out that although it was nine months since his last visit we still had only the same experimental engine to work with that he had seen then.

Tizard seemed to be of the opinion that Power Jets ought to be responsible for the design, but that the manufacturing firms should be allowed to make small alterations to suit their planning and to ease production, provided these did not affect the operational efficiency. He thought that Power Jets should be the judges of this. I agreed with him, and said that what he was saying was equivalent to making Power Jets finally responsible for the design.

At one point we discussed the matter of responsibility for the drawings. In this connection I showed him Rover's letter blaming us for the breaking of a tool because of an error in one of our drawings. Tizard turned to Tedder and remarked that it was clear that Rover's were trying to get it both ways. They wanted to be able to say that the drawings were theirs and yet at the same time to throw the responsibility on to Power Jets when anything went wrong. He remarked to Whyte and myself that in putting that particular letter on record, the Rover Co. had played into our hands and given us a very powerful weapon.

Tedder and Tizard also visited the Rover Co. and possibly as a result of this there seemed to be a further slight improvement in the willingness of the Rover Co. to co-operate, because a few days later M. C. Wilks visited to discuss the W.2.B. design, and he and I agreed that there should be no real need for the committee which had been proposed. He assured me that the Rover Co. would not dream of doing anything we might consider would interfere with the aerodynamic or thermodynamic performance, because they did not pretend to know as much about such matters as we did. I said, in turn, that Power Jets were not likely to be difficult about any minor modifications in design necessary to suit the plant available. There was also some indication that Rover's would give us a limited amount of help in manufacture.

In this particular conversation I gathered that Wilks knew more about the B.T-H. design than we did.

What little we heard about the work the B.T-H. were doing on their own W.2.B. came in dribbles and indirectly. For example, it was disclosed at a conference at Gloster's that the engine, though designed for the same performance as our W.2.B., would have a compressor casing 6 in. larger in diameter, and would therefore not be interchangeable with it in the Meteor.

On the 12th November, 1940, Mr. (later Sir Harry) Ricardo paid us a visit. He explained that Lord Beaverbrook, the Minister, had asked him to do so to see what could be done to speed up the work. He had already seen Tizard and had agreed with him that the proposed committee to control the design was not a good idea.

We had a long general discussion about the past history and the Ministry's policy. Ricardo was very sympathetic to my point of view — he said that his own organisation had received treatment very similar to that which Power Jets had received, on such matters as the sleeve valve for piston engines, etc. He, like myself, could not understand the extent of Tweedie's influence on policy, or the motives that underlay his actions.

It appeared that there had been some changes in the Ministry, and Sir Henry Tizard was now virtually acting as Air Member for Development and Production instead of Sir Wilfrid Freeman.[22] Also at about this time Tedder was posted away from the M.A.P. and ceased to be concerned with the project. He was succeeded by Air Marshal F. J. Linnell.

I believe that Tedder's posting[23] was a most unfortunate thing for Power Jets and myself, because it happened at a time when he seemed to be on the point of recognising that there was a good deal of weight in the arguments I had consistently put forward, and of acting accordingly.

The Ministry's policy took a new turn when Tizard decided that Vauxhall's should be drawn into the orbit of jet engine development to make engines strictly to Power Jets' designs.

A delegation from Vauxhall's visited us on the 19th November, 1940. A week later a meeting was held at Vauxhall's works at Luton with Sir Henry Tizard in the Chair. It was then confirmed that Vauxhall's were to make six W.2.B's to Power Jets' design.

It is not intended to describe Power Jets' relations with Vauxhall in detail, because there was a further change of policy in the new year which led to Vauxhall's dropping out of the development. It suffices to say that, during the short time they were associated with the work, there was very close liaison and we supplied them liberally with W.2.B. drawings and information. In fact, our effort in this direction was quite a considerable proportion of our total effort. Unfortunately, it contributed little to the development in the end.

I asked Tobin whether Rover were supposed to work to our W.2.B. design in accordance with Tedder's letter of October 22nd. He said "no". The latest instruction to the Rover Co. was that they should not make any appreciable departure from our design without reference to us, but if they wished to carry on with any proposed alteration against our advice, then the responsibility for doing so would be theirs.

During December, 1940, there was apparently some tendency to "mark time" on the part of the Ministry. On one occasion during that month, Tobin told me that the Ministry's policy in relation to the other firms was far from crystallising. They were waiting for results. He felt that Power Jets would come well out of it. A further hint that the Ministry was beginning to get "cold feet" was contained in a letter primarily about the test schedule for the W.1.X., wherein it was said that the target to be aimed at was a 50-hour run without having to renew any part of the engine; "should any modifications appear to be necessary, it is hoped that they will be few and quickly incorporated, as the time is drawing near when the Department will have to decide whether or not the Whittle project will play an effective part in this war."

We received delivery of the W.1.X. (less internal combustion chamber components) on the 11th December, 1940, and as we had not completed the flame tubes, etc., we first ran it with combustion equipment borrowed from the experimental engine. It was obvious at once that though very similar indeed in basic design to the experimental engine, it was a very great improvement. We attributed part of this improvement to the fact that the turbine had a greater number of blades in it than the experimental engine (72 as compared with 66). This, in turn, had been made possible by the use of a new method of attaching the blades to the wheel (the "fir tree" blade root). Incidentally this feature of this and subsequent designs was one of the most criticised items on the ground that it was "not a production job" — yet it is almost universal today.[24]

Within the first two or three days we were able to run up to a speed of 16,450 r.p.m. On inspection after one of these runs, we found that the impeller had fouled the casing and that three turbine blades required replacement through damage from some foreign body going through them. However, the performance of the engine was very promising indeed.

It has to be remembered that *up to this moment — ever since April, 1937 — we had been struggling with the one experimental engine* and it was quite a tonic to have our engine testing almost doubled. We no longer had to rely on what was virtually a heap of scrap (though even the W.1.X. consisted largely of parts which had been scrapped from the W.1.).

CHAPTER 25

Despite the compact target presented by the B.T-H. works, the large railway goods yards and junction, and the English Electric Company's works, Rugby suffered little from enemy air raids, and the small town of Lutterworth escaped completely.

In the critical days of 1940 when Britain stood alone, and only the narrow strip of Channel separated us from an enemy triumphant with conquest, I had quite an exaggerated idea of the "bomb worthiness" of Power Jets; not only did I think the Ladywood Works likely to be bombed, but also thought that there was a distinct probability of something in the nature of a raid by parachute troops. Since our sole defence at night, when the Battle of Britain was at its height, was our two night-watchmen, I decided that some of us ought to sleep on the premises as an additional guard. At first my colleagues were reluctant to accept that this was necessary, but after a short period, during which I supplemented the night-watchmen on my own — sleeping on a camp bed in my office — the idea became more generally accepted and a group of us took it in turns. ("Fire-watching" had not yet become a national institution.)

I found an element of fascination in this night-guard business. The nights were mostly fine, and if there were sundry minor discomforts, it was a relief not to do the Rugby–Lutterworth drive in the blackout with the heavily-hooded headlamps that we were compelled to use in those days.

I used to get quite a thrill wandering round the almost deserted works on a still night with searchlights eerily sweeping the sky.

In retrospect, much of what happened in those days seems absurdly melodramatic — the roadblocks and so on (which added greatly to the hazards of blackout driving). When I drove between Rugby and Lutterworth I was always armed with an automatic pistol and my .22 rifle. Later on Power Jets had its own detachment of the Home Guard commanded by Whyte. I, of course, as a serving officer was not a member. I believe the activities of Power Jets' section of the Home Guard did nothing to detract from our "Cherry Orchard" reputation.

On occasions when we were engine-testing at night, we would receive bitter complaints from the local anti-aircraft authorities because we were disorganising the sound-locater system for miles around.

There was one daylight raid on Rugby by a single raider. It happened on a Sunday afternoon and I was at home at the time. A few minutes after the sirens had sounded the "alert" complete pandemonium broke out. I rushed to the window in time to see a twin-engined bomber flying low in the direction of the B.T-H. and saw a stick of bombs fall. The noise was out of all proportion to the raid, chiefly I think because every gun-crew for miles around had been waiting for something to happen for so long that none of them was losing an opportunity to let fly! The excitement was all over in about thirty seconds and nobody was seriously hurt. The B.T-H. escaped with superficial damage to the office block; nevertheless, I heard the next day that our work had suffered, because when the bombs fell, a workman holding one of our compressor impellers was so startled that he dropped it. Out of a series of five impellers, this was the fourth to be scrapped.

There were other indirect delays through bomb damage, but generally speaking, air raids did not cost us more than a few weeks.

My house stood on the highest ground in the district and when Coventry, only twelve miles away, was bombed, it was easily visible. Each of the heavy raids on that city was an awe-inspiring and terrible spectacle. I find it impossible to describe my feelings as I helplessly watched my native city go up in flames. It was particularly maddening to see several raiders caught in the searchlight beams and yet apparently escaping unscathed.

Dr. Taylor featured in rather an amusing incident on one of the occasions when Rugby caught the fringes of a heavy raid on Coventry. He arrived at Rugby station, on returning from a meeting in London, after the alert had sounded, and while the raid on Coventry was in its early stages. He collected his car from outside the station and set out for Lutterworth. The story goes that as he was crossing the bridge over the Avon on the northern outskirts of the town, the car leapt in the air and he hit the roof. He stopped, got out and walked back to see the reason. He found he had struck rubble at the edge of a large crater in the road. To a man who was nearby, Taylor remarked very angrily, "Why the hell doesn't somebody put red lamps round this thing?" The stranger replied, "Keep your hair on, governor, it wasn't there two minutes ago!"

CHAPTER 26

The expansion of Power Jets during the latter half of 1940 was much greater than it had been during the first half; especially during the months of November and December, when the increase in staff was 53, making a total of 134, including personnel on loan (another valuable "loanee" was Mr. J. R. Joyce from Shell, who was lent to us for the special task of burner development). Our workshop equipment included only four lathes and one or two other machine tools. These were, of course, totally inadequate for our needs. We had received a contract for a W.2.B., but were without means of making it, because we had as yet found no alternative sub-contractor to the B.T-H. and Rover Co., who were specifically excluded by the terms of the contract.

A very large proportion of our effort — particularly of the design and drawing-office staff — was devoted to providing information for the other firms now engaged. All this, of course, considerably curtailed the amount of work we could do on direct development ourselves. Not only that, we were also harassed by visitors. There were frequent visits by representatives of Vauxhall's, Rover's and the Lucas Company (who were assisting the Rover Co. in various ways), by Ministry officials and by many others.

I don't think the Ministry officials concerned had any conception of the load that was imposed on me by these numerous visits. Each one would mean the loss of at least half a day; each would mean a tedious repetition of things I had said over and over again *ad nauseam*. At one point things became so bad that I asked Tobin to try and arrange that visitors came in groups instead of one by one, so that we could economise on the time lost on this sort of thing.

There was one visit I shall never forget — that of Air Chief Marshal Sir Hugh (later Lord) Dowding — Commander-in-Chief, Fighter Command, during the Battle of Britain. I felt uneasy before "Stuffy" arrived because certain previous encounters with him were associated with trouble. I felt sure that something was bound to go wrong. It did. While the experimental engine was running, I took him round the outside of the test houses. It was impossible to speak because of the noise. As we stood about three yards away from where the jet nozzle protruded through an aperture in the test-house wall, I pointed to the nozzle, meaning to imply "That's the 'business end' of the engine." He misunderstood my gesture and, before I could stop him, walked rapidly in the direction indicated. Suddenly a mighty invisible force wrenched open his raincoat and sent him staggering across the concrete — his "brass hat" rolling away on to the grass. I stood petrified with horror, and when Sir Hugh recovered himself, apparently unhurt, I could scarcely move and certainly could not speak. Someone had seen the incident through an observation window and shut the engine down. Sir Hugh, pardonably terse, asked me if I wasn't going to show him something, so I dumbly led the way into the test house. Only those in the Service would really understand what a junior Wing Commander feels like when he is responsible for this sort of thing happening to an Air Chief Marshal. At first it seemed remarkable that he should have escaped so lightly, but the fact was that the jet blast was so powerful that it was almost "solid" (a brick thrown on to the top of the jet would almost appear to bounce as it was hurled downwind) and so prevented him from walking right into it.

Until that moment I had not realised how deceptively invisible the jet was to a stranger. There was no trace of smoke or anything else to show the presence of the powerful blast, though several yards downwind it was more obvious because of the haze of foundry sand raised from the ground and the waving trees in the hedgerow. (The cows in the next field used to assemble in the pleasant warmth of the jet on the far side of the hedge — at which distance its blast effect had been largely expended.) By lunchtime Sir Hugh had recovered his good temper sufficiently to joke about the incident. It will be many a long day before some of us forget how we nearly blew an Air Chief Marshal into the next county.

The expansion of Power Jets was only a small proportion of the total expansion. The decision had been taken during October, 1940, that the production of aircraft and engines was to be planned for at the rate of 80 airframes and 160 engines per month. The work of Power Jets, Gloster's, B.T-H., Rover's and Vauxhall's was supplemented by ancillary work in several places. Lucas' were increasing their effort on combustion development. The firm of Ransome and Marles and the National Physical Laboratory had started work on bearing tests. The Ricardo Engineering Co. were assisting Power Jets on certain special problems, the Mond Nickel Co. were now actively assisting on the material side and were working to produce improved materials for turbine blade and combustion chamber parts. The R.A.E. were doing wind-tunnel tests for Gloster's and were advising and assisting Power Jets in sundry ways.

The R.A.E. were also doing experimental work in connection with the development of the F.2 jet engine being made by Metropolitan Vickers. (This project had replaced the earlier propeller gas turbine proposal after we had demonstrated the practicability of the jet engine.)

Also working with the R.A.E. on gas turbine work were Fraser and Chalmers and Armstrong Siddeleys.

It may thus be seen that whatever one may feel about the wisdom or otherwise of the Ministry's policy, at least it was not lacking in boldness, seeing that at this time our experimental engine and W.1.X. were the only engines running under their own power and no flight tests had yet been made. This boldness is all the more surprising in view of the fact that certain high officials in the Ministry believed that the aeroplane might prove to be fundamentally unstable with this novel form of propulsion.

The fact is that too much was being done and there was considerable confusion about who was supposed to be doing what. Vauxhall's, Rover's, the B.T-H. and ourselves were competing for materials, and there were occasions when two or more firms were trying to get castings from the same pattern but from different foundries. It was obvious that a single directing authority was needed, but though several times I suggested the appointment of a controller to co-ordinate the entire development, and though several of the Ministry officials concerned agreed with me that this was necessary, no individual with the requisite terms of reference was ever appointed.[25]

The total expenditure by Power Jets up to the end of 1940 was probably of the order of £50,000, of which about half had been provided by the Ministry. There had been small increases in the amount of private money subscribed — several Power Jets' employees had invested small sums.

CHAPTER 27

The honourable career of the first experimental engine ended on the 22nd February, 1941 — nearly four years after its first run — when it was damaged beyond repair by a failure of the rim of the turbine wheel.

It ended its career in glorious fashion. During the last seven weeks of its life it did approximately 100 hours of running — making a total of just under 170 hours from the completion of the second reconstruction in October, 1938.

We had known for some time that its end was near. The turbine wheel in use had the original De Laval type blade fixing, and the material of the disc had been slowly yielding between the blade roots over a long period. The turbine blades had become so loose that every time the engine was shut down it came to rest with a musical tinkling noise as the blades rocked from side to side in their root slots.

Now that we had the W.1.X., and knowing that the experimental engine had virtually reached the end of its usefulness from the point of view of development, we decided to embark on a series of endurance runs at cruising r.p.m. So the last 100 hours included a number of such runs ranging in duration from 2 hours to over 10 hours. The two most noteworthy were one of a little over 8 hours at 14,500 r.p.m., and one of just over 10 hours at 14,000 r.p.m.

These engine speeds corresponded to cruising conditions only, and so these endurance runs were not of particular value, but fortunately for us they had a psychological effect quite out of proportion to their worth on many people concerned. In my view the condition of the engine had deteriorated so much that any results achieved with it were more likely to be misleading than helpful.

During the early months of 1941, despite several bearing failures, we made substantial progress with the W.1.X. We completed 40 hours running by the end of March.

These bearing failures were really no more than minor teething troubles and were easily overcome by small modifications, but the spotlight was focused so much on Power Jets that there was a tendency to regard them as major disasters by certain individuals whose chief hope seemed to be that the development would not succeed. The last of them was undoubtedly due to an oversight in assembly and this, in turn, was due to sheer fatigue on the part of the personnel concerned who had been working for long hours at high pressure.

The W.1 was received[26] in February, 1941, as a group of sub-assemblies, but, not wishing to risk it until we had eliminated all the snags by experience with the W.1.X., we refrained from putting it on test for the time being. However, it did not stand idle — it was sent to Gloster's to complete the installation arrangements in the E.28 aeroplane.

CHAPTER 28

Though a decision to plan for production of Meteor airframes and W.2.B. engines had been taken in October, 1940, there had been no decision as to *which* W.2.B. was to be produced.

However, the policy took a new turn on 2nd January, 1941, when Sir Henry Tizard called a meeting at the B.T-H. works which was attended by representatives of Vauxhall's, Rover's, the B.T-H. and Power Jets. Roxbee Cox, Tobin and Constant were also present. The official minutes stated that the purpose of the meeting "was to determine the necessary steps to be taken in order to ensure that production of an engine giving a static thrust at sea-level of not less than 1,600 lb. should commence in this country as soon as possible at a rate which should increase to, say, 2,000 engines a year in not more than 18 months".

Both the B.T-H. and Vauxhall's admitted that very extensive facilities would have to be provided to enable them to cope with the production of this kind of engine, whereas the Rover Co. already managed two shadow factories, either of which could be easily converted for the purpose of the production of jet engines. In consequence, it was decided that "a part, if not all, of the labour and equipment of a shadow factory be used for quantity production of the W.2.B. engine" and that, "the Rover Co. be given the contract for the production engines…" but no decision was taken as to which W.2.B. was to be produced, despite the fact that the Power Jets' W.2.B. was the only one for which the design was virtually complete at this time.

As a consequence of the decisions of this meeting, Vauxhall's dropped out of the development. Thus, our hopes of getting a W.2.B. to our design vanished once more (though the Rover Co. had shown some willingness to follow Power Jets' designs a few weeks earlier, they had once more become reluctant to do so).

From time to time I had suggested that all the firms should co-operate in making two W.2.Bs. to Power Jets' design as rapidly as possible, each firm contributing parts most suited to its experience and equipment, e.g. turbine wheels and blading from the B.T-H., sheet-metal work from Vauxhall's and Lucas', and the gearbox and light-alloy components from the Rover Co.

Tobin told me that Tizard was strongly in favour of my proposals, but though the matter was suggested at intervals during the early weeks of 1941 nothing came of it.

On the 8th January, it seemed as though the question "which W.2.B.?" had been definitely settled. I was told by Tobin that the Minister himself had told the Wilks brothers that they were to plan for the production of the W.2.B., and that the W.2.B. referred to was to be based on Power Jets' designs though Rover's would be allowed to modify to ease production provided that Power Jets' agreed to their modifications. Any disputes were to be referred to Tizard. According to Tobin, the Wilks brothers had tended to resist this at first, but had actually accepted. Apparently Roxbee Cox had used our endurance runs on the experimental engine as a powerful argument in favour of the proposal. Accordingly, we sent a large batch of the W.2.B. drawings to the Rover Co. on the 14th January, 1941.

On the 18th January, Tobin re-confirmed that Tizard had emphasised that the Rover Co. was to proceed with the Power

Jets' design. Nevertheless, within four days, Tizard wrote a letter to the Rover Co. which modified this decision, though Power Jets did not hear of this letter until the 5th March.

Some time before all these arguments took place, I had attempted to dispose of my financial interest in Power Jets. In a letter to Tizard dated 20th January, 1941, I told him

> ...that I had offered to make such dispositions of my shareholding as would prevent me from benefiting financially from Power Jets' activities... I am most anxious that my own position should not be subject to the slightest criticism. For this reason I desire it to be as widely known as possible in the Ministry that (*a*) I shall not receive any share of Power Jets' dividends, (*b*) the Ministry has a considerable holding in Power Jets through my shareholding.

I wanted to be able to fight with clean hands. (I was then holding 24 of my 56 "A" shares in trust for the Ministry.)

The next move in our quest to get a W.2.B. made to our designs was to have the W.2., being made by the B.T-H. on Power Jets' contract, converted to a W.2.B. by stages. Tizard asked the B.T-H. to put the highest priority on this conversion.[27]

Rover's were given a pre-production order for 30 engines, and Gloster's were to make 12 aircraft and to plan the jigging and tooling for a rate of production of 20 per week.

In my battle to get the Power Jets' W.2.B. formally recognised as the one for production, and feeling that most people considered I was too biased in the matter, I had suggested in a letter to Tizard that the R.A.E. be asked to carry out an independent investigation and report on the design and design methods of Power Jets, the B.T-H. and Rover Co. I felt very confident that the result of such an inquiry would be wholly in favour of Power Jets. Unfortunately, this suggestion was never followed up.

Bulman, Director of Engine Development and Production, wrote a personal letter to me dated 20th February, 1941, in which he said that Rover's were

> ...to proceed at once to provide capacity, self-contained, for production of 20 Whittle W.2.B. engines per week in a Rover Shadow (Whittle) factory, with premises already earmarked at Clitheroe and Barnoldswick...
>
> As a further step capacity for a further 30 engines per week (making 50 in all) is to be planned, embracing a maximum of sub-contracting. Sub-contracting to be initiated as soon as practicable to supplement the Rover capacity on their 20 per week planning...
>
> As to your own experimental requirements, Mr. Wilks has assured me that he will do his utmost to provide all you want and when you want it. To conserve material and energy it is clearly essential to have one authority for placing sub-contracts and allocating material, and with Mr. Wilks' assurance as above, I am certain that you will agree that this authority shall be Mr. Wilks.
>
> I write to you thus unofficially to inform you fully of how things are going, and I take the opportunity of again confirming to you my verbal assurance that we are all combining and concentrating in the objective of bringing *your* child into effective R.A.F. manhood at the earliest possible moment.

It will be seen that Rover's were not, after all, going to use either of their then existing shadow factories.

It may also be seen that Power Jets were to be virtually placed at the mercy of the Rover Co. for practically all their supplies.

The first hints that the Rover Co. had not, after all, accepted the Minister's ruling that they were to work to Power Jets' designs came on the 22nd February when M. C. Wilks visited Brownsover. It was obvious to me that he put a much wider interpretation on the latitude permitted to him in design than I did.

It was becoming increasingly clear that if we wanted an engine made to our own design we should have to make it ourselves. The situation was paradoxical. Though nearly a year had passed since the Ministry had decided that very considerable support was to be given to the development, we were having more difficulty in getting engines made to our design than ever before. The outside capacity available to us was actually contracting, and our own internal capacity was still very small. This was a scandalous state of affairs in view of the fact that we were the very core of the whole development. The B.T-H. was still our main source of manufactured parts, but the atmosphere of hostility, coupled with their greater interest in their own W.2.B., made it a matter of urgency for us either to acquire sufficient equipment to do the bulk of our own manufacture, or to get reliable alternative sub-contractors. We were beset with what I considered to be unnecessary difficulties in getting material, labour, tools, etc., and we were cramped for space, so much so that the work was affected and morale was going down. When I complained of these things to Tizard, he said we ought to be prepared to put up with difficulties in wartime. I replied that I was quite prepared to put up with difficulties that were unavoidable, but not with those that were avoidable.

The Ladywood Works had become most unsuitable from many points of view. We had used up all the available space and Lutterworth was not a good place to get labour.

We repeatedly sought Ministry sanction for a move. Tizard was less favourable to the idea than he had been a month or two earlier, though we had the support of Roxbee Cox. Tizard then relented to the point of agreeing that we could make plans for a move within six months.

Our first contact with the Rover Co. a year earlier had been with the object of getting them to make parts for us. Except for a small job on a W.1.A. component, they had done nothing for Power Jets. In the middle of January, 1941, there was little sign that this situation would improve.

Despite Power Jets' important position, every small increase in labour and every additional item of equipment had to be fought for. We needed a balancing machine. The Ministry refused to sanction this essential item at first, but later relented when we had managed to locate one at quite low cost. As one way of increasing the labour force available, I asked for more airmen to be attached to Power Jets and eventually received another three, making six altogether — all nominally posted for training.

At this point I would emphasise that we were not in any way fighting to get quantity production of engines — all we were striving for was to be adequately equipped for development and to act as the central design authority. It was absurd that the very cradle of the work was as impeded as it was by lack of skilled men. Our demands were not wild. We had set out our urgent labour requirements and the total was 70 (our strength at the time being 150). The time was getting near when we would have three or four engines on the test benches and, in the light of this and the work we were expected to do, this was a very modest demand indeed.

There was a host of secondary problems, accommodation for the staff, provision of canteen facilities, etc. All these necessary but unspectacular problems were handled by Williams and Tinling. They shared the administration between them under Whyte, with Tinling concentrating mainly on internal administration, and Williams handling matters which required external contacts, e.g. the Buying Department; dealings with the billeting officers, building contractors, and so on.

A bearing failure on the W.1.X. on the 2nd March underlined our labour difficulties. The test section personnel had been working very long hours day after day under arduous conditions, and there was no doubt that the oversight which led to the failure was a consequence of sheer fatigue. I represented to the Ministry that it was dangerous to overwork personnel the way we had been doing, and said I was gravely dissatisfied with action in the past on the labour question. I asked to see the Minister on the matter. I did not see the Minister in fact, but we were promised more energetic action. On the 8th March, 1941, I wrote both to Bulman and to Tizard stressing our urgent staff and labour needs. With my letter to Tizard I sent a batch of photographs to illustrate the conditions under which we were having to work at Lutterworth. In connection with their magneto production, the B.T-H. had been doing a certain amount of building at Ladywood and the surrounding ground and paths had been badly churned up; this, coupled with bad weather, meant that the route from our workshops to the test houses lay virtually through a sea of mud. Not the best of circumstances for testing aero-engines.

CHAPTER 29

On the 5th March, 1941, there was a further modification to policy in respect of the design of the production engine.

Bulman called a meeting at Chesford Grange (a large country house near Kenilworth, which the Rover Co. was using for design).

Bulman said the purpose of the meeting was to settle the W.2.B. design. I said it was Power Jets' understanding that the Rover Co. were to work to Power Jets' designs, and to make only such minor departures from them as would facilitate production, and then only by agreement with Power Jets. We then heard for the first time of Tizard's letter dated 23rd January to S. B. Wilks, in which he had apparently agreed that though Rover's should conform to Power Jets' designs in features affecting the performance, they would have a substantially free hand in mechanical design. I was very surprised indeed to hear of this letter. Amongst other things, it meant that for six weeks we had been working in ignorance of the Ministry's latest policy.

The minutes of the meeting recorded that Tizard had defined the design responsibility as follows:

> Rover Company to be entirely responsible for the general mechanical and structural design and for the production of drawings of W.2.B., but the Rover Company undertake to consult with Wing Commander Whittle on the whole design and to comply with his requirements as far as possible on matters involving turbine or blower design, and the general aerodynamic characteristics of the engine. In the event of

> there being any insoluble difference of opinion, Sir Henry Tizard will make the final decision.

The minutes more or less confirmed this position, though they also recorded:

> ...the Ministry does not contemplate that the Rover Co. will depart from the basic W.2.B. drawings supplied by Power Jets Ltd., other than is dictated by production reasons or their relevant mechanical experience.

We strongly objected to the decision. We felt, with justification, that we had far more experience with all aspects of the engine than anybody else. Indeed, we were still the only people with any practical running experience at all. In a way this fact may have operated against us — being the only people who had done any engine testing, we were also the only people who had experienced teething troubles.

I could not see that anything was to be gained by any of Rover's proposed changes. On the contrary, it seemed that unnecessary development was being added to the programme. Amongst other things, it meant that all the information we had supplied to the Gloster Aircraft Co., to enable them to proceed with installation design for the Meteor, was scrapped and they would be held up pending the completion of design work by the Rover Company which was then only in a very preliminary stage.

I said I thought the only sound course for Power Jets to adopt, in the light of the decisions at that meeting, was to go through the formal action of handing a set of W.2.B. drawings to the M.A.P. and to let the Ministry be entirely responsible for deciding what use was to be made of them. Power Jets to cease work on the detailed design. Bulman said that nominally we could consider that we were doing that, but in order to save time, instructed us to hand the complete set of drawings direct to the Rover Co. Accordingly, on the 11th March, 1941, a set of drawings representing virtually the complete design of the engine was handed to Rover representatives.

I made many protests to the Ministry about the decisions of this meeting; to Tizard and Bulman in writing and to Roxbee Cox and Tobin verbally. I felt that the two latter were in sympathy with my views, but were not in a position to alter the decision.

My views were recorded in a letter (dated 21st March, 1941), to Bulman as follows:

> I wish it to go on record that I disagreed with the decisions reached on the following grounds:
>
> (*a*) The Power Jets' design was virtually complete, whereas much remained to be done by the Rover Co., if they were to be allowed to re-design beyond minor production changes, and that this would entail a further delay.
>
> (*b*) Design features which had been tested were to be replaced by others which had not.
>
> (*c*) Without going through the Rover drawings with a fine tooth-comb it would not be possible for Power Jets to do more than pick out obvious faults in Rover's design, and therefore they might repeatedly find themselves in the position of having to say 'we cannot see anything wrong with this but this does not mean that we positively assert that it is all right'.
>
> (*d*) All the installation information on which Glosters have been working to date was based on the Power Jets' design, and they would now find themselves in the position of having to start afresh in many respects.
>
> I think the record should also include my opinion that the Power Jets' gear box should be used because it was lighter and more compact than the Rover proposal, and in most of its

> essentials it could be described as a box which had been tested... You will recollect that I summed up my views by saying that I would not object to the decisions if they did not involve a single day's delay, but that I thought there would be considerable delay.

The matter was again discussed at a meeting at the Ministry a few days later with Sir Henry Tizard in the Chair. Roxbee Cox and Constant both thought that the policy as defined before the 5th March seemed satisfactory, but Tizard and Bulman argued that Rover's had to be responsible for the engine.

In the course of this discussion I protested once more against the decisions of March 5th, and said that things would be very different if the firm concerned were Rolls-Royce for example, but Tizard said Rolls-Royce would not be interested — they were proceeding with a gas turbine scheme of their own.[28]

However, this meeting did rule that Power Jets were to be equipped to make their own development engines and to be largely independent of sub-contractors. In this connection, Tizard said that this might mean spending another £40,000 on Power Jets and added that this might be difficult to justify for a private company which had only raised £20,000 from its shareholders. I commented that the company was not very private. I might have added that Power Jets was the only Company concerned which had spent any private money at all on the development of jet engines, and that far larger sums of public money were to be found for the Rover Co.

A day or two later there was another attempt to clear the air between Power Jets and the Rover Co. I was invited to Chesford Grange for lunch. Once more there was a very forthright exchange of views. The Wilks brothers said they wished bygones to be bygones, and I said once more that everything I did was directed to providing the R.A.F. with a jet-propelled interceptor fighter at the earliest possible moment. I was invited to visit their drawing office for the first time. (And noted that there was a new design of compressor casing on the drawing board — which was outside their province even according to the decisions of March 5th.)

A week or two earlier the Ministry had agreed to the Power Jets' request that the first Rover-built W.2 (which was now nearly completed) should be sent to Power Jets for test. Rover's had resented this decision and had recorded their opposition to it in writing in very strong terms, but for once, and rather to our surprise, the Ministry had ruled against the Rover Co. I could not understand why the Rover Co. felt so strongly about it. They had not done any testing of this kind before, and any misadventure — and a thousand things can go wrong at a first test — could have been very damaging in more senses than one. They knew they were free to send personnel to Power Jets when the engine was tested so that they would have the benefit without the responsibility. At our talk at Chesford Grange I reminded them that they were at liberty to send anybody they wished to be present, and that, indeed, we would only be willing to run the engine in the presence of and to the satisfaction of Rover representatives.

In insisting on having the first W.2 for test at Power Jets, we were not seeking to score any special point; on the contrary, as already indicated, the design of the W.2 was something we would have preferred to forget. We knew that, short of a miracle, the performance of the engine would be very bad indeed. From the point of view of sheer tactics, the more the Rover Co. identified themselves with it, the better from our point of view, but however badly the engine behaved we hoped to get some valuable information from it, and this was the dominating consideration.

At about this time there was also some improvement in relations with the B.T-H. They sent us a layout of their design and we had agreed to make combustion equipment for their engine.

CHAPTER 30

The Gloster/Whittle E.28/39 which, in my preoccupation with the W.2.B. and Meteor, I had almost forgotten, was completed at the beginning of April, 1941. The W.1 had not yet run, and so it was decided to use the W.1.X. for the taxying trials.

P. E. G. Sayer, Gloster's Chief Test Pilot, had visited Lutterworth on two or three occasions and had handled the engine controls to get some idea of the engine characteristics.

The aeroplane was ready for its taxying trials on the 7th April, and I went to Gloster's with Cheshire that day. Walker and others of Power Jets were already there.

The trials began that evening but there was little done because the light was fading by the time the aeroplane was ready. We had set the throttle stop to limit the engine speed to 13,000 r.p.m. The grass aerodrome was rather soggy from rain so that it required 12,000 r.p.m. before the aeroplane would start moving, and at 13,000 r.p.m. it would only move at about 20 m.p.h.

The look of disappointment on Gerry Sayer's face was obvious. He evidently thought the engine would never develop enough "urge" to get the aeroplane off the ground. We were not worried because we knew how rapidly the thrust increased at the upper end of the engine speed range. I assured Gerry that with increased engine speed he would find things very different. He did not look convinced.

The next morning we removed the throttle stop and adjusted the relief valve in the fuel line to give a maximum engine speed of 15,000 r.p.m. With this limit, I made a few taxying runs in which I reached a maximum speed of about 60 m.p.h. It was a thrilling experience for more reasons than one. It was clear that we would not be short of thrust when we used the permissible maximum of 16,000 r.p.m. Also the complete absence of vibration, the big reduction in noise as compared with conventional aircraft, the excellent view from the cockpit, and the simplicity of the controls, all added up to an impressive combination of characteristics. I felt that the engine instruments left something to be desired, but otherwise, so far as one could judge from a mere taxying run, everything seemed very satisfactory indeed.

Sayer then did a little taxying with the same limit on engine speed.

After lunch we increased the engine speed Emit to 16,000. With this setting, Sayer taxied off to the downwind edge of the airfield. This action caused us to suspect that he intended to do more than merely trundle over the grass, though we had warned him that the engine was thoroughly unairworthy. It had never been intended for flight in the first place, and it had had a number of misadventures on the test bench which had rendered it even less fit to fly than when first built.

Sayer turned into wind, increased the engine speed to the maximum permitted while holding the aeroplane back with the brakes. He then released the brakes and rapidly gained speed. We saw his elevators go up in an effort to get the tail down. He was a little too successful in this, because the tail "blister" struck the ground and the aeroplane pitched forward on to its nosewheel again. Nevertheless, a second or two later it left the ground and, after being airborne for about 200 yards, landed. Sayer taxied back and repeated the performance twice more, the third take-off being very clean and smooth. Each time the airborne distance was 200–300 yards.

These proceedings must have caused very great astonishment to many people who could not help but see the aeroplane but who, up to that moment, had had no knowledge of it. One spectator was an American mechanic, working on the wing of a Stirling bomber. He nearly fell off in his surprise.

Sayer's only criticism was that the aeroplane was a bit reluctant to get its tail down during take-off, but he seemed confident that when the time came he would have no difficulty in making a continued flight.

It was decided that no useful purpose would be served in doing anything further until the W.1 was available, so the W.1.X. was removed and shipped back to Lutterworth to continue bench development work.

Things then moved rapidly. Three days after the taxying trials, the W.1 ran for the first time. The first test had been delayed pending the completion of modifications dictated by experience with the W.1.X. The value of the test running on the W.1.X. up to this time was now made manifest, because the W.1 went through its acceptance test and 25 hours special category test without any hitch whatever. For the purpose of the flight trials, it was limited to a maximum speed of 16,500 r.p.m. at which the thrust was 860 lb. The same speed limit was used for the special category test, except for one run up to 17,000 r.p.m., at which speed the thrust was 1,000 lb.

The W.1 was shipped for installation in the aeroplane at the beginning of May.

An M.A.P. letter to Gloster's cleared the engine for ten hours' flight testing "subsequent to the satisfactory completion of 25 hours bench testing and to about 60 hours bench running of the W.1.X."

"Evening — first test flight of the E.28."

This meagre entry in my diary for May 15th, 1941 — in the handwriting of Mary Phillips — is the only record I made of an event which marked the culminating point of a thirteen-year pursuit of an idea and a generally recognised landmark in aviation history.

Much of the account I give below is based on the notes of others, plus what I can remember — which isn't much. I was in the habit of keeping fairly complete records, and so it seems a little odd that I should have dismissed so important an event in this summary fashion. The truth is that my mind was so firmly fixed on the target of getting W.2.B.-powered Meteors into production that the E.28 had come to seem comparatively unimportant relative to this aim. I was not one of those who needed convincing that it could fly. The short hops it had made during taxying trials had satisfied me on that point, and I felt that neither the engine nor the aeroplane would tell us very much about the Meteor or its power plant. In short, I saw the E.28 purely as an experimental aeroplane which was not going into production, and which would not, therefore, contribute directly to R.A.F. equipment during the war. Nevertheless, these remarks should not be taken as belittling a beautiful little aeroplane. Though today it has an honoured place in the Science Museum at South Kensington, it scarcely looks like a museum piece! It is still, in my opinion, one of the most handsome aircraft that has ever been made. George Carter and the Gloster team have every reason to be proud of their handiwork.

The aeroplane, partially dismantled, but with the W.1 engine installed, was transported to Cranwell by road about the 11th or 12th May.

A day or so later, our own team went to Cranwell; they included W. E. P. Johnson, D. N. Walker, Flight Lieutenant

Bone, Flight Sergeant King and others; Walker, as head of the Engine Test Section, had a general responsibility for the engine, while Bone was immediately in charge of the engine installation.

Cranwell was chosen for various reasons, chief of which was its long runway and clear approaches. Of course, it was a particularly appropriate choice because it was there, as a cadet, that I wrote the thesis which stimulated the train of thought which ultimately led to the jet engine.

R.A.F. Cranwell was commanded by Air Commodore ("Daddy") Probyn, who was very helpful. The R.A.F. personnel were very co-operative generally, and did much to help us in many ways, including the provision of accommodation on the station.

I went to Cranwell with D. G. Tobin (who was then Resident Technical Officer at Power Jets) on the evening of the 13th, expecting the flight trials to begin on the day following. But on the 14th the weather was unsuitable for so important an event as the first flight. Sayer did some taxying trials in the evening, to test out the longer nosewheel leg which had been fitted.

I had not flown since June, 1939, so I took the opportunity to borrow an Avro Tutor from No. 2 C.F.S. I was very pleased to find that I felt as completely at home as though there had been no interruption in my flying practice.

On the morning of the next day, the 15th May, the weather was quite unfit for test flying, and so I returned to Lutterworth. But when I noted that the weather was improving I hurried back to Cranwell in the evening, by which time the weather had improved to the point where it was suitable for the flight. It was by no means ideal, but there was some blue sky and the cloud base had lifted considerably.

While the E.28 taxied to the extreme eastern end of the runway, a group of us went by car to a point about 400 yards along the runway. Sayer was in position at about 7.40 p.m. He ran the engine up to 16,500 r.p.m. against the brakes. He then released the brakes and the aeroplane quickly gathered speed and lifted smoothly from the runway after a run of about 600 yards. It continued to the west in a flat climb for several miles and disappeared from view behind cloud banks. For several minutes we could only hear the smooth roar of the engine. Then it came into sight again as it made a wide circuit preparatory to landing. As Sayer came in it was obvious that he had complete confidence in the aeroplane. He approached in a series of gliding turns as though he had flown the machine for hundreds of hours. Those of us who were pilots knew that he felt completely at home. He made a perfect landing at the far end of the runway and came to a stop somewhere short of where we were standing — the flight had lasted seventeen minutes. He taxied towards us, stopped, and gave us a "thumbs up" sign. We, of course, rushed up to shake him warmly by the hand.

It is difficult to describe my emotions during and after the flight — I was very tense, not so much because of any fears about the engine, but because this was a machine making its first flight. I think I would have felt the same if it had been an aeroplane with a conventional power plant making its first flight. George Carter had much greater reason to feel tense, but if he did, he didn't show it. I do not remember it, but I am told that shortly after take-off, someone slapped me on the back and said, "Frank, it flies!" and that my curt response in the tension of the moment was: "that was what it was bloody-well designed to do, wasn't it?"

Gerry Sayer subsequently reported that "although the fore and aft control was very sensitive at very small movements, the flight was continued". He had had a little difficulty in lowering the undercarriage — he had found it necessary to use the handpump to lock the nose-wheel down.

Sayer had noted a number of points on his knee-pad during this first flight which were incorporated in his flight report. When he filled in the standard flight test report form, his most interesting entry was that for the item "Airscrew Type and No". He wrote, "No airscrew fitted with this method of propulsion."

Despite frantic efforts by Johnson, we were quite unable to persuade the Ministry that the first flight warranted having a proper cinema unit at Cranwell, and so the only film of the event — made with a hand camera — is, to say the least of it, a very amateur effort. One or two photographs were taken while we were congratulating Sayer at the conclusion of the flight, but, possibly because the light was beginning to fade, the results were not good. It is a great pity that pictorial records more appropriate to the occasion were not obtained.

Up to this moment nobody had thought about a celebration, but somehow or other, though the hour was late, the staff of the Officers' Mess managed to produce the necessaries for a very pleasant impromptu party.

With various interruptions due to weather, but no delays for any other reason, the flight trials continued for the next twelve days, and the ten hours' flying for which the engine had been cleared was duly completed. There was no trouble whatever either with the aeroplane or the engine. It was not even necessary to inspect the engine. This last caused particular astonishment to the Gloster crew. In their experience it was usual for the engine mechanics to take off the cowlings immediately after a test flight for a thorough engine inspection. They were therefore dumbfounded when, as soon as the E.28 had taxied into the hangar after the first flight, the Power Jets' crew, in effect, dusted their hands and disappeared. Our people were not as casual as they no doubt seemed. By virtue of their very considerable experience on the test bench, they knew that all was well from the smooth note of the engine as the aeroplane taxied in.

The top speed reached was 370 m.p.h. in level flight at 25,000 feet. This was well above the then top speed of the Spitfire. It was achieved by a temporary increase of rating of the engine for the purpose. The r.p.m. was 17,000 — corresponding to a test bench thrust of 1,000 lb.

Preliminary calculations showed that the performance was very closely in accordance with predictions based on test bench results, but after the results had been more carefully analysed, both Gloster's and the R.A.E. came to the conclusion that the performance was better then prediction. Naturally, Gloster's put this down to the credit of the aeroplane, while we put it down to the credit of the engine. It was probably a little of both, or rather of the combination; because there was reason to believe that the high-velocity propelling jet had a beneficial effect on the air flow over the rear end of the fuselage, thus reducing the drag of the aeroplane slightly — a factor which had not been taken into account in performance estimates. At this time it was a very rare thing indeed for the performance of a new type of aeroplane to be better than design estimates, but later the same thing happened with other jet aircraft. I believe the de Havilland Vampire was 30 or 40 m.p.h. faster than prediction.

There had been no senior officials from the M.A.P. present for the first flight, but there was much coming and going thereafter, and a number of impromptu conferences.

A particularly memorable day was the 21st May, which was allotted for a demonstration flight — the weather was very poor early in the morning, but cleared a little, and Sayer made a short test flight to test a modification to the elevators. This was, I think, the tenth flight. During the afternoon and evening a large number of visitors arrived by road and air for the demonstration flight. Sir Archibald Sinclair (later Lord Thurso), Secretary of State for Air, and Captain Harold Balfour (later Lord Balfour), the Under Secretary of State for Air, arrived by air. Another aircraft brought a party from Hatfield — they were Mr. (later Sir) Geoffrey de Havilland and his son, Geoffrey; Major F. B. Halford; Mr. C. C. Walker and Roxbee Cox. Others present included Mr. (later Sir) Patrick Hennessey, Deputy for the Minister of Aircraft Production, Air Vice-Marshal Linnell (Controller of Research & Development); Messrs. H. N. Sporborg and R. H. Collingham from the B.T-H.; Messrs. S. B. and M. C. Wilks from Rover's; T. O. M. Sopwith of the Hawker Siddeley Group and many others. Williams and Tinling also saw the aeroplane fly for the first time.

Sayer took off at 6.15 p.m. and showed off the aeroplane very well indeed. His impressive demonstration included quite a spectacular flight downwind at a height of about 1,000 feet and at an indicated airspeed of 350 m.p.h. He then swept skywards in a steep climbing turn. The weather held off just long enough for the flight — almost at the instant that Sayer landed, it began to pour with rain.

There were, of course, the most stringent security precautions. The aeroplane was housed in a hangar at the extreme western end of the south aerodrome and was guarded day and night by Gloster's security police. Nobody, except those holding a special pass issued by the Gloster Aircraft Company, was allowed within several hundred yards of this hangar. But however careful the security arrangements were, it was impossible to conceal entirely what was going on. All the R.A.F. personnel at Cranwell were taking a lively interest in the proceedings, and I do not recall that the road along the southern boundary of the aerodrome was closed to civilians. What was seen and heard gave rise to some diverting stories. One of two officers watching the E.28 take off was heard to ask, "How the hell does that thing work?" His companion replied, "Oh, it's easy, old boy, it just sucks itself along like a Hoover!"

Dan Walker was amused to hear one officer — not knowing that Walker was one of the engineers intimately concerned — assure everybody in his immediate vicinity that the power plant was a Rolls-Royce Merlin engine driving a small four-bladed propeller inside the fuselage. He stated positively that he had seen it!

In Newark, a civilian in the bar of a public house was heard to give a highly-coloured description of the aeroplane shooting vertically upwards amid a terrific burst of flame and clouds of smoke (in fact, no flame was ever visible, and the smoke was nothing more than a barely visible trail).

One officer at least was greatly disturbed by what he had seen. He sat in the Officers' Mess with a puzzled frown. When asked what was troubling him, he replied that he had seen a strange aeroplane "going like a bat out of hell" and there was something odd about it, but he could not think what it was. After a pause, he said, "My God! chaps, I must be going round the bend — it hadn't got a propeller!"

CHAPTER 31

By the end of May, 1941, our total engine running time, including the 175 hours on the now defunct experimental engine, was 292 hours. Of this, 108 hours was distributed between the W.1.X. and the W.1 (including the flying time of 10½| hours). We had also started testing the W.1.A. and W.2 for which the running times were then 7 and 2 hours respectively.

Though the original purpose of the W.1.A. had been to test certain features of the W.2 in advance, we actually received the latter built by the Rover Co. two weeks before the former (built by the B.T-H.).

The W.2 was quite as bad as we feared it might be, and it was fortunate for us that we had foreseen and predicted the failure of the engine. I should add that the failure was nothing to do with the design changes made by the Rover Co., but was due to features in the design for which I was entirely responsible. For various reasons, including low turbine efficiency and low compressor efficiency, it was impossible to run the engine at more than about 75% of the design full speed because of surging of the compressor; also the engine ran very hot.

A word about surging is necessary at this point, because it became a severe problem with later engines as well.

Normally the flow through a rotary compressor, whether of centrifugal or axial flow type, is steady, but if at any given speed the flow is reduced below a certain critical value, violent pulsations occur, often to such a degree that there is a momentary reversal of flow. This instability is what is meant by "surging". When it happened with the engine, it was rather alarming until we got used to it, because it sounded rather like a series of explosions.

We continued our work on the W.2 for a time and then returned it to the Rover Co. and they continued to work on it. (Certain of their personnel gained experience in test work whilst attached to us for the testing of the W.2.)

It would have been possible to have saved the engine by modifications, but these would have had to be extensive, and we decided that the effort was not worth while in view of the fact that a modified version of the W.2 design was nearing completion at the B.T-H.

The start of testing of the W.1.A. was also unpromising. We encountered surging again. In this case the cause of the trouble was quickly found and removed, but the engine still ran much hotter than it should have done. However, after re-blading the turbine there was a big improvement and the results then became very promising.

Naturally the flight trials had a number of important repercussions. In a sense they had been too successful in that they generated a feeling of over-optimism. I myself was a victim of this to some extent, but not to the same degree as many others less directly connected with the work. I was very conscious of the fact that the engine destined for production was still on the drawing board, and that much development would be necessary before it was fit for quantity production. My uneasiness was in part founded on the belief that the M.A.P. policy would not work.

At a meeting at the M.A.P. presided over by Tizard, it was decided that the production target was to be a total of 1,200 engines and 500 aircraft — these to begin to appear in June and July of 1942 with production rising to 80 aircraft a month by November, 1942. It was estimated that there was a chance of completing the 500 aircraft by the Spring of 1943. (The Ministry's optimism on this point may be gauged by the fact that one prototype only had flown by the end of March, 1943.)

My uneasiness about the position was expressed in a letter I wrote to Tizard on the 27th May, 1941, in which I said:

> I want to say with the greatest possible emphasis that what is now needed is the maximum possible concentration of effort on the development work at Lutterworth for the next two to three months, and that anything which detracts from this concentration should be cut out until our primary object is attained, i.e. the development of the W.2.B. up to the point when it can safely be launched into production.
>
> The responsibility that rests on my shoulders is very heavy indeed. We are faced with two alternatives — either we place a powerful weapon in the hands of the Royal Air Force or, if we fail to get our results in time, we have falsely raised hopes and caused action to be taken which may deprive the Royal Air Force of hundreds of aeroplanes that it badly needs. Therefore I say that we must be given every help in the task and be kept free from all unnecessary strain or else I must ask to be relieved of the responsibility.
>
> Everything now turns on getting the test bench results and we have not got them yet, and we shall not succeed in getting them in time unless the effort is as intense as I have indicated above.
>
> I feel confident that the job can be done in the end, but that is not enough, it has to be within the next two or three months, and nothing that Rover's or the B.T-H. or anybody else tries to do, starting virtually from scratch, can really affect the development within that time.
>
> What is required is concentration of effort on those features of the W.2.B. which are in doubt, rather than the frittering away of energy on the design and making of alternative structure, gear boxes, fuel systems, etc., etc., such as is going

on in the B.T-H. and the Rover Co., all of which will be a costly waste if nobody succeeds in making a turbine which will do its job.

We know the gear box works, we know the fuel system works, we can feel fairly confident of the combustion chambers and blower, but there is grave doubt about the turbine end at present, and by far the greater part of the total effort should be directed to solving that problem. The B.T-H. can help immensely, by making a series of alternative wheels for several W.2.Bs. (to Power Jets' drawings), otherwise made by the Rover Co. with the assistance of the Coventry Gauge and Tool Co.

Failing this, it is my duty to say that I cannot guarantee success before the end of this year.

(I have to admit that subsequent events were to show that I was over-confident about the blower[29] and combustion chambers and unduly pessimistic about the turbine.)

In a talk I had had with S. B. Wilks during the flight trials I had told him that I thought there was still a long way to go. He said he was pleased to hear me say that, because that was also his opinion. He expected that great pressure would be put on him to get on with production. This, he thought, would be premature. He said he agreed with me that what was now needed was three months of very intensive development, with preparation for production going along in parallel. He therefore proposed to ask the Ministry for sufficient facilities and skilled operatives to enable them to turn out large quantities of experimental engine parts, and concentrate on making a few W.2.Bs. with various modifications instead of thirty of one design straight off (I did not say so, but the thought was prominent in my mind that Power Jets would make very much better use of these facilities than the Rover Co.).

Next day I heard that he had already been to the M.A.P. to press his demands for increased facilities for experimental work.

Though S. B. Wilks had seemingly accepted the inevitability of design changes, yet when we wrote to the Rover Co. (27th May) warning them of certain probable changes, they replied expressing concern about them. When S. B. Wilks visited us a few days later (15th June, 1941), he said they were worried about the prospect of design changes, because it would throw their production programme out of gear. The next day Bulman called a meeting at which Roxbee Cox, Tobin and I were present. Bulman said that Wilks had been complaining about the effect the design changes would have on the production programme, and that he himself was also disturbed to hear that we felt that important modifications might be necessary. I told him that recent experience on the test bench had caused us to have doubts about certain features of the W.2.B. design. I said that I did not doubt that the W.2.B. could be made to give its predicted performance ultimately, but I was uneasy about how long it would take to do it. I was, however, able to say that any changes we contemplated would not result in the scrapping of material already ordered.

The logic of the Rover complaint was quite beyond me. It struck me as very odd, to say the least of it, that so much fuss should be made about the possible effects on production of modifications proposed by us, when at the same time Rover's were themselves making a large number of design changes, most of which, in our view, were entirely unnecessary and in a number of respects undesirable. Not only were they re-designing the gearbox for auxiliary drives, the bearings, the fuel system and so on, but, as I heard at this meeting, they had also placed a contract with Rolls-Royce for the manufacture of an alternative (Rover) design of compressor casing. This was a clear case where Rover's were going beyond their functions as defined on March 5th. The design of the blower casing very clearly affected the aerodynamic design of the engine, and such design changes were not supposed to be made without my knowledge and approval. This alternative design was, in fact, very similar to our first W.2.B. design at the time we were collaborating with Vauxhall, but from which we had changed after it had been strongly represented to us that it would be costly in foundry man-hours to produce. (In other words, we had made a change from what we considered to be aerodynamically desirable in in order to ease production, and Rover's, who were supposed to be developing for production, were doing the very opposite.)

It later appeared that they had even more far-reaching changes in mind because, after a visit by Hawthorne to Clitheroe on the 26th July, 1941, he reported that M. C. Wilks "also showed me a tentative layout of a unit comprising a two-stage single-sided compressor arrangement followed by a 30-in. straight-through combustion chamber and turbine wheel".

Hawthorne also reported "the establishment seemed to be primarily devoted to development and testing, with the main engine building work being sub-contracted. It appeared to me that Waterloo Mill was a Rover version of the Power Jets' set-up with probably more facilities for production in the offing". Hawthorne's report thus confirmed that Rover's were putting a very elastic interpretation on their function of "development for production", and that they intended to embark on all aspects of the development.

The flight trials appeared to have a favourable effect on our relations with the B.T-H. One evening Collingham, whose home in Rugby was only a few yards away from mine, visited me and we had a very friendly talk in which I told him of the events at Cranwell. He invited me to go and see the design of their version of the W.2.B. during the next few days. Later, the B.T-H. agreed to help us further by making experimental sets of turbine blading.

It might be supposed that the successful flight trials would have had a dramatic effect on the Ministry's policy towards Power Jets, but though there could scarcely have been a more forceful demonstration of our capabilities, this did not happen. On the contrary, there were many signs that the Ministry intended to place even greater reliance on the Rover Co., and that if the latter ventured beyond their already very elastic terms of reference, the Ministry was unlikely to stop them.

On July 4th, 1941, L. L. Whyte resigned as Chairman and Managing Director of Power Jets. Though the immediate cause of this was a serious disagreement between Whyte and myself about the organisation and space requirements of the Company, it was really the culmination of a long period of disharmony between us.

In a letter to him I paid tribute to his ability and energy, and admitted that he had often received the blame for situations for which the M.A.P. were really responsible, and that he had been unfortunate in having had to deal with individuals whose motives and business morals left a lot to be desired. I told him I did not wish him to break all his ties, and would not resent his remaining on the Board.

We agreed that he would be resigning because of irreconcilable differences of opinion with myself and the other managers.

At the Board meeting at which Whyte's resignation was accepted, it was resolved "to place on record the Directors' appreciation of the valuable services rendered by Mr. Whyte in the early stages of the Company's development and their gratification that they would continue to benefit by Mr. Whyte's collaboration as a member of the Board".

I appointed Tinling as Chairman, and he and Williams became joint managing directors.

Shortly after the flight trials we became aware that the campaign of adverse propaganda to which we had been subjected for some time, had, if anything, been intensified. For example, during a visit to Firth Vickers, Dr. Taylor learned that someone had been spreading the story that the fuel consumption during the flight trials had been far too high. Similar stories had come back to us from other sub-contractors. In my view this propaganda was likely to undermine any belief they might have in the value of the work they were doing on the job.

I felt it necessary to write to Bulman (22nd June, 1941) mentioning particularly Taylor's visit to Firth Vickers and said:

> ...this is one of a number of similar instances and it is clear that a large amount of unnecessary talking is going on, and that this includes a good deal of harmful propaganda, which I believe to be deliberate. Similarly, I frequently find that before I have ever met certain individuals someone has managed to convey the impression that I am difficult to get on with, etc. etc. These things are undoubtedly impeding the development and something must be done to stop it.

This propaganda began to have its effect at the Ministry. Bulman told me that several people were beginning to feel some concern about the high fuel consumption. I told him that the fuel consumption during the flight trials was by no means as much in excess of design prediction as rumour made out.

When he said that S. B. Wilks in particular had expressed some concern on the subject I was very indignant. I pointed out, as I had done many times before, that high fuel consumption was at least partly a consequence of the high power developed, and that to consider fuel consumption alone was very misleading. The true criterion was whether the aeroplane would do the job for which it was designed and whether it would have a performance which could not otherwise be obtained. I stressed that the very low engine weight and the effect of the clean installation of the engine on the design of the aeroplane were important factors which had to be taken into account as well as fuel consumption and that, in my view, judgment on these matters was not within the competence of the Rover Company. I reminded Bulman that, according to the terms of reference which he himself had laid down on March 5th, 1941, Power Jets were primarily responsible for the aerodynamic and thermodynamic design, namely, those design features which affected thrust, fuel consumption and so on and that though he had given the Rover Company considerable latitude in mechanical design, they were only supposed to make departures in the interests of ease of production. Bulman said that Wilks was flat out to get on with the job and was naturally interested in all aspects of it. I replied that it was my impression that, on the contrary, his comments appeared to me to reflect his doubts as to whether the scheme was worth while going on with at all.

Bulman said I was misinterpreting a natural desire on the part of S. B. Wilks to avoid a waste of public money.

Again, in a phone call to me (4th July, 1941) Roxbee Cox hinted that some anxiety was being felt about the fuel consumption. I replied, with some warmth, that a great deal was being said about the fuel consumption that was not justified. It constituted malicious propaganda and ought to be stopped. Fortunately, I was able to cite some test results we had achieved within the preceding few days with the W.1.A. These had shown that the fuel consumption was not more than 8% higher than the predicted value and was probably less.

A few days later in a talk to Constant of the R.A.E. I showed him the test results of the modified W.1.A. He was very impressed and urged us to report on them as soon as possible, so that they could be used as a counterblast to some of the harmful propaganda which was going around.

The matter again cropped up at a meeting in London at which Bulman was in the chair and S. B. Wilks was present. The minutes of this meeting placed on record that if the fuel consumption of the W.2.B. proved to be as close to design estimate as the test results of the modified W.1.A., then the Meteor would have an operational endurance comparable to the Hurricane II.

At this meeting I had again protested against the Rover Co. and their associates concerning themselves with aspects of the design which did not fall within their terms of reference as I understood them, and so the minutes also recorded:

> ...it was emphasised to Wing Commander Whittle that the Rover Company and the Lucas Company were naturally anxious to assure themselves on many technical points and were entitled to full answers to all their queries having regard to their heavy responsibilities to the Ministry for production and their complete unity of interest with the Ministry and himself in carrying the project into effective R.A.F. use at the earliest moment.

When I saw these minutes I wrote to Bulman about that particular paragraph, and reminded him that at the meeting I had said that we always did our best to answer all queries, but pointed out that we were bombarded with questions from a large number of sources including Rover's, Joseph Lucas Ltd., C.A.V., Rolls-Royce, B.T-H., Gloster Aircraft Co., Vickers Armstrong's, the Bristol Aeroplane Company, de Havilland's, etc., but we had not the staff to cope with the correspondence involved. I might, with justice, have added that we would be more willing to supply information if we could feel confident that it was not required merely for use as a weapon against us. We had a natural reluctance to supply fuel consumption figures when we had reason to believe that they were wanted solely to support propaganda against the jet engine as such.

Various other features in the design were the subject of adverse criticism. In the case of our method of attaching the turbine blades to the wheel, the story was that it was not a production job, and both the B.T-H. and the Rover Co. made attempts to find alternative designs. It is a sufficient comment to say that our method is now virtually universal. Similarly, a feature of the discharge ducts from the W.2 compressor casing, which was the subject of criticism, (an "elbow" with corner vanes) was successfully incorporated in later Power Jets' designs and in the designs of many engines derived from them. In fact, that particular feature also is virtually universal in engines with centrifugal type compressors.

CHAPTER 32

On the test bench we experienced delays due to inexplicable accidents. The W.1.X. was considerably damaged as a result of a foreign body passing through the engine. We had had a blade failure on the W.2 which also seemed to be due to a similar cause. Then later in the same month we found a loose nut lodged on the compressor casing of the W.1.A. in the test house, in such a position that it could easily have fallen into the compressor intake and gone through the engine. We held an inquiry into this last incident, because these events suggested either deliberate sabotage or serious carelessness. No positive conclusions were reached, but thereafter there was a very considerable tightening up in the supervision of the work, particularly engine assembly.

With the W.1.X., which was then being used mainly for detail development, we achieved a noteworthy advance in starting technique. Hitherto the starting sequence had been fairly complicated. The following drill had been observed:

(*1*) Ensure that the throttle was in "Closed" position.

(*2*) Turn on main fuel cock.

(*3*) Switch on electric starter motor.

(*4*) Press ignition switch at about 500 r.p.m.

(*5*) Cut out starter motor when engine speed had reached about 2,000 r.p.m.

As a pilot I felt that all this was too elaborate and I had therefore instructed D. N. Walker to try and evolve an automatic starting system. This was duly done. G. B. R. Fielden was chiefly responsible, and his efforts led to successful automatic starting near the end of August, 1941. The starting procedure was greatly simplified. It was only necessary to turn on the fuel, switch on a safety switch (which was just an extra precaution) and press a starter button and the rest of the starting sequence was operated automatically.

In our work on fuel system development we had the very valuable assistance of the Ricardo Engineering Company. We were indebted to them for such important components as a speed limit governor, a barostat relief valve (which automatically reduced the pressure in the fuel line as the aeroplane climbed, thus relieving the pilot from continuous adjustment of the "throttle" control) and so on. If others had shown the same exceptional degree of co-operation, and the same unselfish disregard of proprietary interests, as we received from Ricardo, months, or even years, would have been saved.

A new engine, designated the W.2.Mk.IV. was delivered by the B.T-H. and we began testing on the 23rd July, 1941. This was our original W.2 which had been modified in stages to bring it near to the W.2.B. design.

Because of its similarity to the W.2.B., testing of this engine was of special importance.

In some ways the results were encouraging and in others very disappointing. On the favourable side, analyses of test results showed that the turbine — of the same design as the W.2.B. — was better than we had lately come to expect, but on the other side our misgivings about the compressor design proved to be well founded. As with the W.2, we found that the speed was limited by surging of the compressor (but by no means as seriously as the W.2).

At first sight, the remedy seemed to be simple — to increase the quantity of air flowing through the engine until the surging stopped, but when we tried to do this by slight modifications we found that the resulting drop in efficiency was such that the speed was limited by a rise in the exhaust temperature above that permissible for the material of the turbine blades. We had cured surging in the W.1.A. easily enough, but it proved a much more difficult problem with the W.2.Mk.IV. (and — later — with the W.2.B.).

Observations made on the W.2.Mk.IV. suggested that the turbine efficiency could be raised by a small change to the turbine blades, namely, altering their setting by about five degrees, and so I strongly recommended to the Rover Co. that they should provide for this modification in the W.2.B. (phone call on the 29th July; letter 12th August and another phone call on the 13th August). It is most unfortunate that no action was then taken on this recommendation, because when this experiment was eventually tried about eighteen months later, it resulted in an astonishing improvement in performance. We were, of course, keeping Rover's fully informed about our test work on the W.2.Mk.IV. and other engines — sometimes by phone, sometimes by letter, and at other times verbally during visits either of Rover representatives to Power Jets or vice versa.

At a discussion in London between Bulman, Roxbee Cox, Tobin and myself about the test results of the W.2.Mk.IV., I once more stressed our urgent need for more engines and engine components. Bulman promised that something would be done about this. Later the Rover Co. were instructed to deliver the first and third W.2.Bs. to Power Jets, the first of them to be delivered as a set of parts for Power Jets' to assemble. This was another of the rare occasions on which the Ministry ruled in favour of Power Jets.

The Minister of Aircraft Production, Lt.-Col. Moore-Brabazon (later Lord Brabazon), was taking a very active interest in the development; indeed, he was taking too much interest for my peace of mind.

After a visit to Lutterworth, during which he witnessed a demonstration run of the W.1.X., the Minister wrote: "my short visit gave me more interest and enjoyment than any which has fallen to my lot since joining this Ministry."

His interest increased. Early in August, 1941, Roxbee Cox told me that the Minister was apparently rather disturbed about the slow rate of progress. Roxbee Cox said he had done his best to reassure the Minister, but the latter had asked to be informed daily on how things were going. Next day the Minister rang me direct to ask me how we were getting on, and about the troubles of the W.2.Mk.IV. He sounded very disappointed when I told him that a modification we intended to make would take a week. My note on this conversation records that we had reached a thrust of 1,000 lb. on the W.2.Mk.IV. at a speed of 14,000 r.p.m., which was more or less in accordance with expectations for that speed. (The design full speed was the same as for the W.2.B., namely, 16,500 r.p.m.)

In a phone conversation with Roxbee Cox later that day I told him of the Minister's call and said I was beginning to feel like a hunted man. He said he had asked Air Marshal Linnell to pass on a hint that all was being done that could be done and that I should not be worried by inquiries. He said the Minister had seen him and instructed him to get me another engine, but he had replied that he did not know where it was to come from.

However, the Minister was not without consideration and he sent me a handwritten letter of encouragement about two weeks later (22nd August):

> So sorry things are not behaving themselves. I am afraid there are going to be a lot of headaches coming your way. Don't be discouraged. Just plug along, it will all arrange itself. Any way I can help, just ask, everything is at your disposal. You've got a good crowd round you. I have nothing but confidence in the future.

In a letter to the Minister a few days later, I gave him some indication of the rate at which we were working in our efforts to get over our difficulties. I told him that with the W.2.Mk.IV., we had dismantled, modified, reassembled and tested the engine no less than five times in the preceding ten days in attempts to cure the surging trouble. I went on:

> ...it is a case of getting the most detailed observations and analysing them, and the fact is that we are getting the readings almost faster than we can digest and analyse them so that diagnosis tends to lag behind the testing.
>
> You may rely on me to keep plugging away. We have been up against worse troubles than these, and I am quite confident that we shall overcome them, and in normal times I wouldn't be at all worried, but it's this terrible race with time which is so dominant in my mind. All the time I have to weigh the desirability of a certain modification against the time needed to make it. This situation will be much eased as soon as there are several sets of parts available. (Unfortunately, Rover's have gone back three weeks on their promise of the first set of W.2.B. parts.) Then it will be possible to carry out a modification on a spare component without interfering with our ability to try the effect of other more easily made changes...
>
> You are right in saying that I have a good crowd round me. They are all working like slaves, so much so, that there is a risk of mistakes through physical or mental fatigue.

The sense of a race with time, coupled as it was with a shortage of experimental components and lack of facilities, weighed heavily upon me, and left an indelible imprint on my nervous system. If I had had the courage then to sacrifice time by making fairly extensive modifications, much time might have been saved later, but in my own defence I must add that throughout this period it did seem probable that the troubles we were meeting might be cured by quite small changes. The answer always seemed to be "just around the corner".

Two days later the Minister phoned me again to find out how we were getting on. I had to tell him we weren't.

Soon after this I had a short talk with him in London. After giving him a report of progress (or lack of it) on the W.2.Mk.IV., I hinted that one of the most trying factors in my situation was the knowledge that every move we made was being closely watched. He told me not to let that worry me.

I followed up part of this talk by sending the Minister an interim report on the running of the W.2.Mk.IV. In his acknowledgment (24th September, 1941) the Minister said he was very impressed with the difficulty of diagnosis when the principal components of the engine were so inter-dependent, and he expressed himself as being enthusiastically in favour of the separate testing of the compressor, turbine and combustion assembly:

> I think that is the most pressing problem at the moment and at this end I am pursuing the matter to see what can be done in conjunction with your needs.

I was very glad indeed that the Minister at least had come to recognise our needs in the matter of full-scale test plant. I had raised this subject over and over again, but we were at this time no nearer getting sanction for it than at any time before. At one moment it seemed as though Roxbee Cox was prepared to support us in the matter, but later, opinion in the Ministry veered in the direction that if such equipment were to be provided, it should be installed at the R.A.E. In a phone conversation on the 1st August, Roxbee Cox stated specifically that the Ministry was opposed to Power Jets having this equipment.

Encouraged by the Minister's views on the subject, I wrote to him (28th September, 1941) and said:

> I hope the proposals to put such test plant down at the R.A.E. will not be considered to be sufficient to meet our needs, because this type of work is extending so rapidly that one establishment will be quite unable to meet the needs of the different firms engaged on the development.

However, it was not until May, 1942, that my persistence was rewarded and this equipment was sanctioned.

During September, 1941, in spite of repeated dismantling, modification and re-erection, we did over twenty-four hours running on the W.2.Mk.IV. We then thought we had accumulated sufficient information to see our way out of the surging difficulties. My records show that on the 4th October I told Roxbee Cox what I thought should be done, and our much later work showed that we were then on the right track, but we were foiled in our experiments on the W.2.Mk.IV. because of its total destruction just under a week later.

To test certain modifications we believed desirable (and had recommended to Rover's), we had had a spare rotor made in which the compressor impeller was to the W.2.B. design and the turbine had 80 blades (as compared with 72 for the

W.2.B.). The first and last run with this new rotor fitted was made on the 10th October.

At the comparatively modest speed of 9,000 r.p.m. the new impeller burst with explosive violence and shattered the engine. Though this was a major disaster from the point of view of the development — it probably cost us six months — we were fortunate in other ways. It happened at about eleven o'clock at night and there were four people actually in the test cell when the explosion occurred — R. C. McLeod (who had recently joined us as a design engineer); W. Podmore, one of Walker's test engineers; Sergeant Allen (R.A.F. on loan) and H. Havard (test fitter). By almost a miracle, nobody was killed. Podmore and Allen were both slightly injured and, by a remarkable coincidence, their injuries were practically identical — each had a small piece of metal embedded in the side of his nose. McLeod and Havard escaped completely. It was scarcely possible to put one's foot down anywhere without stepping on debris. The impeller, weighing about 56 lb. had burst into two pieces which had hurtled round the test cell several times before coming to rest. The shaft linking the compressor impeller to the turbine wheel had fractured within half an inch of the turbine and remained attached to one of the two portions of the impeller. Another astonishing feature of the accident was that, though without a bearing and with only half an inch of shaft, the turbine remained in position in what was left of the rear part of the engine.

The explosion occurred after only about four minutes' running with the new rotor, but during that four minutes it had been observed that the exhaust temperatures were much lower than usual, which was a reasonably certain indication that there was an improvement in efficiency.

Inspection of the pieces of the impeller showed that the fracture was discoloured over a large part of its area. This indicated that an extensive crack had existed for some time before the impeller was ever assembled into the engine, and that up to the speed at which the burst occurred it had been mainly held together by the two portions of shaft bolted to it.

The new rotor had been made by the B.T-H. and had passed inspection.

On the 14th October, a meeting was held at Brownsover to inquire into the failure. Major A. A. Ross (Bulman's deputy) was in the chair. It transpired that similar defects had occurred in two other impellers, but had been detected before the completion of the component.

It was decided that Power Jets were to take immediate action to provide an overspeed rig in which it would be possible to spin new rotor components up to a speed well above the design full speed before fitting to engines. Rover's were advised to do the same.

CHAPTER 33

The principal aero-engine firms were Rolls-Royce, Armstrong Siddeley (a subsidiary of the Hawker Siddeley group), Napier's, the Bristol Aeroplane Company, and the de Havilland Engine Co. With the exception of Napier's, all these firms became interested in aircraft gas turbines during 1941.

After the flight trials, and probably as a result of them, Rolls-Royce began to take a very active interest in our work and became linked with it as sub-contractors both to Power Jets and Rover's for the manufacture of engine parts. They were also preparing to do compressor tests for us with a test rig powered by a Vulture engine.

Before this they had been working on a turbo-jet engine scheme to the design of A. A. Griffith — a very ingenious but much more complex arrangement than anything we were doing — which was still in an embryo stage.

The fruitful technical co-operation between Power Jets and Rolls-Royce had started with a meeting at their Derby works in June, 1941, at which E. W. (later Lord) Hives had promised to help in a number of ways. Thereafter there was a frequent exchange of visits which I do not propose to detail. From the commercial point of view Rolls-Royce were much more to be feared than the Rover Co., in that they were far more powerful. Nevertheless, there was no reserve whatever on the part of Power Jets in technical collaboration. This was based on our respect for their outstanding engineering ability, particularly in the field in which we were engaged. I believe that this respect was mutual.

The de Havilland Engine Co. had also been drawn into jet engine development by Sir Henry Tizard after the trial flights. Major F. B. Halford, their Chief Engineer, had already had some association with the project as an adviser to Vauxhall's before they dropped out. The de Havilland proposals were beginning to take definite form at the end of June, 1941. They were embarking on the design of a jet engine and of an aeroplane to be powered by it — this was the birth of the Goblin-engined Vampire. The engine was to be much larger and more powerful than the W.2.B. and was to be designed for a thrust of upwards of 2,700 lb.

Once more Power Jets were expected to co-operate fully and supply all the necessary information, but this was by no means easy because we were grossly overloaded. However, most of the information they required reached them via the R.A.E. who were closely in touch with both ourselves and Halford. In addition, there was more positive direct assistance, particularly on combustion chamber design and testing.

As I discovered later by comparing notes with Halford, the activities of third parties hampered good relations between de Havillands and ourselves. We were told that they preferred to seem independent of us, and they were told that we were unwilling to collaborate for purely selfish reasons. I admit that on our part we felt some opposition to what we regarded as a diversion of effort, but this was based on our view that nothing should detract from the task of getting the Meteor powered by W.2.Bs. into production at the earliest possible moment. I did not believe that any major departures in engine design could lead to an engine which would be in production in time for the war. On the contrary, the additional competition for sub-contract capacity and material supplies was likely to put back the date at which the Meteor would become operational. I think I can claim that events were to show that these views were well founded. Nevertheless, from the longer term point of view, de Havilland's work proved of great value because, though the Goblin-engined Vampire never became operational during the war, it proved to be a very fine aeroplane.

Armstrong Siddeley had been aware of our work from pre-war days. They had also had some connection with gas turbine work in making experimental compressors for the R.A.E., so it was natural that they should wish to break into this field. Initially they did project work on a rather complex scheme proposed by an engineer named Heppner. However, this did not proceed beyond the paper stage and was subsequently abandoned in favour of more straightforward projects.

Certain contacts between Power Jets and Mr. (later Sir Roy) Fedden and F. M. Owner of the Bristol Aeroplane Company led to proposals for combining jet engines and piston engines, but these were subsequently dropped and Bristol's concentrated on the development of propeller turbines.

The very considerable extension of the scope of activity and interest in the field of aircraft gas turbines in the few months following the flight trials, led to the formation of the "Gas Turbine Collaboration Committee".

I understand that the original suggestion for this committee was made by Hives of Rolls-Royce, but the first reference to it which came my way was on the 23rd August, 1941, when Roxbee Cox said that he was considering having regular meetings between all the parties concerned in this type of development.

The matter was taken a stage further at the beginning of October. We received a letter (3rd October, 1941) from Air Marshal Linnell (Controller of Research and Development) saying:

> ...to encourage and guide collaboration, it has been decided to form a committee under the chairmanship of Dr. Roxbee Cox on which all the firms engaged on gas turbine projects will be represented with the object of:
> (1) avoiding duplication of effort;
> (2) pooling ideas;
> (3) pooling testing facilities;
> (4) pooling experience;
> (5) relating power units to the most appropriate airframes.

The first meeting was fixed for the 1st November, 1941.

Frankly, we at Power Jets did not receive the proposal with any enthusiasm at first, because it seemed likely to complicate matters rather than otherwise, and to add yet further to the burdens on us in the way of supplying information, but we later became enthusiastic supporters, and I am firmly convinced that Britain owes much of its technical superiority in this field to the Gas Turbine Collaboration Committee. There were many intrinsic difficulties in the proposal, but somehow or other, under the skilful chairmanship of Roxbee Cox, a good deal of thin ice was skated over very successfully.

Shortly after the formation of the G.T.C.C., it seemed to me very desirable that a document should go on the record outlining the relative contribution made to the jet development by the various firms connected with it up to the date of the first meeting. I, therefore, prepared a summary (January, 1942) of the position so far as it was known to me. Copies of this document were sent to the M.A.P. with a letter suggesting that it should be a contribution to a memorandum which we recommended that the Ministry should have prepared, and which should go on the record as having been accepted as a true statement of fact by all the firms in the G.T.C.C. In our view, such a document would have had important reference and legal value and would be particularly useful to any official or other person coming new to the work and requiring to pick up the threads. Unfortunately, the Ministry did not take any action on this suggestion.

CHAPTER 34

The first of the W.2.Bs. manufactured by the Rover Co. and delivered to Power Jets as a set of components, was assembled during October, 1941, and ran for the first time on the 31st of the month. For the first few tests we were obliged to use a W.2 impeller, because two W.2.B. type impellers delivered by the Rover Co. had had to be scrapped, one because it was cracked and the other because of excessive dimensional errors. Once more the primary difficulty was surging of the compressor at a very moderate speed. Later, when we fitted a W.2.B. impeller, we managed to get up to a speed of 15,750 before surging occurred (at the expense of high exhaust temperatures) as compared with the design speed of 16,500. We were also hampered by failures of sheet-metal components supplied by the Rover Co. (Messrs. Joseph Lucas, who were making the sheet-metal components for Rover, had not yet got into their stride and we attributed these failures to manufacture rather than design.)

We were not the only ones in trouble with surging. Rover's were testing a W.2 fitted with their own design of compressor casing, and this engine was also surging at speeds well below full speed. The B.T-H. were in the same boat and reported surging at 10,700 r.p.m. (first G.T.C.C. Progress Report).

No other firms, of course, had any engines running.

At that time every day seemed like a month and the apparent intractability of the problem caused a general wave of pessimism. It was decided that the first twelve Rover/Whittle W.2.B. engines were to be cleared at a reduced rating. Bulman (letter dated 18th November, 1941) instructed the Rover Co. to complete four engines for flight trial with a thrust rating of not less than 1,000 lb., and to complete the other eight for a thrust rating of 1,200 lb. In connection with this instruction, it is interesting to note that by the 23rd November, we were getting results from the W.2.B. as follows:

1,000 lb. thrust at 14,750 r.p.m. with a jet pipe temperature of 590° C.

1,190 lb. thrust at 15,500 r.p.m. with a jet pipe temperature of 620° C.[30]

Surging occurred at 15,800 r.p.m. at which the thrust and temperature were 1,270 lb. and 640° C. respectively. We seemed to be quite near our target and could scarcely be blamed for hoping that comparatively minor changes would enable us to reach it.

Our intensive efforts were still impeded by lack of facilities. This, and the urgency of the need to solve the surging problem drove us to desperate measures. We even resorted to making experimental parts (diffuser blades) out of hard wood, hoping that they would last just long enough to give us the answer we needed, and indeed they nearly did. With them we obtained a thrust of 1,350 lb. at 16,000 r.p.m. without any sign of surging. The wooden blades failed at that speed.

An informal meeting of the G.T.C.C. was held at Brownsover to discuss the surging problem. No formal minutes were taken, but there was reasonable agreement about the causes and possible solutions. The R.A.E. representatives were rather pessimistic about compressor efficiency and thought that we were aiming too high. They produced a chart of collected results from work on aero-engine superchargers to support their point. I protested against the attitude that because the thing had not been done so far, it could not be done in the future. (Our target figures of those days have since been well surpassed.)

The R.A.E. representatives also produced calculations which suggested that the W.2.B. probably could not run at full speed without excessive exhaust temperatures. This implied that there must be some important discrepancy between their calculations and ours. After a long and rather confused discussion it came to light that the R.A.E. had used a wrong dimension for the size of the exhaust duct. I registered a strong protest about the whole matter — to quote from my own notes: "pointing out that the R.A.E. representatives were giving their considered opinion that it was virtually impossible for the W.2.B. to reach full speed, in front of a number of individuals who, without going through the calculations in detail, were not in a position to judge between the R.A.E. and Power Jets' calculations, and had an important discrepancy not come to light, a most unfortunate impression must have been created."[31]

The programme set forth in a note I had written on the problem of surging received general approval.

By the beginning of December, 1941, Rover's also had a W.2.B. on test, and succeeded in getting a thrust of 1,400 lb. with the W.2.B. ostensibly as designed except for an oversize propelling nozzle.

Whilst surging was the main obstacle to development, we were now beginning to get indications of another major problem — turbine blade failures.

Though we had had a number of failures in the past, they had all been associated with some exceptional circumstances, e.g. a tip rub or damage due to a foreign body going through. But now the need for improved materials began to become urgent. Nevertheless, we had gone a long way with the materials we had used hitherto, all of which had been supplied by Firth Vickers, and so on the 10th November, 1941, I was moved to write to the late Dr. W. H. Hatfield, their Chief Metallurgist, as follows:

> The contribution which you and your firm have made to the development on which we are engaged has been very important, and indeed, without the special steels which you have developed, it would not have been a practicable proposition. You have, therefore, provided an essential link.

A few days later, Dr. Hatfield replied and said, *inter alia*,

> Your letter is particularly generous and I do not think I remember ever having received such a charming acknowledgment of our work.

Tests by the National Physical Laboratory (at the end of 1941) of a new alloy known as Nimonic 80 were very promising. Nimonic 80 was a product of the Mond Nickel Co. and was an alloy mainly of nickel and chromium. This material was to prove very important in the subsequent history of the development.

Shortly before the formation of the G.T.C.C., another M.A.P. Committee had been formed specially to deal with the problems of high temperature materials — it was known as the High Temperature Materials Research Committee, and held frequent meetings throughout the war.

Unfortunately, turbine blade manufacture was a long job and set a limit to the rate at which experimental work was possible, so we were devoting considerable thought to ways and means of removing this bottleneck. Two engineers attached to us on loan from the United Shoe Machinery Co., of Leicester — J. A. Kestell and B. Barton — were very experienced in the design of special machines, and so I set them the task of designing a new type of blade-making machine. Kestell was chiefly responsible, and was successful in evolving a very ingenious machine tool which ultimately greatly speeded up turbine blade manufacture. The first experimental Kestell machine was later rendered obsolete by more specialised machines also to his design. This was one of the many ways in which Power Jets made important contributions to the development of manufacturing methods. (I remember getting quite a thrill of pleasure two years later when I saw a battery of Kestell blade-making machines at work in the Rolls-Royce factory with "Power Jets Limited" embossed in a prominent place.)

Some time earlier I had tried to get Firth Vickers to experiment with forging blades close to final shape, but it was not then considered practicable. Nevertheless, the matter was not forgotten, and I received a pleasant surprise one day when Dr. Hatfield sent me a forged blade which they had succeeded in making very close to the design shape. Some time later I learned that the practice of forging blades to shape was already well established in the U.S.A. (for exhaust turbo-superchargers).

CHAPTER 35

From time to time there had been suggestions that Power Jets should become partly or wholly Government owned. As early as September, 1940, certain senior officials of the Directorate of Contracts had hinted that public ownership of the Company might be the best way out of a complex situation.

At the time of the flight trials and thereafter, Tizard repeatedly took a similar line, on the ground that the sums of public money being spent on Power Jets could not be justified unless there were at least a substantial increase in the holding in the Company which the Government held through me. Eventually, he invited the Company to submit proposals along these lines.

While we did not understand why these arguments should apply to Power Jets and not to others, at the same time we recognised that a large Government share in Power Jets might provide the protection we needed. So, shortly before his resignation, Whyte formally submitted proposals on behalf of Power Jets, the essence of which was that the M.A.P. should purchase a controlling shareholding of just over 50% for £192,000.

However, though the initiative in this matter had come from Tizard and other Ministry officials, the Treasury turned down the proposal on "broad grounds of public policy". I understand that Roxbee Cox and others who favoured the plan in principle tried to get the Treasury to relent, but without success.

The decision came both as a surprise and as a painful shock to Power Jets. A surprise because we could not see why it had been rejected on grounds of "public policy", in view of such well-known precedents as the Suez Canal and the Anglo-Iranian Oil Company, and a shock because we felt that our chief hope of ensuring survival had been destroyed.

Now that many firms, all of whom were potentially dangerous competitors, were entering the aircraft gas turbine field, Power Jets' chances of ultimate survival were becoming increasingly slim. What — in more normal times — would have been vital trade secrets had been freely supplied to possible future rivals. The whole of the equipment we operated was the property of the State. Indeed, Power Jets' only tangible assets were its patent rights, and such protection as these afforded applied only to non-Government contracts.

Williams, Tinling and Johnson made repeated efforts to get the Ministry to recognise that, having put us in this dangerous position, it was up to them to do something about it. Many of the Contracts Directorate officials concerned were sympathetic to Power Jets' point of view and recognised the danger in which we stood, but seemed unable to find a satisfactory solution to the problem.

In a further attempt to clear up the matter, Tinling addressed a long and very carefully considered letter to the Minister of Aircraft Production (10th September, 1941) setting out in detail the difficulties of the Company's position as a consequence of Ministry policy, and requesting that the following broad principles should be recognised:

(1) that the Company ought not to be prejudiced, or placed in financial jeopardy by the Ministry's policy, but, on the contrary, had a special claim to security;

(2) that the Company was entitled to be regarded as the main seat of the development of the Whittle and ancillary inventions both during the war and after;

(3) that my services should continue to be at the disposal of Power Jets for as long as was required to fulfil the objects of the Company;

(4) that the Company was entitled to protection against the competition of other organisations to whom its technology had been divulged;

(5) that if and when a similar situation arose in respect of developments in the United States, the Company's American rights should not be prejudiced.

In effect, Tinling was seeking something more specific than Tedder's assurance of a "moral obligation" to protect the Company.

After a lapse of over two months, the Ministry replied in a long letter (dated 24th November, 1941) which was extremely evasive and of doubtful relevance in many respects. Not one of the points of principle which Tinling had sought to have recognised was conceded. Indeed, if anything, it seemed to represent a retreat from Tedder's undertaking, because the letter contained the following:

> The Company is being financed from public funds and this will continue so long as it is deemed necessary. It is impossible for the Minister to give any undertaking in this respect beyond what may be contained in current contracts.

The letter contained an important admission that while the Ministry had forced Power Jets to disclose all its technology, they had been too weak to make the other firms "toe the line". The relevant section read:

> In so far as information or knowledge has been divulged which is not the subject of a patent the position is more difficult. The Company is aware of the attempts made by the Department to secure certain undertakings from third parties

> and the lack of success attending these efforts. The Minister is not unsympathetic to the Company's representations although the Company was bound to make disclosure. It is not possible at this stage for the Minister to define the Department's attitude to this question more closely than to say that the Department would not be an assenting party to the exploitation for commercial purposes by third parties of information obtained from the Company for military purposes and not otherwise procurable. The Minister considers that this problem must be left for consideration in the light of the circumstances prevailing if and when it arises.

At one point the Ministry's letter contained the curious statement: "the Company is in no different position from others engaged in comparable undertakings." Nothing, of course, existed which could be described as a "comparable undertaking". Power Jets' position was quite unique. No other firm had the development of the jet engine as its sole activity. To the established firms then engaged it was not yet more than a sideline.

The Company made many further attempts to get the position clarified but, as I was only on the fringe of these exchanges, I do not propose to detail them. It seemed to me that it was almost beyond the power of the human mind to sort out the appalling muddle. Eventually, the "Gordian Knot" was cut by the nationalisation of the Company in 1944.

CHAPTER 36

During the latter half of 1941 it was at last conceded that Power Jets should be equipped to make experimental engines. The capacity authorised was defined as that necessary to make engines and spares up to an equivalent of twelve complete engines per year.

This meant that our need for increased space became greater than ever.

For some time we had been seeking permission to find alternative premises, and eventually the Ministry belatedly recognised that it was impossible to accommodate the necessary expansion at Lutterworth in view of the space, labour and other difficulties. Had sanction for a move been given some time earlier, it would not have been difficult to have transferred to any suitable alternative premises, but our commitments had now become such that a move of any appreciable distance from Lutterworth would have meant a very severe interference with our work and serious personnel difficulties, and so we sought authority to build a factory on a site just outside the village of Whetstone, about four miles south of Leicester and about nine miles from Lutterworth. After protracted discussions in which Ministry officials repeatedly argued that we ought to find an existing factory (such places as Nottingham and Bradford were suggested) our point of view was at last accepted and the Whetstone factory sanctioned (end of October, 1941).

The combination of overwork and frustration was beginning to tell on me severely at the latter end of 1941. Exhausted by a four-and-a-half-year struggle with formidable engineering problems, and depressed by pessimism about the outcome of M.A.P. policy, I began to suffer from insomnia, irritability, lack of appetite and other symptoms of nervous strain. I became "jumpy" and very easily startled. These things gradually grew worse until I had to stop work on the 10th December, 1941.

On that day — three days after Pearl Harbour had brought Japan and America into the war — the dreadful news of the loss of the *Prince of Wales* and the *Repulse* was announced. I heard the news from Cheshire who burst excitedly into my office to tell me. I was so shocked that I temporarily lost all self-control. I sprang to my feet and pointing to the door, shouted "Get out — get out!" I find it hard to explain why I acted so violently in those particular circumstances, especially as Cheshire and I were close friends and there was nothing he personally had done to annoy me. Somehow the sinking of those two mighty ships affected me profoundly, partly, perhaps, because I had spent sufficient time at sea with the Navy in the past to know to what extent one's ship becomes one's home; partly also, I suppose, because, to my mind, the Navy still symbolised the might of Britain. In my depressed state the news sounded like the knell of doom.

I realised that if I could behave like this, there was something seriously wrong, so I stopped work there and then and went home. The thing to be wondered at is that it had not happened before.

Group Captain Symonds (later Sir Charles Symonds), the R.A.F.s senior specialist in neurology, came to see me. A few days later he urged me to go into the Military Hospital, Oxford, where he was based, so that he could attend to me personally. I found the hospital atmosphere extremely depressing, and so after a week of it, I succeeded in persuading Symonds to allow me to return home. I remained at home for another week and then returned to work after an absence of one month. Though I regarded myself as being on "light duty" for a time, there was no doubt that I returned long before I was fit to do so, but I found almost complete inactivity intolerable.

When I did return I found that even my illness had been used against me. It was reported back to me that at one meeting, when someone quoted my views on a certain matter, a senior M.A.P. official had said "it's no use taking any notice of Whittle — he's gone round the bend".

During my absence, another crisis over technical policy developed. A meeting, held on 23rd December, 1941, at the Lucas Works in Birmingham under the chairmanship of Major A. A. Ross (Bulman's deputy), was used to re-define the relative functions of Power Jets and Rover's, though, ostensibly, its purpose was to make decisions on certain technical matters relating to the W.2.B., especially the fuel system.

The official minutes recorded:

> ...the Rover Company were ... responsible to the Ministry for the production development and design of the thrust power units designated as the Rover Whittle W.2.B., complete with all the major components for the accessory services and control systems required for the satisfactory functioning of the power unit in the aircraft.

Also:

> ...the Rover Company are responsible to the Ministry for the production design which includes that for the accessory service and control system and may experiment and submit for approval to the Ministry for embodiment in the

> production, changes in the basic Power Jets' design made in the interests of ease of production, increased reliability, simplicity and improvement in operation or performance.

There were a number of other paragraphs which indicated that these minutes were being used to re-define the responsibilities of Rover's and Power Jets. In effect, all the former restrictions on the latitude of design permitted to Rover's were removed.

Williams, Tinling and Johnson visited the M.A.P. on the 30th December and learned that Air Marshal Linnell had virtually changed the position overnight, in that he had ruled that Power Jets' work was to come under the Director of Engine Research and Development instead of under the Director of Scientific Research. This meant that Ross could give rulings affecting Power Jets.

Tobin explained that the position now was that the Rover Company were responsible for their W.2.B. research, development, and production independently. Power Jets were responsible for such research and development as might be put upon them. Power Jets were also to act as consultants to Rover's. The Power Jets' representatives pointed out that they had been advising continuously, but their advice was rarely taken.

Before this Tinling had written to the Minister (3rd January, 1942) setting out Power Jets' views on policy. This letter stressed that Power Jets had only two immediate objects, namely, the most rapid success of the venture and the least possible wastage of resources. After reminding the Minister that originally Rover's had been introduced to the venture because Power Jets hoped to invoke their aid as manufacturers, the letter went on:

After many months of contact, we are convinced that it is not efficient for the activities of our collaborators, the Rover Company, to include Research and Development save in respect of production; and we have serious misgivings even as to production. It is our conviction that no substantial contribution to the technology is likely to be afforded by them. We have information that the incursions of Research impede manufacture of superchargers[32] for flight or bench running. The result of research and development by Rover, up to this date, is unimpressive. The original basis of collaboration has, by Departmental processes, been gradually changed. We agreed to act as consultants in detailed (mechanical) design and as the authorities (under your Ministry) on thermodynamic-aerodynamic matters. Our experienced advice as consultants has been largely and detrimentally ignored, whilst our function as authorities is being abrogated. We can no longer agree to this position since in our opinion safety, performance, and celerity, are being and will be impaired thereby.

Major modifications introduced by Rover into our design (we are dealing only with their W.2.B.) have been rejected by us; but our advice has not prevented their appearance in Rover superchargers; important modifications or departures evolved by us and communicated to Rover have not been adopted. This has retarded, and will further retard, the programme as a whole. In some cases departures from our design and practice have been made without reference whatever to us before manufacture.

Whilst the original basis of collaboration intended that Rover should develop the designs for production, we believe that they are, in important respects, far behind production methods evolved by us; thus it would appear that their progress towards efficient and free-flowing production has suffered from the diversion towards research of their energies and capacity…

> We are now brought to the second of our main issues, which is that we find ourselves the servants of too many masters. We have up to recently operated, under instructions which in the main came from D.S.R. and that is a term *de facto* if not *de jure* in our Contracts. It has recently been indicated to us that we are to act on the instructions of D.E.D. Now, it is the fact that our relations under D.S.R. have been smooth and, we are bold enough to believe, successful in principle and in practice. We are, in short, happy in that relationship. We cannot ignore, however, that it is D.E.D. who have sponsored those decisions and acts of which we most seriously disapprove. This is not in any sense an aspersion on this Directorate, it is simply that they are, necessarily, not fully apprised of the facts and circumstances which are part of our everyday experience. In our opinion and experience, it is not sufficient that an extensive knowledge of ordinary aero-engine work be applied in this development; a close personal familiarity being quite essential.
>
> We ask therefore that our duties and responsibilities and those of Rover be made clear, and be decided in the light of the fact that we are in every significant sense the senior party in this venture. We also ask that Departmental authority be clearly and specifically defined, so that wasteful conflicts and contradictory rulings be avoided henceforth. We ask that a review of the activities of Rover should be held in order that the launching of useful aircraft be not further retarded, and so that the many problems which they are deemed to be suited to solve should be dealt with to the limit of their capacity…

The Minister's reply (dated 10th January, 1942) clearly confirmed that Ross's meeting at Birmingham on the 23rd December had indeed been used to change the terms of reference to give the Rover Company much wider scope than they had nominally been allowed hitherto. For the rest, the letter was a defence of policy, and though it contained remarks recognising that Power Jets were the rightful parents, were actuated by the highest motives, and had co-operated loyally, there was no hint that our views had made any impression or that the "review" asked for was likely to be held.

We thought that the decisions of the 5th March, 1941, had given the Rover Company far too much scope, so it may be guessed how indignant we felt at this further extension of their functions, particularly as nothing had happened in between the 5th March and the 23rd December to show any justification for this course of action. On the contrary, in the interval, Power Jets had had the successful flight tests to their credit, and had continued to produce results which any competent and unbiased judge might reasonably have described as remarkable in proportion to our strength in personnel and resources, whereas such results as Rover's had obtained worthy of note were obtained with an engine to Power Jets' design in all important respects.

In a talk with Air Marshal Linnell at the M.A.P. on the 24th January I referred to the unfortunate developments during my absence. I severely criticised the Ministry's policy up to that date, especially the way in which Rover's had been allowed to ignore strong recommendations made by Power Jets. I gave it as my opinion that drastic changes were required in the Ministry if future mistakes were to be avoided. He admitted that, in his opinion, a number of mistakes had been made and used the phrase "I have taken over an unfortunate legacy."

I urged most strongly that time would be gained rather than lost by a complete change in policy, including the formation of a separate Directorate in the Ministry to deal with jet engines. He said this last had been considered and rejected. He expressed himself as horrified by the atmosphere of distrust and suspicion he had found to exist. He was most emphatic in his assurance that the intentions of all concerned were sound and that the work of Power Jets and myself to date was fully appreciated.

I repeated much of what I had already said, in a letter to Linnell dated 20th January giving my views about the then position with the W.2.B. I recorded that we had been to full speed and obtained full sets of readings, and that we had achieved a thrust of 1,560 lb.

I said that though the results might seem a little disappointing when compared with expectations, "the circumstances were such that we regard them as highly satisfactory and constituting an important landmark in the development — I will go so far as to say that the most serious aerodynamic and thermodynamic troubles which were limiting the development have now been overcome, and the main purpose of this letter is to put this opinion on record". I added that with certain modifications recommended earlier and greater accuracy of manufacture, I felt reasonably confident that there should be no difficulty in getting the 1,600 lb. thrust which was expected from the engine.

Having thus expressed my confidence on the aerodynamic side, I stressed that there had not been enough test running to make it certain that all mechanical weaknesses were known, and that in my opinion "the Rover Company should be attending to this matter instead of experimenting with aerodynamic design, and thereby limiting their ability to put in running time".

CHAPTER 37

By the end of January, 1942, Power Jets had three engines of the W.2.B. type, namely, two Rover-built engines and a third which we had built with the aid of sub-contractors. It would scarcely be true to say that we had three complete engines at any one time, because, in practice, a good deal of "cannibalising" was going on through shortage of parts, and more often than not we could only run one particular engine by borrowing parts from another.

The W.1.A. which was destined for flight in the E.28 was successfully cleared for flight during December, 1941.

Much useful development work was done on a W.1 type of engine which, since it was used purely for miscellaneous test work, was denoted W.1.T.

In their progress report covering the period up to the 4th February, 1942, Rover's also claimed a substantial advance with the surging problem. They recorded that they had delayed surging to above the full speed of the engine, and to have obtained a thrust of 1,644 lb. at the surge speed, namely, 16,750 r.p.m. with an exhaust pipe temperature of 628° C. This was with their own design of compressor casing; thus they were closely in parallel with us even to the extent that they found that several of the turbine blades cracked and that they had exhaust assembly failures. They had also had a thrust bearing failure.

The B.T-H. were also doing better. They also succeeded in raising the surge speed to a little above the full speed and claimed a thrust of 1,667 lb.

The axial flow engine known as the F.2 at Metropolitan Vickers had been completed and testing had begun.

It may be seen that the bogey of surging was receding, and being replaced by the bogey of turbine blade failures. The other failures though tiresome were not of a fundamental nature. They were frequently due to insufficient care in manufacture. This was particularly true of the sheet-metal failures in the exhaust assembly and combustion chambers (Rover's reported splitting of the combustion chamber casings).

The odd thing was that the apparently encouraging results of the beginning of 1942 were not maintained during the rest of the year. The development seemed retrograde rather than progressive.

CHAPTER 38

In a letter dated 12th January, 1942, Hives of Rolls-Royce invited me to Derby to discuss a proposal that they should build their version of a Whittle engine. Hives said, *inter alia*,

> I want to impress upon you that this is not put forward with the intention of competing with the Whittle; it is with the sole desire of helping with the national effort. We want you to look upon our contribution as an extension of your existing facilities for development, both as regards technical assistance and facilities for producing the pieces.

In my reply to Hives I said:

> We are very pleased to hear that you wish to go ahead with a Rolls-Royce version of our unit, and you can count upon us to give you all the assistance in our power. You need have no fear that we shall regard it as a competitive effort — on the contrary, we have frequently advocated to the Ministry that if any other firm were to be asked to do such a thing it should be Rolls-Royce, as we have for a long time felt that, as far as we knew, you were the only people who had a technical staff sufficiently competent for the purpose.
>
> Hitherto other firms have been requested or allowed to undertake work on this development much beyond their capabilities (in our opinion), instead of being confined to functions for which they were fitted, and this has placed a heavy load on us and created an atmosphere which, in some quarters, may have been interpreted as a resentment of competition on our part, whereas in fact, our objection has been to the uneconomic expenditure of effort, waste of time, and the risk of failures and mistakes of a kind likely to bring

unmerited discredit on the whole development, and to cause unjustified pessimism in high quarters. We have no such misgivings in respect of any contribution you may wish to make to the project.

I have quoted this letter extensively, because it clearly shows that Power Jets were quite willing to co-operate cordially with anyone whom they regarded as competent.

The matter was taken further in a meeting at Derby on the 21st January, 1942, attended by Johnson, Walker and myself. Sidgreaves and Hives headed the large number of Rolls-Royce representatives at the meeting. They outlined their proposal which was to make a larger engine generally similar to the W.2.B., but based on very conservative design assumptions and to give a thrust of 2,000 lb.

Hives emphasised that they had not lost faith in the Griffith engine and they would go on with it, but it was still regarded as a long-term development. He said that they had examined the position from a very broad point of view, and the simplicity of the Whittle type engine appealed to them very strongly, and so they had concluded that their aim should be to develop such an engine on a short-term basis.

It appeared that they did not intend to lose any time and had already ordered some material.

They accepted our suggestion that the best way of going about it would be for Power Jets to be the main contractors and to place a sub-contract for the work with Rolls-Royce.

The M.A.P. eventually approved of the Power Jets/Rolls-Royce proposals (though after some months' delay), and Power Jets received contracts for the design and development of six engines. We immediately placed corresponding sub-contracts with Rolls-Royce. These contracts included combustion test work and other supplementary testing. The engine was known as the W.R.1.

The R.A.E. were not very enthusiastic about the W.R.1.; they felt that the proposed power in proportion to weight and size compared very unfavourably with the W.2.B. We at Power Jets really agreed with them, but felt confident that Rolls-Royce would rapidly develop the W.R.1 to a power well above that originally specified. In a letter to Elliott (20th February, 1941) I said that we looked upon the design as being extremely conservative, but that we thought it should be possible to increase the rating to 3,000 lb.

On the 30th January, 1942, Hives and Sidgreaves visited Lutterworth and Brownsover. They made it clear that Rolls-Royce intended to be in the post-war field in jet engine manufacture, and said that in their view it was essential for the smoothness of future co-operation that there should be some kind of link-up between Rolls-Royce and Power Jets. He said that they were a little worried by the possibility that after our joint efforts had proceeded some way, they might find Power Jets linking up with one of the other aero-engine firms.

Williams and Tinling were very much involved in these discussions as well as myself.

The talks were in very general terms and no concrete suggestions were made, though various possibilities were mentioned, e.g. joint ownership of a subsidiary company.

We made it clear that we were agreeable in principle to a commercial link with Rolls-Royce, but explained that it was very difficult indeed to make any definite proposals until the extremely complicated contract position with the M.A.P. had been sorted out. Until that was done, Power Jets did not really know what their assets were.

I personally stressed repeatedly that commercial negotiations should not cause any upset or disturbance which might cloud the technical collaboration.

Towards the end of the discussion we gave them an assurance that we would give them the option of a first refusal in respect of any scheme put forward.

The next day I visited the Rolls-Royce works at Derby in company with Cheshire and Bone, mainly for further technical discussions about the W.R.1, but during the visit I had a private talk with Hives and we went over some of the ground of the discussion of the day before.

Hives expressed himself as being most anxious that nothing should occur to upset collaboration, and said that there was no hurry in the matter of the proposed alliance. He explained that a factor operating powerfully with them was that they realised that at the end of the war there would be an absolute glut of Merlin engines, which threatened stagnation in the aero-engine business unless they had something on the go which rendered the Merlin obsolete.

My net impression after this private talk with Hives was that their eagerness of the day before had cooled off somewhat.

At a later date I had reason to be thankful that I had made fairly detailed notes of these discussions, because it transpired that there had been a most unfortunate misunderstanding. When the matter was reopened several months later, it came out that each party was under the impression that the next move lay with the other, so both Power Jets and Rolls-Royce waited for a move which never came and a golden opportunity was lost. No doubt a factor in the situation was that neither side wished to appear too eager lest they should weaken their bargaining position. Power Jets was further hindered by not knowing what their bargaining position was.

CHAPTER 39

During February, 1942, flight trials of the E.28 powered by the W.1.A. engine began at Edgehill. As before, Gerry Sayer was the pilot.

Early in the tests, an interesting fact was established, namely, that though the W.1.A. was developing more power and burning correspondingly more fuel than the W.1 at ground level, the endurance of the aeroplane was increased for a given amount of fuel because the extra power made a much more rapid climb possible, and so the fuel available for cruise at height was increased. This confirmed our prediction of what, on the face of it, seemed an improbable result.

Flight trials continued intermittently during February and March, but were suspended temporarily when a turbine blade failed in flight. The failure occurred during a climb and at a height of about 4,000 feet. In his report, Sayer said that the first indication of trouble was a "howling" noise and vibration, but he found that he was able to keep the engine running at about 10,000 r.p.m., which was sufficient to enable him to get into position for a safe landing on the airfield.

In the course of these trials a speed of 430 m.p.h. was reached at a height of 15,000 feet.[33]

By the beginning of April, 1932, Rover's had completed eight W.2.B. engines. They were working on five; one was on loan to Joseph Lucas Limited (for fuel system development, etc.), and Power Jets had two.

Though promising performance results had been achieved, development was otherwise bogged down in a morass of troubles which fell into three main categories — mechanical unreliability, manufacturing defects and turbine blade failures.

We felt that Rover's, who were responsible for the mechanical design, were not paying sufficient attention to improving mechanical reliability. We repeatedly expressed this view at meetings and in correspondence. In a letter to the Rover Company (10th February, 1942) we said:

> We can summarise our views by saying that experimenting cannot go on indefinitely before a decision is made on the first production model, and in the meantime if we have the correct picture of the situation the mechanical side is being seriously neglected. It seems to us that mainly because of the blower experiments, a negligible amount of running time is being put in, with the result that nobody knows how far off we are from having a mechanically reliable unit.

The bearing situation in particular was causing anxiety. Both Rover's and ourselves were having bearing failures — more than once both main bearings failed at the same time — and in order to keep the engines running we found it necessary to modify the Rover-built engines back to our own bearing design.

The matter of bearing design was one of a number of technical controversies which had been raging for some time, but our views, which were repeatedly expressed, carried little weight. It was one of the matters which had been discussed at length at a meeting at Barnoldswick on the 11th February, 1942, under the chairmanship of Ross, yet Power Jets' views were omitted from the official minutes. When we noted this we wrote to Ross to point out the omission, and said, *inter alia*, "every Rover arrangement which we have attempted to use has failed in a very short time… We believe Rover's experience with their own bearings has been no happier." This letter emphasised that our own bearing design had the blessing of the N.P.L. and of the bearing manufacturers, and that we had had about 500 hours' test running without trouble. We inferred that "ease of production" could not be used as an excuse for departing from Power Jets' design, because we had converted a Rover engine to our own type of bearing arrangement in less than four days.

We did not know to what extent manufacturing inaccuracies were affecting the performance, because at that time we were not equipped to check components to make sure they were in accordance with the drawings. Strictly speaking, we should not have needed such equipment for the Rover-built engines, because inaccurate parts ought not to have passed their own inspection, but we experienced striking variations in performance which could only be explained by differences in components which were nominally of the same design. An outstanding example of this occurred when we changed an impeller in one of the W.2.Bs. The new impeller was supposed to be the same as the one it replaced, yet the engine with the new impeller surged at a speed well below full speed, whereas before it had reached full speed without surging. These experiences led us to develop our own special gauges for checking.

Because of our uneasiness about the mechanical design of the Rover W.2.B., we started to press strongly for flight testing in a Wellington flying test bed. This proposal had been discussed on and off for several months and the firm of Vickers Armstrong had been working on the drawings, but hitherto there had been no clear ruling that the scheme should proceed. Johnson wrote to Air Marshal Linnell on the 25th March, 1942, stressing the advantages of this method of flight-testing the W.2.B., and recommending that the installation and testing should be done by Rolls-Royce at Hucknall. Linnell replied that he was very attracted by the proposal, and ultimately he gave it his blessing.

The M.A.P.'s agreement to flight-test the W.2.B. in the tail of a Wellington was really one indication of their increasing uneasiness about the project as a whole. There were signs that the feeling was growing that everybody had been over-optimistic about the job and that it was not yet ready for production.

The increasing frequency of turbine blade failures was causing much concern. Unfortunately, the problem was clouded by the fact that in most cases accidental circumstances could not be ruled out and so there was great uncertainty about the real causes of the failures, but there was little doubt that the higher speeds and higher temperatures at which the engines were being run was an important contributory factor.

The R.A.E. were giving much thought to the blade failure problem and the N.P.L. were doing experimental work in connection with it. As a result of their combined efforts there was a strong recommendation from the R.A.E. that fewer and stiffer blades should be used. We decided to adopt this recommendation as soon as was practicable. This change, plus the change to Nimonic 80 for the turbine blade material, was to make important advances possible at a later date, though at that time Nimonic 80 was not yet considered sufficiently reliable (in the sense that its strength-temperature properties were very variable).

On the 13th March, 1942, we started a complete re-design of the W.2.B. The new design was known as the W2/500. We had come to feel that our work on the W.2.B. was largely a waste of time, since advice based on our experience with it seemed to have little effect on the production engine. Also we believed that the best way to get the most advantage from a number of improvements — such as the increased size of turbine blade recommended by the R.A.E. — would be to make a fresh start. By this time we had sufficient equipment to make a substantial part of the engine ourselves, though we would still be dependent upon sub-contractors for turbine blades and other parts.

CHAPTER 40

During April, 1942, the tension between Power Jets and Rover's reached a new climax when we learned that the Rover Company had been secretly at work for some time on a rearrangement of the W.2.B., which they later designated the B.26. They had first run this engine early in March, about three weeks before we ever heard of its existence.

To understand Power Jets' indignation about this, it is necessary to bear in mind that though, by a succession of Ministry rulings, the Rover Company had been given increasing latitude in design, there had been no relaxation of the requirement that there should be a full and frank interchange of information (so far as we knew).

The chief difference between the B.26 and the W.2.B. was that the former had "straight-through" combustion chambers instead of the Power Jets' counter-flow arrangement.

For some time we had ourselves been contemplating changes of the kind which Rover's had incorporated in the B.26. Indeed, we had a contract for an experimental engine along these lines — the W.3.X. — but had been unable to make it through lack of facilities.

Our counter-flow type of combustion chamber had been dictated by sheer necessity. In the first place, when the experimental engine had been reconstructed for the second time in 1938, we had been obliged to keep the cost down to a minimum, and hence the combustion chamber design had been governed by the need to use the same rotor assembly. Thereafter, we continued to use the same basic arrangement, because we had learned from bitter experience that the combustion process was very sensitive to the air-flow within the combustion chamber, and any major change would have meant another long period of combustion experimental work, the time for which, in the circumstances, we could not afford.

In the light of the facts as they were revealed during April, 1942, an incident which had occurred at a meeting at Barnoldswick on 11th February was of some significance. It was recorded by Johnson as follows:

> Just as the meeting broke up Rover tabled what was called a further production idea, stated to be arrived at by re-arranging components. A general assembly drawing was shown, and it was found to represent a straight-through combustion system resembling the Halford design, but with double-sided compressor. We heard a good deal of sales talk for this project… Production would be enormously easier… As the Power Jets' representatives were literally putting their coats on to depart when this was going on they made no comment whatever.

In the M.A.P. minutes there appeared:

> …a general arrangement drawing of a re-arranged W.2.B. engine, submitted as the first serious attempt to productionise the design, was examined and the production advantages explained.

The minutes went on to record that

> DD/RDE[34] agreed that Rover's could proceed with the detailing for manufacture and assembly of one experimental unit to the proposed design, provided that the development and production of engines to the present design arrangement was in no way prejudiced during the present year. As soon as

found convenient the firm should submit further details to M.A.P. for discussion.

The full significance of this entry in the minutes was not brought home to us until some time later. It was another example of the way the Directorate of Engine Development was "slipping things across" in official minutes. I should mention that these official minutes were so verbose (fourteen closely typed foolscap pages) and we were so busy that we could not afford the time to go through them as carefully as we would have liked.

No reference to the B.26 had been made in any of the G.T.C.C. Progress Reports, and it now became obvious that when reference was made to a possible re-arrangement of the W.2.B. at the meeting at Barnoldswick on 11th February, Rover's must have had their "tongues in their cheeks" because the engine must then have been nearing completion.

The revelation that the Rover Company had been secretly at work on the B.26 both shocked and surprised several M.A.P. officials as well as ourselves. Wing Commander G. E. Watt, Roxbee Cox's deputy, who first told me of it, also said that Roxbee Cox was very angry about it, and that Air Marshal Linnell, Controller of Research and Development, had expressed amazement at the state of affairs and had instructed D.S.R. to hold an inquiry into it. Watt advised Power Jets not to take any hasty action which might alienate C.R.D., as the latter was very sympathetic towards Power Jets in the matter.

I discussed the situation on the phone with Roxbee Cox on 8th April. My main theme was that though there was a lot to be said in favour of the arrangement, the key fact was that it was not one which could be described as representing a production unit for at least a year, owing to the mechanical and combustion development which would almost certainly be required. He agreed, but said that Rover's were submitting it as a "scheme *per se*". I pointed out that on the contrary, Rover's were representing the B.26 as being the first real attempt to productionise the W.2.B. I referred him to the minutes of the Barnoldswick meeting of the 11th February. This appeared to be a shock to him. He had apparently not seen it in this light before.

He said he wanted to avoid any acrimony over the business. I said that was not possible. This was the culminating act on Rover's part, and I personally at least could not co-operate with them in the future. He then admitted that he felt much the same way about it as I did, but asked — somewhat plaintively it seemed to me — what were they to do about it? I replied, "Use the big stick, but not on me!"

The next day a meeting was held at Clitheroe to discuss the general position of the W.2.B. development, but no reference whatever was made to the B.26 in the minutes. (Ross and Schlotel represented M.A.P.). The lengthy minutes recorded a number of details, and indicated that though Rover's were modifying a certain number of bearings in accordance with Power Jets' design, they intended to persist in trying to make their own bearing arrangement work. The minutes also stated that Rover's could not introduce a compressor modification recommended by us into any of the first thirty engines, and that there was little prospect of its immediate introduction into the first batch of fifty production engines. Thus, though they found time, material and labour to rearrange the W.2.B., in the form of the B.26, yet they were unable to introduce a comparatively small modification which Power Jets had made and tested some time before.

The minutes of that meeting recorded that no prolonged endurance running had been possible with the W.2.B. at

Rover's; up to then the longest non-stop run was about two and a half hours.

A delegation from Power Jets went to the M.A.P. to see Linnell about the B.26 situation. The Power Jets' representatives were Williams, Tinling, Sir Maurice Bonham Carter and Johnson. They first saw Roxbee Cox, who commented that it was clear that there was something very wrong with the administration of the whole project. He was under the impression that the B.26 was a private venture, so the Power Jets' representatives pointed out that the official M.A.P. minutes of the meeting at Barnoldswick (11th February) might be interpreted as an instruction to proceed and so Power Jets were wary about assuming that it was a private venture. Roxbee Cox had not read this meaning into the minutes (neither had we at the time), and he was of the opinion that the wording was ill-chosen. It was suggested to him that it was possible that the wording was intended to be deliberately ambiguous, and he did not seem to disagree.

They then saw Linnell who told them that the B.26 was a private venture, and that he himself had not heard about it until the week before. The relevant part of the minutes of the Barnoldswick meeting was then pointed out to him and he appeared to be badly shaken. The Power Jets' representatives told Linnell that it was very difficult to conform to policy when it appeared to be changed periodically, and particularly when it was stated in minutes which they felt bound to challenge for accuracy every time. Linnell asked why Power Jets had not protested at the Barnoldswick meeting. He was told that the decisions quoted in the minutes, if they had been made at all at the meeting — which Power Jets doubted — had been made after the Power Jets' representatives had left. In any event, Power Jets had rebutted the minutes as a whole.

There was then some discussion about the technical merits of the B.26 as claimed by Rover's. Linnell asked whether Power Jets would resist the job even if they thought it was likely to be a success. He was told that we would resist nothing which was an honest contribution to the success of the venture, but if he wanted alternative designs we could produce possibly ten at very short notice, any of which might have its own special advantages, but that was an insufficient reason for proceeding with them at the expense of the main job. In any case this type of work was not within Rover's province. He was then reminded that we had a contract for a "straight-through" arrangement of the engine, but had been unable to do anything about it through lack of facilities.

Power Jets said that the whole affair was a serious affront to myself and to Power Jets. Linnell admitted that he himself had been very upset when he had learned about it, but he did not propose to comment officially until he had all the facts.

Two or three days later (12th April) I wrote a long letter to Air Marshal Linnell and referred to the possibility that the result of the inquiry into the B.26 affair might be either a reaffirmation of past policy or a change in the policy for the future, and went on:

> The purpose of this letter is to request most earnestly that I may have a hearing before any changes in policy are made. My grounds for requesting this are:
>
> (1) I am the engineer most familiar with *all* aspects of the jet propulsion project, in addition to being an Engineer Officer of the Royal Air Force with high engineering qualifications, and possessing a combination of Service and engineering experience which is probably unique.
>
> (2) The burdens resulting from policy decisions fall more heavily on me than on anybody else.

Later I continued:

> It is perhaps not unnatural that there should have been a tendency for the views of the originators to have been to some extent submerged; but I respectfully point out that this process has no logical foundation, and implies strongly that the ultimate authority has either lost faith in the parents of the project or has acquired an increasing degree of faith in those I have referred to as newcomers.
>
> I feel it my duty to remark that the technical history of the venture over the last two years has involved a rising tide of unfortunate or wrong decisions, a series of failures of control, and an atmosphere which is the very reverse of co-operative.
>
> It is a matter of record that although I am chronologically the senior technician in the venture, and I believe that my technical achievements and status carry substantial weight, I have never been either consulted or even forewarned of any change of policy or of administration. Practically every important step which has been taken by the Ministry has been a *fait accompli* before I have had an opportunity to comment on it. At the risk of being challenged with egotism, I say that it is again a matter of record and fact that events have proved that virtually every comment which I have made on such *faits accompli* is shown to have been well founded.

I made it clear that I was speaking on matters in relation to production as well as matters of design, and said:

> It has been the custom of certain individuals to treat me as a 'gifted amateur', inventor, etc., and to talk of 'taking my child and sending it away to school', to say that I have no production experience, etc., and, I believe, to represent me as a somewhat difficult and temperamental individual. On the one hand a good deal of lip service has been paid to my achievements, but on the other it has been implied that I am fit only to have 'bright ideas' with the results that, as it seems

to me, I have been regarded as being either too biased or too incompetent to make a good judgment or to give good advice on major matters of policy.

I am in a far stronger position now to say these things than I was a year ago, because the advice, etc., that I gave them, in so far as it is on record, can be weighed against the events as they have turned out.

I then submitted:

(1) Little had been done by others to improve the design of the engine in respect of production;

(2) Little had been done to improve the mechanical design; rather, on the other hand, attempts had been shown to be retrograde;

(3) No other firm had succeeded in improving on the thermodynamic and aerodynamic design, 'and in fact events have shown that where Power Jets' practice has been abandoned temporarily, as in the case of the turbine blading of the B.T-H. W.2.B., a reversion to Power Jets' practice has been found necessary';

(4) Power Jets' manufacturing technique had proved to be the best up till then;

(5) The calibre of the Power Jets' team was probably unequalled.

I then suggested that:

...the time has arrived when nothing less than a full inquiry is required to establish the truth or otherwise of the propositions I have stated, and to examine the qualifications, judgment, and experience, of the Civil Servants who have had such a powerful influence on the project, in order that future policy can be laid upon a solid basis and be placed under the direction of the right type of personnel.

...I feel entitled to request either that matters of policy affecting the progress of the venture should be discussed with me before they are laid down, or that I should be informed definitely of what I already have grounds for suspecting, namely, that my judgment and experience in such matters are believed to be inept. In the latter event it would appear that but little useful purpose could be achieved by my remaining in my present position.

In a letter to Power Jets (dated 19th April, 1942), Air Marshal Linnell said that he had received full reports about the Rover "straight-through" engine and went on:

I wish to make it clear in the first place that my policy remains what it was, namely the maintenance of full collaboration between all the firms concerned, and in particular between yourselves and Messrs. Rover. It is my expressed intention that Wing Commander Whittle should be kept informed of any intended changes of design.

That such collaboration has been jeopardised by the way in which this matter of the 'straight-through' version has been handled I fully agree, and I am taking steps to ensure that a failure in this respect, which is fatal to a policy of collaboration, shall not recur...

In a letter to me (also dated 19th April) he assured me

...that no changes of policy are in contemplation, and I hope that arrangements which I shall make will ensure that you are kept fully in the picture in future when any changes of design are under discussion. That there will have to be modifications of the design from time to time must be accepted, and it may be that for good reasons the design which seems to you the best may not be acceptable on grounds of production, maintenance, etc. Nevertheless, before any decision on a matter of this kind is to be made, it will be my purpose to ensure that your views are taken fully into account.

Up to this point there was still a general belief which was shared by Pye, Roxbee Cox and Watt that the B.26 was a private venture, but on 22nd April, Tinling and Johnson had a meeting with Linnell and Pye, at which Linnell said that he regretted to have to tell Power Jets that a mistake had been made, and that the B.26 was not a private venture but had been officially authorised. He said he assumed full responsibility for the error. He explained that M. C. Wilks had convinced the Directorate concerned that Rover's needed to keep the thing secret until it should have established itself to some extent. Apparently the written authorisation upon which Rover's had acted had been given at the end of 1941. On hearing this, Johnson commented very strongly that in the light of this information the conduct of the Barnoldswick meeting of the 11th February had been blatantly dishonest, and if proof were required it was only necessary to read the minutes. This very strong comment drew no rebuke nor denial.

Some wider aspects of the whole position were discussed at this meeting, and the Air Marshal seemed to appreciate the contract difficulties of Power Jets. One point stressed by Johnson and Tinling was that Power Jets' position was so insecure that they could not even give reasonably long employment contracts. Linnell asked if the position would be improved if Power Jets were guaranteed possession of the Whetstone factory, but it was pointed out that this wouldn't help much if we could not pay the weekly wages bill.

According to Johnson's notes on this meeting, Linnell "definitely appreciates now that we cannot live on air and goodwill and a possible academic reputation".

As the Power Jets' representatives were leaving, Linnell appealed to them to accept from him — and he was supported by Dr. Pye — that Major Ross was actuated entirely by disinterested motives, whatever might be said of certain others. Linnell stressed that Ross was a man of absolute integrity who only had the proper progress of the job at heart. It was his very keenness to see it through that had misguided him in the particular matter of the B.26. I accepted the view that Major Ross had acted disinterestedly.

Later, Johnson and Tinling had a talk with Roxbee Cox and Watt, and learned that Linnell had discovered that the B.26 was an officially authorised project only about half an hour before a meeting with S. B. Wilks a few days earlier.

In short, a most astonishing situation had come to light. The Rover Company's work on the B.26 had been sanctioned by the Directorate of Engine Development, but had been kept secret not only from Power Jets, but also from the Controller of Research and Development, the Director of Scientific Research and other officials intimately connected with the project, particularly Roxbee Cox and Watt.

In one sense the whole affair was very helpful to Power Jets, because it provided clear and welcome proof of the state of affairs at which we had hinted from time to time, namely, that the Rover Company intended to go their own way, and that in this course they were receiving moral and practical support from the officials of the Directorate of Engine Development. There were times when I suspected that these officials, who had spent the greater part of their lives in the familiar field of piston engines, subconsciously resented the advent of a type of engine which rendered useless much of their specialised knowledge slowly acquired over many years.

In view of the fact that one of the reasons given by the Rover Co. for their work on the B.26 was "ease of production", it is of interest to record that Group Captain F. R. Banks (Director of Engine Production) and one of his staff visited Lutterworth on 22nd April, 1942. After commenting favourably on the quality of our sheet metal and other work, Banks made the significant remark that production need be little more than a scaling up of what he had seen at Ladywood Works that day, and that if anybody was experiencing any production difficulties, they had only to spend a few days at the Ladywood Works to find out how to get over them.

In the course of a visit to Lutterworth (29th April, 1942), Ross expressed the view — which to us was very startling — that one of Power Jets' responsibilities was the development and improvement of the W.2.B. in all respects up to the stage where it was a reliable production engine giving its proper performance. This was evidently his own view, and he stated there were many officials in the M.A.P. who held it, and that Power Jets had been criticised for not having "done their stuff" in this direction and had, so to speak, left Rover's "holding the baby". We could hardly believe our ears when we heard this, and we said so. We pointed out that we had been told repeatedly that Rover's were responsible for the design for production with freedom in mechanical design, and we, in spite of vigorous protests, had virtually been frozen out of the W.2.B. development and had been relegated to the position of consultants. We pointed out that Power Jets' position in the matter had been laid down in writing in the minutes of the meeting of the 23rd December, 1941, when Ross himself had been chairman, and had subsequently been confirmed by a letter from the Minister and statements by Linnell. We reminded him that we had protested strongly against the policy then laid down, and against similar policy laid down by Sir Henry Tizard before that date. Once again it appeared that we were being blamed for not doing something which we had virtually been specifically forbidden to do, and for which facilities had not been provided. We had, in fact, as we explained to Ross, done quite a lot of mechanical development. We had been driven to it in order to keep the Rover-built engines running on the bench, so that we might fulfil what we took to be our function, namely, development for performance. Of course, if Ross and others were under the impression that Power Jets' functions were quite different from those which they themselves had laid down, it explained a possible source of a great deal of misunderstanding, though it should have been obvious that we could not possibly do the work that Rover's were supposed to be doing while we had three rather battered W.2.B.-type engines only.

Ross also appeared to be under the very wrong impression that Power Jets had not been co-operating with the Rover Company as much as they should have done. We made it clear that, on the contrary, we had done our best to ensure that we should not expose ourselves to criticism in this respect, and that, having foreseen some time before that accusations of this type might be made, we had kept most careful records of the transactions with the Rover Company, from which we could prove that we had continuously kept them supplied with test results, drawings and advice.

In preparation for a meeting to discuss the merits of the B.26, the Rover Company produced a brochure entitled "W.2.B. Adaptation for 'Straight-Through' Combustion," in which they set out their arguments in favour of it. I do not propose to make a record of the technical pros and cons here, because, in our view, the matter was not one which really turned upon the question "Was it a better form of the engine?" but rather on the question "Was it a form of the engine which could be regarded as a production version of the W.2.B., producible in time to meet the laid-down airframe and engine programme?" and on the further question "If this is a desirable form of the engine, were the Rover Company competent to undertake it?"

I wrote a commentary on the Rover brochure, in which I said:

> ...the attitude of the writer towards the proposals is very dependent upon what basis the scheme is put forward. Is it to be viewed as:
>
> (*a*) an immediate production version of the existing W.2.B., or
>
> (*b*) a future production version of the W.2.B. to be introduced at a relatively distant date, or
>
> (*c*) as a long-term piece of development work intended to contribute to the general development of the 'species'?
>
> With the information supplied, the writer finds himself unable to comment adequately under any of the above heads, but is of the opinion that (*a*) cannot be entertained at all. Much more information is required before adequate comment can be made under the head of (*b*) above.
>
> Under (*c*) there is a strong favourable case, and it appears to the writer that, like so many other equally attractive schemes, the question is whether the deflection of effort required for the development is justified in the present urgent circumstances. This, of course, is a question for the Ministry to decide.
>
> The writer and Power Jets' engineers have repeatedly been attracted by the 'straight-through' arrangement, as is witnessed by the fact that Power Jets have had a contract for such an arrangement for over a year, the unit being described in the contract as the W.3.X. This unit was to have been based on a

> layout earlier known as the W.2.Y., which made use of W.2 parts in much the same way as the B.26 makes use of the W.2.B. parts...
>
> It was rapidly realised that there was a number of somewhat severe mechanical problems to be solved and, though their solution was not regarded as impossible, the work was looked upon as being too 'long term' for the urgency of the need for developing a production unit as soon as possible... The uncertainty of the outlook, and the urgency of other work, were such that all this side of the development was given a very low priority, and in fact never proceeded beyond the paper and model stage...

We did not accept as valid many of the reasons put forward by the Rover Company for offering the B.26 as an early solution to the production problem. They complained of sheet metal failures, and assembly difficulties with the sheet metal components of the W.2.B. design, which we were not getting with our methods of construction.

In our view there was no doubt that if the B.26 were regarded as the production version of the W.2.B., then production of the engine would go back for many months. Moreover, the installation of the B.26 in the Meteor meant a major modification to the rear spar of the aeroplane. In short, it all boiled down to the question, "was the B.26 an engine which could contribute to the war effort?" Power Jets felt it was most improbable that it would.

It is fortunate for the reputation of Power Jets and myself that our views went clearly on record, because, at a later date, there were some who alleged that we had opposed the B.26 on purely technical grounds. Had this been true, of course, we would have looked rather foolish, because such highly successful engines as the Derwent V. and the Nene had the "straight-through" combustion chamber arrangement. Another belief which became widely held, and which needs exploding, is that the Rover Company were the originators of the arrangement, whereas, in fact, the first engine to be designed and made with "straight-through" combustion chambers was the de Havilland H.1 (the Goblin). Moreover, M. C. Wilks had seen the drawings of the W.2.Y. at Power Jets in 1940.

For some time before and during the controversy, I had standing on my desk a wooden model of a shaft coupling which we were proposing to use in our own "straight-through" engine when we could get around to it.

I sent a copy of my commentary on the Rover brochure to Air Marshal Linnell accompanied by a letter (dated 17th May, 1942), in which I placed on record many of my views as follows:

> I would like to take this opportunity of expressing my views on the more general aspects of the proposal. I do not intend to discuss the ethics of the case, because I have agreed that it is better to forget the shortcomings in conduct which the affair revealed.
>
> My general opinion is that a good case can be made out to justify an attempt to solve many of the problems involved in the 'straight-through' arrangement, but that it should be looked upon as a relatively long-term development because of the nature of these problems. It would, for example, be a useful thing in itself to develop a satisfactory coupling because such a coupling may be wanted for other reasons in the future. Such development work would, however, inevitably mean the deflection of a part of the total resources available, and dispersal of effort (already serious) would therefore be increased. This has to be weighed against the advantages to be expected, and the decision on this must of course be made by the Ministry. If that decision were in favour of the development proceeding, the next question becomes, who is

to expend the necessary manpower and resources? And once more this is a question for the Ministry to decide, but my personal wish is that none of this load should fall on Power Jets beyond such as is involved in giving what advice they are able.

It seems, from the meagre information supplied, that the design of the B.26 is anything but finalised (I especially draw your attention to the significance of the fact that even today, after all the fuss and bother there has been, we are asked to give an opinion on a 10 in. x 6 in. photograph of a G. A. drawing, and five photographs of the 'lash-up').

It would of course be wiser to leave any such decision until after a substantial amount of bench running.

All the above is based on purely engineering considerations, but I have lately come to think that one may have to take psychological factors into account.

I am convinced that the Rover Company *has not the will* to produce a W.2.B. as it now stands, and that nothing can be done to fire them with any enthusiasm in relation to it, especially now that they have the B.26 bee in their bonnets. I am also of the opinion that some of their alterations to the Power Jets' designs have got them into considerable trouble, and they would rather do anything than admit it. (This also seems to apply to certain officials who gave them too loose a rein on these matters.) This unfortunately is a fairly common fault of human nature and one very difficult to deal with. Power Jets have done everything they can to prevent them 'running off the rails', but in vain. (I return to this point again below.)

I have also lost confidence in their general ability to handle the job, and one way, though an expensive one, of proving this would be to give them every facility they ask in the way of latitude of mechanical design and general arrangement; thus, if they say that the B.26 would enable them to produce these units much more quickly than the existing W.2.B., then they might be allowed to go ahead and prove it. They would then presumably either succeed in proving their case, or in demonstrating their incompetence in an unmistakable manner. There is no doubt that the Rover organisation has a number of very capable production engineers, but as far as one can see they are not being allowed to get on with the job by their own people. This would be a very wasteful way to obtain evidence of incompetence, but, unless the true state of affairs can be otherwise made clear, it may be the best thing in the end (on the principle of 'allowing sufficient rope').

In brief, ought they to be allowed to go ahead on the B.26 in order to remove any possible excuse for not 'delivering the goods'? I suggest that if this policy were followed they should be committed to a very specific promise of delivery, and told in the clearest possible manner that if they fail to live up to their promises the penalties will be very severe. This I think would call their bluff with a vengeance. But for two considerations this course would appeal to me personally very strongly. The first consideration is the waste and delay involved in the event of failure. The second consideration is the danger that a failure of the Rover Company would be looked upon, in many quarters, as a failure of the jet propulsion engine 'per se'. To minimise this, it would, in my opinion, be necessary, as a corollary, to make alternative arrangements for the production of a pure Power Jets' design.

This second consideration is an ever-present danger in any case because, as things are, it seems to me that the W.2.B. situation is going to drag on indefinitely in the hands of the Rover Company, with the attendant risk that the Whittle engine will come to be looked upon as a 'white elephant' (while Power Jets can do little to save this situation through sheer lack of W.2.B. parts). Should such a thing happen (which Heaven forbid!) it would not be the first time in British engineering that a promising project had come to be looked upon as basically impracticable, or 'before its time', simply because it had been incompetently handled. In reality very little indeed really remains to be done to make the W.2.B.

fit for Service use. (The problem of the turbine blades is the only serious outstanding difficulty, and I believe that this will soon be solved.)

In effect the reputations of Power Jets, of the Ministry officials who have backed the project, and of myself, are in the hands of the Rover Company. They all stand to be discredited (even to the extent of being charged with a waste of national resources) if the Rover Company fails. (This alone would be a sufficient incentive for Power Jets and myself to do all we can to see that they do not fail, and explains a good deal of the anxiety we feel.)

I summarise the questions which have to be decided as follows:

(*a*) Is the design of the B.26 sufficiently finalised for it to be contemplated as a new mark of the W.2.B.?

(*b*) If the answer to (*a*) is negative, is the B.26 arrangement nevertheless a worth-while development as a contribution to the general development of the 'species'?

(*c*) If the answer to (*b*) is affirmative, then can we afford the energy and resources available to be further dispersed to embrace it?

(*d*) If the answer to (*c*) is affirmative, then which organisation is to expend its energy and resources on this development?

(*e*) Would it be worth allowing the Rover Company to proceed as they wish in the matter for psychological reasons in order to remove all excuses for delay?

(*f*) If (*e*) were decided upon, ought not alternative arrangements be made for the production of a pure Power Jets' design?

In recent talks I have had with various officials, it has become apparent that there exists a belief that Power Jets and myself have not done their best to help the Rover Company. As I said to Major Ross during his recent visit here with the greatest possible emphasis I could, the more the facts are examined the more apparent would it become that this is an entirely mistaken view, and can only be based on ignorance of the facts. Major Ross, for example, appeared greatly surprised to learn that we send the Rover Co. a copy of every internal report on each W.2.B. test series (though I understand that both Mr. Tobin and Mr. Schlotel have each told him this more than once). Moreover, Rover representatives are allowed to see everything they wish to see. We do our best to answer every question and to give information which we think might be of special interest. It should not be supposed that the privileged views expressed by me to Ministry officials is representative of my outward attitude to the Rover Co., and if, as I suspect, these views are passed on to the Rover Co., then the officials who pass them on are guilty of a breach of privilege and are the primary cause of a bad atmosphere. It is significant that in this connection Major Halford writes in a letter dated 14th May: 'I consistently obtained the impression, admittedly second-hand, that you rather resented the work we were doing.' This explained a lot, and shows that there has either been deliberate sabotage of collaboration or else most unfortunate indiscretions and misrepresentations on the part of Ministry officials, whose names 'I could with a ready guess declare'. (It seems certain that what were in fact criticisms of Ministry policy made to Ministry officials were distorted into the form cited by Major Halford.) It seems to me to be most important that something should be done to make it impossible for organisations like Power Jets to be accused of non-collaboration, when in fact they are doing their best. To give advice, to have it ignored, and then to be accused of not giving it, is unreasonable to say the least of it. It is for this reason that I have suggested to Dr. Roxbee Cox that it should be the duty of the Secretary of the Gas Turbine Collaboration Committee to keep records of all exchanges between the collaborating firms, and that for this purpose the firms should each send one copy of letters, reports on visits, memos on telephone conversations, etc., to the Secretary.

The Air Marshal replied in a letter dated 22nd May, 1942, and *inter alia*, said:

> ...as regards your summarised questions, my answers would be as follows, subject to anything which may have transpired at the meeting at Clitheroe:
>
> (*a*) No. (*b*) Yes. (*c*) In the circumstances we must. (*d*) Messrs. Rover, (*e*) Yes. (*f*) In general I am not unfavourably disposed to your suggestion, but I must reserve decision till I see results of yesterday's meeting.

The meeting to discuss the merits of the B.26 was the one referred to, and it was held at Clitheroe on 21st May with Ross as chairman. It was a large meeting and I headed a delegation of four from Power Jets.

The discussions were naturally very technical, but nothing transpired in the course of the meeting to cause me to vary from my commentary on the Rover brochure, and so I requested that this be attached as an appendix to the minutes. This was duly done. Also attached as an appendix to the minutes was a letter signed by Constant giving the views of the R.A.E., which, in general, coincided with my own.[35] The last paragraph of the R.A.E. letter read:

> ...summing up, we agree that the general layout of the B.26 offers some attractive features, but none of the improvements suggested are essential to the development of the engine. We suggest that with the production programme delayed by blade failures, time should not be spent at present on non-essential modifications, and we recommend that the Rover Co. be instructed not to proceed with the manufacture until a Whittle-type engine has been proved to be reliable.

The decision recorded in the minutes of the meeting at Clitheroe was that the Rover Co. would be allowed to proceed with the B.26 development, but that this should not be at the expense of the W.2.B. production development.

I think that Power Jets can claim that, despite their strong feelings on the ethics of the whole business, they made a number of constructive suggestions at the Clitheroe meeting.

Power Jets naturally did not believe that work on the B.26 could continue without affecting the W.2.B. development. It was quite clear that the enthusiasm necessary for such work was, in Rover's case, directed towards the B.26, and the more trouble with the "Power Jets" W.2.B. the stronger the case for the "Rover" B.26. Yet it was the W.2.B. which went into active service in the end, in spite of all that had been claimed for the B.26.

CHAPTER 41

Much that had happened had brought it home to me with great force that a great many of the difficulties and much of the confusion of the past stemmed from sheer lack of precision of such words as "design", "research", "development", "production" and so on, and so, during May, 1942, I prepared a document in which I attempted to explore and clarify what was meant by these words. Then, as a corollary, and starting from the basis that the primary function of Power Jets was "research and development", I wrote a second paper giving my views on what these terms should cover. I concluded that if we were to carry out the functions of research and development in a complete sense, we ought to be required and to be equipped to carry out the following duties:

(1) To design and develop up to the production stage such types of aircraft gas turbines as might be considered by the M.A.P. to be likely to be required in quantity, including the manufacture of the prototype engines necessary for this work, and if necessary to produce for this purpose (say) fifty prototypes in nine months from the initiation of design.

(2) To do all forms of work directed towards development of the "species", and for this purpose to design and manufacture experimental engines, experimental compressors, turbines, etc.

(3) To design, make and try out tools and production equipment suitable for quantity production of any type of engine developed by Power Jets, and to obtain the complete data required to plan a factory for large-scale production, and generally to perform the functions of a "production nursery".

(4) To undertake a certain amount of research and development on production methods and technique, such work to include:

(*a*) extension of applications of (the then) existing processes to meet the needs of gas turbine production;

(*b*) to devise and develop new processes and tools.

It will be seen that the most ambitious part of this proposal was what I described as "nursery production". I was to find out during my then impending visit to the U.S.A. that this concept was already well accepted over there and was known as the "pilot line".

One thing I was seeking was a clear recognition of the fact that development of manufacturing technique was an integral part of the total development. Up to that time Power Jets had been compelled to devote much attention to methods of manufacture special to this type of engine, and I think we can claim that our work in this direction had met with considerable success.

We could, at this time, afford to contemplate some extension of our activities because, at long last, the situation was improving rapidly in the matter of facilities; the full-scale test plant, for which I had been asking for over two years, was authorised during May, 1942, and was to be installed at Whetstone. The Whetstone factory itself was nearing completion and manufacturing work had started in one of the two shops.

Once the Whetstone factory had been authorised, work had proceeded very rapidly. The planning and building of this factory was an achievement in itself, for which much of the credit was due to Williams, Tinling and Peasgood. When I paid my first visit to the site with Roxbee Cox and others during April, 1942, I received quite a shock. I think Roxbee Cox did as well. It was one thing to have approved the plans, and quite another to see the result. The plant looked far larger than I had visualised after being so accustomed to our small workshop at Lutterworth. I remember well that Roxbee Cox and I looked at each other with somewhat uneasy expressions, and I think the unspoken thought in both our minds was that somebody had "put over a fast one" and that the place was far larger than had been authorised. I was having uncomfortable visions of an official inquiry into the expenditure of public money. Williams assured me that the plant was in accordance with the plans approved by the Directorate of Aircraft Factories and with the figures I had myself agreed. We had reason later to be grateful for the fact that Williams and Co. had looked well ahead, because the space, large as it seemed then,[36] proved to be barely adequate for our later needs. Indeed, it became necessary to put up one or two additional buildings for special purposes.

CHAPTER 42

During the latter half of 1941, proposals to have a corresponding development started in the U.S.A. had culminated in the sending of the W.1.X. engine, a complete set of drawings, and a team of three from Power Jets to the General Electric Company at Lynn, Mass., at the beginning of October.

It is worth emphasising that this very important piece of Anglo-American co-operation began before Pearl Harbor (December 7th, 1941), i.e. before America's entry into the war.

During the three months before sending the engine, drawings and personnel across the Atlantic, we had already supplied much preliminary information to U.S. Army Air Force officers and other officials who had visited us from time to time. One U.S.A.A.F. officer — Major Donald J. Keirn — had spent four days with us to study all aspects of our work. He became largely responsible at the American end for the turbo-jet liaison between the two countries. His ability and pleasant personality fitted him very well for the task, and the smoothness of the transatlantic collaboration owed a lot to his good work.

It was decided that all these matters should be channelled through the M.A.P. and the offices of the British Air Commission in Washington. The officials primarily concerned were Wing Commander G. E. Watt at the M.A.P. and Major J. N. D. Heenan at the B.A.C.

On the 29th September, 1941, the W.1.X., broken down to packing-case size and with an armed guard provided by the Power Jets' section of the Home Guard, had been duly shipped by road to Prestwick from whence, accompanied by Walker, Flight Sergeant King and G. B. Bozzoni, it had been flown to the U.S.A. in a Liberator. The W.2.B. drawings and other information were sent by sea. I was very much amused when I heard later that Bozzoni wasn't altogether happy about having to cross the Atlantic by air. He was reported to have said (with some feeling): "The first time I fly, I have to fly the ruddy Atlantic!" But Bozzoni wasn't one to let a little thing like that discourage him.[37]

I cannot, of course, give a first-hand account of what happened on the other side when they arrived, but according to Walker's subsequent reports, the most elaborate secrecy arrangements had been made. I gathered that there was a "cloak and dagger atmosphere" about the proceedings, which Walker and co. found both exciting and diverting.

I received my first news in a very cautious handwritten letter from Dan Walker about the middle of October. He said that "things" were rather slow in getting started, but "they" were planning to do big "things", and he expected that when "things" did get going, "they" would move fast.

Later, a signal from the British Air Commission told us that the G.E. were to build engines in accordance with the W.2.B. design, but modified to take American accessories. It was planned to complete the first engine in six months. The message also said that the Bell Aircraft Corporation had started work on a twin-engined fighter, the first of which was expected to be ready in eight months. The signal contained other points, including the fact that "the Whittle project at the G.E. is to be known as the 'exhaust turbo-blower Type 1' for security purposes".

The G.E. had expected to have their first engine running in May, 1942, but, in fact, they worked so fast that they beat their own target date, and their first engine went on to the test bench on April 22nd.

Walker arrived back from the U.S.A. on 1st December, 1941, but King and Bozzoni stayed on for a while and returned early in March, 1942.

It was arranged that I should visit the U.S.A. myself for a few weeks to assist in their part of the development. Accordingly, I arrived in New York on June 4th, 1942 (having crossed the Atlantic by flying-boat).

Being chiefly concerned with the development in progress at the Lynn Works of the G.E., the greater part of my time was spent in that area, but I also visited Washington, Buffalo, Schenectady, Dayton (Ohio) and Los Angeles.

During my first series of visits to the Lynn factory, I stayed in Boston, but for my other stays in that area I was the guest of Mr. and Mrs. R. G. Standerwick at Marblehead. Standerwick was the senior G.E. executive directly concerned with the Type 1 project.

During my stay in Boston I had my first experience of American security measures. In the suite reserved for me in the Statler Hotel, a special telephone had been installed which bypassed the hotel switchboard. Also I was expected to use an assumed name. Not being used to this sort of thing I thought my new name had better be fairly similar to my real one and so decided on "Whiteley". The trouble was that I could not remember from one day to the next how I had decided to spell it. Also there were times when I forgot about it altogether and signed bills for room service with my usual signature. The hotel staff must have been very puzzled by the intriguing variety of signatures they were getting from me, but it probably didn't matter, because I understand that the waiter who attended to my needs was specially chosen and probably belonged to the

F.B.I. Much later I heard that I was under the friendly protection of the F.B.I. throughout the visit, but if so, it was done so unobtrusively that I saw no visible evidence of it, though there were times when I sensed that I was being watched and, sometimes rather restricted in my movements.

During my frequent visits to the Lynn Works, about ten miles north of Boston, I worked closely with the late Donald F. Warner, the engineer chiefly responsible for the work, and his staff of engineers and draughtsmen. My contacts with them were almost as intimate as with my own team at Power Jets.

Their engine was chiefly based on the Rover drawings, but they had preferred Power Jets' practice in certain features of the mechanical design, especially bearings, and in some ways they had modified from the British drawings as a result of their own experience (the G.E. had primarily been selected for the work by the U.S. Government because of their extensive experience with turbo-superchargers — which had a number of features in common with jet engines).

I found, as Walker had reported, that their test house was a very robust affair with concrete walls eighteen inches thick. Walker had christened it "Fort Knox" (after the place in Kentucky where the U.S. Government stores its gold), and this name was painted above the steel door.

At the time of my first visit to the Lynn factory they had only one engine running, but another one was almost ready and a few others were nearing completion. The W.1.X., having fulfilled its purpose in giving useful experience, had been dismantled. (It was later returned to Power Jets, and some years after that — in 1949 — it crossed the Atlantic yet again to be formally presented to the Smithsonian Institute.)

During my visits to Lynn, Buffalo and elsewhere, I was often accompanied by Dundas Heenan and Don Keirn, and they often took a prominent and very useful part in the technical discussions. Their hospitality and assistance also helped to smooth my path considerably.

At Buffalo, the Bell Aircraft Corporation were working with considerable speed and enthusiasm on the P.59A. prototype aircraft, of which there were three under construction at the time of my visits, the first being nearly completed.

At the main works of the G.E. at Schenectady, a team of engineers were working on a propeller gas turbine scheme. This engine was well beyond the preliminary design phase. Indeed, manufacture was then well advanced, but nevertheless by comparison with our work it was still very much in the embryo stage.

During my visit to Los Angeles, I visited an aircraft factory where another propeller gas turbine project was in a very preliminary stage. It was sponsored by the U.S. Navy Department.

When I saw the drawings of the engine and studied some of the figures and assumptions on which the design was based, it had a very depressing effect upon me because I felt that they were biting off more than they could chew. When I was shown round the part of the plant allotted for the work, it had a further depressing effect, because it was clear to me that the equipment available was hopelessly inadequate for the magnitude of the task they had undertaken. I was in an embarrassing position because, if I were to be strictly honest, I had to say that I thought they were wasting their time. This was a very painful thing to have to do and required a good deal of moral courage, especially as it implied severe criticism of enthusiastic engineers who were doing their best. When the firm's president asked me outright for my opinion, I was obliged to tell him as tactfully as possible what I really thought.

I feel able to say this now without giving offence, because the firm decided to drop the scheme a short time afterwards.

The work at Lynn and the two propeller gas turbine projects I have mentioned by no means represented the whole of the U.S. effort in this field. Though I had no direct connection with any of the other projects, I heard about them in the course of many talks with senior officials in Washington. For example, the Navy Department was sponsoring about four schemes altogether, of which the most important was a turbo-jet engine project at Westinghouse — generally similar to the R.A.E./Metropolitan Vickers F.2. This and the other Navy sponsored schemes were still in a very preliminary stage and none of them had yet reached the test bench. My impression was that they were all regarded as relatively long-term projects.

During a visit to the U.S. Army Air Force Experimental Base at Wright Field near Dayton, Ohio, I had many talks with senior technical officers. From the Commanding Officer, Brigadier-General Vanaman, downwards, their enthusiasm for the jet engine was impressive, and there already existed plans for test equipment on a scale far greater than anything we contemplated in Britain. Indeed, a plant for testing jet engines under high-altitude conditions was already under construction.

A letter from myself to Roxbee Cox dated July 7th, 1942, recorded my general impressions up to that date. I told him that it seemed to me that I had arrived at the G.E. at about the right time, because though they had done very well up till then, they had begun to run into a lot of trouble, much of which was of a kind that we had already met and overcome, and so I had been able to give them the benefit of our experience. I also recorded another of my impressions —

> ...the enthusiasm and ability here is such that I feel that the best that can be done will be done.

In another letter to Wing Commander Watt of the same date I amplified this point slightly —

> I get on very well indeed with the engineers over here because they have both enthusiasm and ability, which is a pleasant change from some we know of, and it is a real pleasure to do all I can to help the job along and I think my efforts are appreciated...

After I had been in the U.S.A. about five weeks, during which I had had to maintain a high level of mental alertness, I began to feel severe strain once more. At most of the engineering meetings I was, as it were, outnumbered by several engineers, all of whom were eager to make the most of my knowledge and experience. This meant that I was obliged to attempt to pass on the experience of years in a matter of a few days, and in such a way that there were no misunderstandings. All this was very exhausting and I began to feel seriously in need of a rest.

I found that Heenan and Keirn had sensed this and had discussed the matter with Air Marshal Hill, the senior R.A.F. officer at the British Air Commission, and that it had been arranged that after completing my official business in the Los Angeles area, I was to remain in California for two weeks' leave.

It had been assumed that what I needed was sun, rest and peace, and so at first I was left very much on my own at a hotel right on the Pacific coast at Santa Monica. Though this hotel was very comfortable and pleasant, I soon tired of my own company and so appealed to Group Captain Adams, in charge of the Beverly Hills office of the British Air Commission, to arrange that I should return east. Adams commented that he thought the treatment was wrong, and that if I would give him the chance he proposed to change it. He asked me to give him twenty-four hours after which he would arrange for me to go back east if I still wished to go. It was then four o'clock in the afternoon. Adams suggested that I should go to the Beverly Hills home of Edward Hillman, Jr., there and then and remain on for a barbecue party that was to be held there that evening. I did as he suggested and from that moment life became anything but dull. On arriving I was greeted warmly by Eddie Hillman (who was dressed only in bathing trunks) and told to "relax". Not an easy thing to do, because the situation I found myself in was so very different from anything I had experienced before. I have a somewhat confused impression that though there were always several people present — some of them well known in the film world — there was a continuous going and coming, with my host as the only element of continuity in an ever-changing scene.

Meanwhile, he spent most of his time on the telephone. He repeatedly told me to relax and, presumably to assist me to do so, ordered his secretary to bring me a bowl of chicken noodle soup (which I did not in the least want at that time of day). The sight of a strange R.A.F. officer sitting in the corner with a bowl of chicken noodle soup appeared to excite no surprise or comment from the new arrivals.

Amongst Eddie's many telephone calls was one to his wife, formerly the famous British dancer 'June' who was then at their Santa Barbara home about eighty miles to the north. Eddie told her that he had a young Wing Commander fresh from England whom she ought to meet and so would she come down to the party. So far as I could make out, June did not feel well enough to make the journey at the time — nevertheless, she arrived later in the evening.

In the course of the party that night I succeeded in "relaxing" to such an extent that at about 3 a.m. I was induced to join three others in the swimming pool and ruined my wristwatch which I had forgotten to remove. By then I had quite abandoned my intention to go back east immediately.

My diary of the remainder of my stay in California is very sketchy and my memories of it are somewhat disjointed. Most of the time either Eddie or June or both looked after my entertainment, and there was no doubt that I found the treatment much more congenial than the "sun, rest, etc.", which had been originally prescribed, so much so that after ten days, despite the fact that I was having a very good time, I felt the urge to return to work three or four days before I need have done.

During my last few days in Washington before returning to England, I heard that the G.E. were thinking in terms of a production rate of 1,000 engines a month and were already planning for this. They were also planning a full-scale test plant for the individual testing of compressors, turbines, etc., on a far bigger scale than anything we had visualised, and for which the cost was estimated to be about three million dollars, i.e. about twelve times as much as we were spending on our full-scale test plant at Whetstone. The Americans generally were astounded at the parsimonious attitude of the M.A.P. towards the work of Power Jets.

I arrived back in England on the 14th August, 1942.

Subsequently, Air Marshal Hill sent a message to Air Marshal Linnell which included:

> In my opinion, Whittle's visit has been of major significance in promoting closer understanding between the two countries. It has made a direct contribution in accelerating diagnosis of the causes of a number of teething troubles experienced by

> the G.E.C. Whittle's personal relationships with all of those whom he has met have been of the most cordial nature. He has won great respect from American engineers in the circle which is acquainted with this development…

Unfortunately, I had not been able to stay in the U.S.A. long enough to witness the successful flight trials of the Bell aeroplane, which began at Muroc Lake in California on October 2nd, 1942. In spite of their very much later start, their prototype twin-engine fighter started its flight trials before the Meteor, and just under a year from the date of the arrival of Walker and company with the W.1.X. in the U.S.A. This was a very remarkable achievement indeed. (During my absence the first Meteor prototype had done taxying trials fitted with two de-rated W.2.Bs., but Sayer, who was the test pilot again, had deemed it unwise to attempt flight trials until more powerful engines were available.)

One important consequence of my visit was that the G.E. decided to proceed with a new engine based on the Power Jets W.2/500. This was known as the Type 1.16.

I do not propose to record further the continuous interchange of information and visits between Britain and the U.S.A. It will suffice to say that mainly through the activities of Wing Commander G. E. Watt at the M.A.P. and Heenan and Keirn in the U.S.A., Anglo-American co-operation was excellent throughout the war.

CHAPTER 43

There were some very important policy changes at the latter end of 1942, and as these were very much influenced by what was happening on the engine test benches at the various firms, it is important to give a summary of the background of engine development before describing them.

At Power Jets by far the most important event was the completion and testing of the first W.2/500. This engine began its tests on September 13th, 1942, exactly six calendar months from the date on which we had begun the drawings. *After a preliminary run of only thirty minutes to make adjustments it was run up to full speed* and full sets of readings obtained. A thrust of 1,750 lb. was recorded at full speed, and 1,800 lb. at a slight overspeed. These observations and all the others taken were almost exactly in accordance with predictions. The engine then did its official acceptance test in the course of which it ran five minutes at full speed. This was the first time that running at full speed had been included in an acceptance test. This achievement demonstrated what could be done when ability, the will and the means were combined.

As a result of this very satisfactory performance, Tinling wrote to Air Marshal Linnell reporting on the results and said:

> …for the first time we have been able to design an engine with a background of experience. You will recall that when the W.2.B. was designed there was no experience except the limited running with the original and pre-war W.U.[38]
>
> I am glad to tell you that the design predictions for the W.2/500 have been fulfilled in practice with an accuracy

which seems to confirm that the design of these engines can now be regarded as almost an exact science.

(I was responsible for suggesting this bit about the "exact science", and my engineers got a lot of pleasure in quoting it back at me on sundry occasions later when we ran into trouble.)

I received a letter from Roxbee Cox, congratulating us on the very impressive achievement with the W.2/500.

The weight of the engine was 835 lb.

Unfortunately, there was some doubt about the safety of the compressor impeller. Experiments and calculations made by the R.A.E. and ourselves suggested that there was a risk of failure through resonant vibration, of the same kind as was happening about that time on W.2.B. engines, and so, pending the manufacture of a re-designed impeller, we continued test-running with interim modifications designed to make the impeller safe enough to enable us to test the rest of the engine for reliability. Unfortunately, these modifications reduced the full-speed performance to about 1,600 lb. thrust, and throughout the period under discussion the compressor was not in a satisfactory state. Nevertheless, apart from this the engine was otherwise showing up very well, and, during December, 1942, a 25-hours' special category test was done of five 5-hour cycles, each of which included 40 minutes at full speed, and 4 hours at 97% of full speed.

Next in importance to the testing of the W.2/500 was a 100-hour test on the W.1.A. *which thus became the first engine to complete a 100-hour test.* More than half of this 100 hours was at over 95% of full speed. There were some minor sheet-metal failures, but no trouble of any real importance. In particular, though the turbine blades were made of Rex 78, which was now under grave suspicion after many blade failures, they survived the test. One important reason for making the test had been to try out a theory I had had about one possible cause of turbine blade failures. Puzzled by the curious fact that the place where the blades cracked or broke was very variable, when one would expect failures due to a particular mode of resonant vibration to occur more or less at the same place along the blade, I had concluded that a thermocouple inserted into the exhaust pipe was creating a disturbance which caused severe "buffeting" of the blades, and that the variation in the point of fracture was associated with the changes in the position of the thermocouple. The W.1.A. did its 100-hour test with this thermocouple removed, and the fact that the blades survived seemed to be strong evidence in support of the theory. Nevertheless, though it was true that there was a big drop in the incidence of blade failures in general after the removal of the exhaust thermocouple, they were not entirely eliminated, and so the decision to change over from Rex 78 to Nimonic 80 was not affected. (During my absence in the U.S.A. Power Jets had done 34 hours of endurance running at full speed with a W.2.B., having turbine blades made of Nimonic 80. Though this test ended in a blade failure, it nevertheless demonstrated that Nimonic 80 was a very much better material than anything we had so far tried — 34 hours' full-speed running on the bench corresponded to many more hours of flying time.)

Another W.1.A. was used intermittently for flight tests in the E.28 at Edgehill. Later the aeroplane was handed over to the R.A.E. and the flight testing continued at Farnborough.

During the period there were some interesting experiments to increase the thrust of the engines by the injection of cooling liquids at the compressor intake. We first tried the injection of finely atomised water with the W.1.A. and found that we could get an increase of thrust of about 10%.

While I was in the U.S.A. it had occurred to me that a very large temporary thrust increase could be obtained by ammonia injection. When liquid ammonia evaporates it has a very powerful cooling effect indeed, and I estimated that we ought to be able to achieve a temporary increase of thrust of at least 50%.

With the W.1 we certainly had a very dramatic demonstration of what ammonia injection could do. A large steel bottle of liquid ammonia was placed outside the test house, and we arranged to spray the ammonia into the duct through which the air entered the test house. We had realised that since ammonia was combustible it would, in all probability, be necessary to cut down the normal fuel supply during ammonia injection, to avoid overspeeding the engine (which was not then fitted with a governor). The operator had been warned about this. A test fitter was stationed outside the test house, whose duty it was to turn on the ammonia on receiving a signal. When the signal was given nothing happened for a few seconds, and so, believing that the ammonia was "on", the man at the engine control relaxed. But the cock of the ammonia bottle had jammed, and it was some little time before it could be turned on. When it did come on there was virtually an explosion. The engine speed went "off the clock" before the operator had time to snatch back the throttle. The rev. counter scale ended at 20,000 r.p.m. and the designed top speed of the engine was 17,750! Many other instruments went off their scales and the mercury was blown out of several "U" tube manometers (instruments for measuring pressure) and sprinkled all over the control-room. We judged that the engine had momentarily produced a thrust of 2,000 lb. at least, as compared with its designed maximum of 1,240 lb. The remarkable thing was that the engine was not scattered all over Leicestershire.

When ammonia injection experiments were resumed on the W.2.B. we injected the liquid ammonia in a series of fine sprays round the compressor intakes. We achieved thrust increases of the order of 33%. The cooling effect was so intense that it proved too drastic and caused the compressor casing to contract rapidly and foul the impeller. The outside of the casing became covered with a very heavy coating of frost in a second or two. We could have dealt with this trouble by turning on the ammonia more slowly, but since we had by then found that the ammonia was having a corrosive effect on alloys containing copper in the engine, we decided to discontinue the experiments.

With the W.2.B., a new "disease" had made its appearance, namely, compressor impeller failures. There were three such failures at Power Jets, two in September and one in October, 1942. The G.E. in America and the Rover Co. had had similar trouble. This had now become a more serious problem than the turbine blade failures. Modifications based on suggestions from the G.E. and the R.A.E. were agreed by Rover's and Power Jets, and ultimately led to the elimination of the trouble. When there was an impeller failure the damage was frequently extensive, and so the three failures at Power Jets severely impeded the amount of development work we were able to do on the W.2.B.-type engines.

The total running time during 1942 at Power Jets was just over 709 hours.

The foregoing, of course, is a very brief summary of what was, in fact, an immense amount of experimental work during the period, not only on the engines but on the combustion test rigs, on aerodynamic test rigs and other experimental apparatus.

At Rover's the number of engines on development work increased until they had about twenty by the end of 1942. Their total running time during the last five months was just over 578 hours — almost entirely devoted to comparative tests of different modifications, and experiments to improve performance. Not until December did they attempt any serious endurance running, and in that month three 25-hours' special category tests were completed at a maximum thrust rating of 1,250 lb.

In August and September one of their W.2.Bs. was given ten hours' flight testing in the tail of a Wellington at the Rolls-Royce flight test unit at Hucknall.

Rover's were still having a lot of trouble with their combustion chamber sheet-metal work of a kind which we were not getting at Power Jets (in the flame zone of the combustion chamber were short stub pipes attached to the flame tube wall — their function was to duct additional air into the combustion region. In the Rover engines these stub pipes were being overheated and distorted).

Rover's had continued experimental work on their "straight-through" engine and during November a second B.26 was completed. According to the G.T.C.C. Progress Report for December, 1942, their total running time on the two B.26-type engines was just under 57 hours, of which nearly 34 hours was on the first one which had started its running the previous March. This compares with the 57 hours which we had done on the one W.2/500 since the middle of September, a large proportion of which had been at and near full speed. I think this is a sufficient comment on the "first serious attempt to productionise the W.2.B." Rover's progress reports gave little information as to why their running time was so limited. For example, the 7 hours 33 minutes on the second B.26 during November, 1942, was described as "running in and plain bearing tests". In December they also described the 14 hours 40 minutes on the same engine as "preliminary running in". (We, of course, never felt it necessary to do any "running in" at all, and I am not aware that any troubles could be attributed to our "neglect" in this respect.) The Rover Progress Reports for the period also indicated, as we had foretold, that the changes in the combustion chamber arrangement had made a further and intensive programme of combustion development necessary.

The limited amount of running on the B.26-type engines would not normally be a cause for comment (since that is what one would expect for an engine in which such important changes had been made), had not such extravagant claims been made for the engine and had not these been swallowed "hook, line and sinker" by the senior officials in the Directorate of Engine Development at M.A.P.

The amount of test-running at the B.T-H. was very small. They had two engines, but they only did 11½ hours' running during the last five months of 1942. Their progress reports were too meagre to explain why so little running time was put in.[39]

At the beginning of 1942 Rover's, the B.T-H. and Power Jets had reported maximum thrusts of 1,600 lb. and above with their W.2.B.-type engines. At the end of the period all three firms were showing much more modest figures. It was an extraordinary thing that a year of development work should have resulted in a reduction in performance, yet that, in effect, was what happened. My own view is that the chief explanation was lack of accuracy in manufacture, largely due, presumably, to the increasing proportion of unskilled labour which had to be used. So far as Power Jets were concerned, part of the explanation was that we were repeatedly obliged to use salvaged parts.

De Havilland's completed 156½ hours' running on their H.1-type engines during the last five months of 1942. They had a third engine on test in September, and a fourth was completed in November. Though they were showing a distinctly higher specific fuel consumption than the W.2.B., and running into sundry mechanical troubles, the net result was so promising that it had a distinct effect upon policy as will be seen hereafter.

During December they did a five-hour test which included ten minutes at a thrust of 2,680 lb. By this time it was planned to install two H.1s in one of the prototype Meteors, and during November and December the third and fourth engines were sent to Gloster's for this purpose.

The Metropolitan Vickers F.2 type engines completed 125½ hours' running during the five-month period under review. For most of the period they had three engines on test. They were also to have engines flight-tested in a prototype Meteor and much of their testing was in preparation for this.

At Rolls-Royce the amount of running on the Griffith engine was very limited, amounting to only 4¾ hours under power during the five-month period. The whole of this at speeds far below the design full speed. No performance figures were reported.

Rolls-Royce completed the first W.R.1 engine during November and did about 3¾ hours' preliminary running on it up to moderate speeds during December.

It may be seen that the record of engine development for 1942 presented a very gloomy picture, illuminated only by two bright spots — the Power Jets W.2/500 and the de Havilland H.1. The Metropolitan Vickers F.2 might also have been accounted as one of the bright spots had this engine not been considered to be in a very preliminary stage with no provision for production.

An M.A.P. Technical Committee had been formed in August, 1942, the function of which was to advance the development of the W.2.B. for the F.9/40 and to this end to bring Power Jets and Rover's together to discuss the problems which arose during the development. The committee was also to be the authority for modifications to the W.2.B.

I do not propose to record the proceedings of this committee in any detail. For the most part the discussions were highly technical and the proceedings accounted for a lot of paper, but it was a short-lived committee, and was wound up early in 1943 as a result of policy changes.

My dominant impression after re-reading the minutes is that though Power Jets made a large number of recommendations for the improvement of the W.2.B., Rover's usual answer was that to embody the modifications recommended would mean a serious set-back in production.

A point of particular interest was that Power Jets placed on record that if the modifications which they recommended were incorporated in the engine, it would give 1,550–1,600 lb. thrust with reliability. The Rover representative, on the other hand, was minuted as saying that they did not consider this performance to be possible with the W.2.B. arrangement of combustion chambers. A few months after this opinion went on the record, the W.2.B. completed a 100-hour test at a rating of 1,600 lb. — but by then Rolls-Royce had taken over the Barnoldswick and Clitheroe factories.

Among the many problems which the Technical Committee attempted to solve was the curious difference in experience between Rover's and Power Jets on the burning of the combustion chamber stub pipes. Independent investigators were called in to look into this matter (Dr. Saunders and Professor Lander of the Imperial College), and they found that there were substantial dimensional differences between Rover's combustion chamber components and those of Power Jets. However, it was by no means certain that this was a sufficient explanation of the differences in experience. A curious thing about this particular business was that though Rover's and Lucas were well aware that Power Jets claimed to be free of the trouble, they made virtually no attempt to benefit from the Power Jets' experience which was fully available to them.

CHAPTER 44

The sorry story of the W.2.B. development, the relative success of the Power Jets' W.2/500, and of the de Havilland H.1, were the chief factors which had an influence on policy at the latter end of 1942.

Another factor of no small importance was that the initiative in the air was clearly passing over to the Allied side, and so the operational requirement for a very high-altitude interceptor, which the Meteor was intended to fulfil, had become less urgent. The other operational needs of the R.A.F. were being met by improvements in conventional fighters.

According to information which reached me from various sources, opinion in the M.A.P. was sharply divided. Roxbee Cox, Watt and other officials in the Directorate of Scientific Research tended to back Power Jets and the W.2/500. Their opposite numbers in the Directorate of Engine Development, who by now were beginning to lose faith even in the B.26, wanted to put their money on the H.1. It might seem at first glance that the H.1, being much more powerful than the W.2/500, was a much better bet, but this was more apparent than real, because a Meteor to take the H.1 would, because of the much larger size and greater fuel consumption of the engine, have had to be rather drastically modified, and would, because of the larger nacelles, have a substantially greater drag, which would have largely offset the increased thrust. On the other hand, Power Jets had expressed their confidence that the W.2/500 could, in a relatively short time, be developed up to 2,000 lb. thrust. Either engine as power plant for production aircraft was rather a long-term proposition at that stage, because no provision had as yet been made for their manufacture in quantity.

As time passed the arguments of the advocates for the H.1-powered Meteor seemed to be having an increasing effect, and so a corresponding pressure was brought to bear on Power Jets, by the champions of the W.2/500 in the M.A.P., to complete a 100-hour type test at the earliest possible moment, particularly as Linnell, not wishing a repetition of the W.2.B. situation, had said that he would not contemplate the production of the W.2/500 until it had done such a test.

In a letter (dated 10th October, 1942) to Tinling, Air Marshal Linnell said that the aim would be to introduce the W.2/500 as a replacement for the W.2.B. as early as possible because of its much greater promise, but that he was not prepared to risk a repetition of the troubles which had resulted from attempts to force the W.2.B. into production before the prototypes had done any serious running.

Linnell also indicated his intention to authorise a contract for a further twelve W.2/500 engines plus spares to be made by Power Jets at Whetstone. His letter hinted that subject to successful development he might authorise Power Jets to undertake "pilot production" of the engine. He ended by stressing that the emphasis still remained on the W.2.B., because it would be some time before there could be a satisfactory replacement in production and that Power Jets should therefore not relax in their efforts on their part of the W.2.B. development. (A comparatively small part of necessity because, of the thirty or so engines which had been made by the Rover Co. by the end of 1942, Power Jets had only received four.[40])

In his reply (16th October, 1942), Tinling pointed out that Power Jets was far from being equipped to manufacture a sufficient number of engines for intensive development. He said that labour was a greater bottleneck than machine tools, because at that time there were more machine tools at Whetstone than there were operatives to man them. (We then had the capacity to make about four engines per year.)

The development troubles of the W.2.B. had important repercussions on the airframe programme; the planned production was first cut back from 80 a month to 30 a month — later the programme for the Meteor I was cut back to a total of 50, pending a decision as to whether or not the H.1 would power the Meteor II.

Since quantity production of the W.2/500 by Power Jets was out of the question with the then available resources, we suggested to Rolls-Royce that they should consider taking on the job. As a result, Sidgreaves and Hives paid a visit to Power Jets on 8th October, 1942. They were cautious but seemed to be generally favourable to the suggestion. They made it clear that they intended to stay in the jet engine field, and would make every effort to become the leaders in that field.

Though there were frequent exchanges of visits and discussions between Power Jets and Rolls-Royce engineers, the matter was not taken any further until Power Jets repeated the suggestion more formally in a letter (dated 16th November, 1942). Hives visited Brownsover Hall on the 4th December and told us that he and Sidgreaves had discussed our proposal with Sir Wilfrid Freeman (who had retired from the R.A.F. and returned to the M.A.P. as Chief Executive) and Air Marshal Linnell. Hives said they had summarised Rolls-Royce views as follow:

(1) As a matter of policy Rolls-Royce were quite definitely entering the aircraft gas turbine field.

(2) They were interested in the Power Jets' W.2/500 and would like to undertake production of it.

(3) Their heavy commitments on the Merlin were such that in order to undertake the production of the W.2/500 they would require extra facilities.

Hives said Freeman and Linnell had agreed that the W.2/500 was the best bet, but that its production would have to be done within then existing facilities.

We were startled to hear from Hives that Freeman had suggested that Rolls-Royce should take over Whetstone for the purpose of the W.2/500 production. Hives said that he had replied that they could only think of such a course in complete agreement with Power Jets. I said we were willing to go a long way to help to bring the W.2/500 into production, but if Whetstone were to be used for the purpose it meant that tools and labour would have to be found in the Whetstone area, and if they could be found for Rolls-Royce they could equally well be found for us. On the other hand, there existed at Barnoldswick a plant which was both manned and tooled for the production of jet engines, whereas Whetstone was destined to be equipped for research and development only. I thought it of considerable national importance that Whetstone should be retained for this purpose.

As the discussion continued, it seemed that we were all thinking in terms of the same thing, namely, that Rolls-Royce should take over the management of Barnoldswick from the Rover Company.

We were generally agreed that facilities for the production of the W.2/500 existed at Barnoldswick, and that since it had earlier been decided that the production of W.2.B. engines was to be limited to a total of 100, these facilities would become available as soon as that task was completed.

Hives seemed to be very impressed with the work we had done on the W.2/500, and in particular with the speed at which it had been designed, made and tested.

On 11th December, 1942, I was summoned to the M.A.P. to see Sir Wilfrid Freeman. I do not claim to be a good descriptive writer, and it would be very hard indeed for me to convey the atmosphere of that rather extraordinary interview.

My health had been poor throughout the year and this was one of my bad days. I was not feeling well when the interview began — I was feeling much worse at the end of it!

During most of the talk I was seated, while Sir Wilfrid paced back and forth speaking forcefully and rather abruptly, emphasising his remarks with vigorous arm movements. Air Marshal Linnell sat at one side of the room and said very little.

Freeman opened by saying that every jet engine up to then was either a flop or likely to be. Three years had passed and there was little to show for it. When I protested that this was not a true representation of the facts, he admitted that he might be exaggerating slightly. He then concentrated on the W.2.B. situation — he laid great emphasis on what he described as the failure of the W.2.B. and inferred that I was primarily to blame. I said I refused to accept the blame, and that on the contrary I had repeatedly protested against the course of events which had led to the situation as it then was.

Here was the state of affairs I had long foreseen. Though I had been deprived of any effective control of the development of the W.2.B. long before, I was being blamed for the results of a policy which had failed.

Freeman said that his first impulse, when he first took up his new post, was to close down the whole job. After this he had felt that the best thing would be to bring all the different firms together into one organisation, which he inferred would be dominated by Rolls-Royce. Though he had been dissuaded from so sweeping a step, he had nevertheless made up his mind to bring together the resources of Rolls-Royce, the Rover Co. and Power Jets under the primary control of Rolls-Royce. The Rover management would cease to have anything more to do with the job. Though he did not say so explicitly, I gathered that Power Jets would cease to have an independent existence. At this point he stopped in his peregrinations and asked, abruptly, "Well, what do you think of it?" I felt I had to gain time and so I replied that I had not really grasped what he was proposing, so he went over more or less the same ground once more.

He seemed to be antagonistic to the Board of Directors of Power Jets; he admitted that Williams and Tinling had done a good job of work in initiating the venture, but thought that they had ceased to have any useful function. He went so far as to say he would have them called up. I gathered that he proposed to include Johnson amongst those he intended to call up. I protested vigorously, and said that all the people he had referred to were still doing very important work. Williams and Tinling had done far more than initiate the venture — amongst other things they were mainly responsible for the expansion which had taken place, and in particular for the bringing into being of the Whetstone factory.

Once more he stopped and asked me what I thought about it all, so again I stalled by saying that I had not clearly grasped what it was he had in mind. I was almost sure that what he really meant was that Power Jets was to be handed over to Rolls-Royce, lock, stock and barrel, but that he could not bring himself to put it quite as bluntly as that. So once more he stalked up and down embroidering his theme. I told him that any proposal which disturbed the Power Jets' team as an entity would be disastrous. He replied that what he had in mind did not involve the disbanding of the team. He went on to argue that a firm like Rolls-Royce with their vast resources could obviously do much better than a small organisation like Power Jets. I asked him whether the record of the past year supported his point. I pointed out that no one had equalled, let alone beaten, the Power Jets' record in the time of manufacture of the W.2/500 or in test-running results after completion of manufacture.

He made it clear that he had quite definitely decided to transfer Barnoldswick and Clitheroe to Rolls-Royce management. He remarked that he had yet to break the news to the Wilks brothers. I said that that at least was a feature in his proposals which had my full approval.

I asked him who would be the effective Chief Engineer of the integrated scheme he had in mind. Sir Wilfrid countered by asking whether I would prefer —— (a well-known aero-engine designer whom he knew was not likely to be acceptable to me); he presumably meant as an alternative to Rolls-Royce. I replied that I would prefer me. He said he could not very well put Rolls-Royce under my orders.

I tried to make it clear that anything which in my view would really be for the benefit of the project would have my approval. Freeman said the Ministry fully recognised that I always did what I considered to be my duty and was not actuated by personal motives.

At the end of this further harangue, in which he still had not explicitly stated that Power Jets were to be handed over to Rolls-Royce, though he had again inferred it, he once more asked me what I thought about it, so I told him that I was not feeling well enough to take in what he really meant. At this point Linnell intervened and asked me what was the matter; I told him very bluntly that I was tired, and sick to death of the whole business. Freeman said that they could not afford to dispense with my brain for some time yet, and asked me whether what he had said had made me feel any worse. I replied that I did not know until I understood it. This more or less brought the interview to a close. Freeman told me to go away and think about it over the weekend and then have a talk with Roxbee Cox and Hives the following Monday.

Throughout this interview I sensed that Linnell was not in entire agreement with Freeman. After the discussion he took me along to his own office — his manner was very friendly and sympathetic, and he managed to convey to me that he felt I had been rather roughly handled. He hinted that much of what Freeman had said was a "try-on" to test my reaction, and that I could discount about half of it. I repeated to him what I had already said to the two of them together, that the basic idea of combining the resources of Rolls-Royce and Power Jets had my full approval, but I was unable to follow Sir Wilfrid's ideas as to how it should be done.

Freeman had told me that he had made important changes in M.A.P. organisation, and that thenceforward Roxbee Cox would become responsible directly to C.R.D. (Linnell) for all gas turbine development. I told Linnell that I welcomed this change which, in my opinion, was long overdue.

The next day there was a G.T.C.C. meeting at the Derby works of Rolls-Royce which I attended. This occasion provided an opportunity for the talks between Roxbee Cox, Hives and myself which Freeman had suggested. Elliott[41] was also present.

I gave an account of my interview at the M.A.P. the day before, and said that though I was in entire agreement with the basic principle of a very close technical liaison between Rolls-Royce and Power Jets, I had not been able to form a clear impression of the machinery Freeman had in mind for this. Roxbee Cox and Hives evidently had a much less drastic outlook on the problem than Freeman, and we were all agreed that the necessary degree of close co-operation could be secured without a major upheaval.

After the discussion Roxbee Cox made a summary of the points on which we were all agreed. These were:

(1) Machine tools and labour at Barnoldswick must continue to be used to the full.

(2) Rolls-Royce should undertake the production of the W.2/500 at Barnoldswick.

(3) Production of the W.2/500 would be to a design agreed between Rolls-Royce and myself.

(4) That in relation to the W.2/500 and future engines of the same series, Power Jets' engineering policy would be one agreed between Rolls-Royce and myself — this engineering liaison to be so close that any blame or credit was carried jointly.

(5) That research and development especially in relation to new designs should remain the function of Power Jets, and that it should continue to take place at Whetstone, etc.

(6) Rolls-Royce to undertake such manufacture of experimental parts as was necessary.

(7) Rolls-Royce would do all they could to increase the efficiency of Whetstone.

(The above points were as written down by me as Roxbee Cox summarised them and simultaneously made his own notes.) Two or three days later (in a letter dated 15th December, 1942) Roxbee Cox placed on record the points agreed at this discussion. His version was in good agreement with mine.

In a phone call on the 19th December, Hives told me that the Minister of Aircraft Production had seen S. B. Wilks the day before, and as a result had sent out a minute saying that Wilks had agreed to handing over the job to Rolls-Royce.[42]

On the 5th January, 1943, at a meeting in my office at Brownsover Hall, Hives stated that the Rover Co. had agreed that Rolls-Royce would be responsible for all engineering work at Barnoldswick and Clitheroe thenceforward, though the administrative takeover would take a little more time.

It was agreed that Power Jets were to send W.2/500 drawings to Rolls-Royce at once to enable them to go ahead with production planning, though Hives was of the opinion that it was still too early to embark on quantity production of the engine. It was revealed that six B.26 engines were being made at Barnoldswick and Hives argued that since these engines were virtually in existence, their development should continue.

Roxbee Cox told the meeting that the airframe programme at Gloster's had recently been reduced to seven prototype Meteors and twenty Meteor I's, pending the availability of an improved design of engine. He also thought it was as yet too early to regard the W.2/500 as ready for large-scale production.

It may thus be seen that the end of 1942 saw profound changes, both in the technical direction of the W.2.B. development at Clitheroe and Barnoldswick and in the M.A.P. organisation controlling it, and in so far as this was so, it marked the beginning of a new and brighter phase in the story, and though, as will be seen hereafter, things did not go altogether as Power Jets had hoped, the technical quality of Rolls-Royce plus their enthusiasm helped to change in dramatic fashion a situation which had become very gloomy. The pity is that these changes were not made much earlier. As it was, I believe that the policy of the M.A.P. had cost us at least two years.

CHAPTER 45

At Barnoldswick, the vigorous technical policy of Rolls-Royce made itself apparent almost immediately. The W.2.B. which had virtually been dying a lingering death throughout 1942 was rapidly revived. During January, 1943, the total engine-running time at Clitheroe and Barnoldswick on the W.2.B. and B.26 engines jumped spectacularly to nearly 400 hours. In particular, in view of the difficulties which had previously been experienced with the sheet-metal work of the combustion chambers, it was significant that 100 hours' running was completed on one engine with one set of flame tubes and burners.

The next few months saw a steady increase both in reliability and the rating of the engine until, in May, 1943, a 100-hour development test at a rating of 1,600 lb. thrust was completed. The following month even more severe 100-hour tests were successfully completed, one of them at a rating of 1,700 lb. thrust.

The work included a substantial amount of flight testing in the tail of the Wellington flying test bed and in the second Gloster/Whittle E.28 in which, by the end of June, 50 hours flying had been completed.

After the conclusion of the 100-hours test at 1,600 lb. with the W.2.B., J. P. Herriot phoned to tell me about it (7th May, 1943). After congratulating me, he told me that the engine had been stripped and that such defects as were found were very minor. Herriot emphasised that a very important contribution to this result had been the twisting of the turbine blades through an angle of 5; (which we had recommended nearly two years earlier).

I felt that the occasion called for a special letter and so wrote to Herriot as follows:

> The recent completion of 100 hours on the W.2.B. at a rating of 1,600 lb. is an event constituting an important landmark in the history of jet propulsion, and one on which I most heartily congratulate you. I should like you also to convey my congratulations to the team at Barnoldswick which has assisted in the achievement which, coupled with the success of the W.2/500 and the recent noteworthy flights of the E.28, should go a long way to putting jet propulsion well and truly on the map. The record of development running carried out by you since the latter end of last year is most impressive and satisfying. As you know, we had felt for a long time that endurance running with progressive increase in rating was what was most needed to set the W.2.B. on its feet, and this has now virtually been proved. Power Jets could not contribute much to this because of lack of engines and the capacity for making them.
>
> We are of course very gratified with this excellent result because the rating was the one counted on when the decision was taken, on the basis of P.J. drawings and calculations, to gamble on the production of the W.2.B. and hence, in so far as this was so, that gamble has been justified.
>
> It is not to be overlooked that the policy of emphasis on endurance running was largely brought into effect by you personally, and it is gratifying that you have been enabled to continue — as the 'highest common factor' linking the old management with the new — the effort so well initiated by yourself previous to the change. I believe that it is also correct to say that the important though apparently trivial changes such as '50 twist' which have made recent achievements possible, though having been dormant for many months, owe

their resuscitation very largely to the efforts of yourself and your colleagues to whom all credit is due.

There has in the past undoubtedly been a certain amount of ill-feeling, based largely on the poor view Power Jets took of the development policy of the former management, but now that you have demonstrated that you are flat out for rapid progress in this field you may rest assured that as far as Power Jets is concerned not a trace of this remains.

To this Herriot replied:

I would like to thank you very much on behalf of myself and the Development Staff at Barnoldswick for the kind things you have said in connection with our efforts at Bankfield, culminating in the satisfactory completion of the 100-hour Type Test of the W.2.B. engine at a rating of 1,600 lb. You will, I know, agree from your own experience that it is not so much the effort of the individual as the team work of the Department as a whole which finally results in ability to reach the desired goal.

I have been particularly fortunate in having as my assistant, Mr. J. N. Dening, who has handled all the type tests for me, and who as you know gained his first experience in jet propulsion engines whilst stationed at Power Jets in the early days; he is therefore particularly gratified at your kind remarks.

We at this end fully realise that whereas a number of modifications have been made as a result of the development running, the basic design still remains almost 100% in line with your own original ideas, and we feel honoured in having been allowed to play our small part in what we hope has been the first step in putting the jet propulsion engine on the map as a tried and going concern, backed by *very* extensive test-bed running.

Personally I do not think we have reached finality in the W.2.B. at a rating of 1,600 lb. and I shall be very disappointed if, by the time you return from the R.A.F. Staff College, I have not been able to satisfactorily complete 100 hours Type Test at at least 1,700 lb. for take-off.

Thanking you again for your letter and with all good wishes for the future.

It may be seen from this exchange that there had been a very great improvement in the atmosphere between Power Jets and the technical team at Barnoldswick.

Part of the flying of the second E.28 powered by the W.2.B. was done by the Gloster Aircraft Company at Edgehill.

An event of special interest was a demonstration flight at Hatfield before the Prime Minister, Mr. Winston Churchill, on 17th April, 1942. I was not invited to be present on this occasion. The aeroplane was piloted by Mr. John Grierson. For its flight from Edgehill to Hatfield it was provided with an escort of two Mark V. Spitfires from No. 11 Group and a Hawker Typhoon flown by Mr. Crosby Warren, another of the Gloster test pilots. This escort was to ensure that none of our fighters should mistake the E.28 for an enemy aircraft. According to Grierson the three escorting aircraft took off first and then joined up with him over the airfield, but though he only maintained cruising speed, he subsequently reported:

I never saw the Spitfires again for the rest of the flight, and apparently the Typhoon could only just keep up with me at maximum cruising power having to use absolute maximum occasionally to keep abreast of the E.28. The navigation was tricky because we were both intent on keeping contact in formation, and neither of us knew how lost or otherwise the other one was. The result was that we deviated some seven miles south of our course, and instead of traversing the direct track of 57 miles we actually covered 71 miles between

> Edgehill and Hatfield. The elapsed time was approximately fourteen minutes for the greater distance, and this included climbing from 5,000 feet to 8,000 feet.
>
> After making several circuits at Hatfield so as to lose height and speed, I landed…
>
> The machine was taxied straight into the special hangar. As I came out of the hangar one of the escorting Spitfires reached the aerodrome in a power dive.

I have no record of the subsequent demonstration, but I understand that the Prime Minister was duly impressed.

At Power Jets the emphasis was on the testing of the W.2/500. A second engine to this design was on test in February and a third in March. The second was short-lived, because, also during March, it was damaged beyond repair by a failure of the turbine disc due to a heavy rub on a part of the stationary structure, and so we continued our work on the two remaining engines until another one was completed in June. It may thus be seen that during the first six months of 1943 we had, in effect, only two W.2/500-type engines. These did not give us much scope for intensive development, particularly as one of them was allocated for a 25-hour special category test and flight trials in the first E.28.

Meanwhile, the work of the de Havilland Engine Company gathered momentum. By January, 1943, they had four engines completed, of which two were allotted for flight tests in an F.9/40[43] specially modified to take them. The engines for flight test were first installed in January, but for a number of minor reasons the first flight did not occur until the 5th March. It was then completely successful. This was the first time that the F.9/40 had done more than "hop" during taxying trials (flight trials with an F.9/40 powered by W.2.Bs. did not take place until June). Michael Daunt was the pilot. (He had become Gloster's chief test pilot after the tragic loss of Sayer in a flying accident some months earlier while on loan to the R.A.F.)

Daunt had a very lucky escape. He walked too near the intake orifice of an engine nacelle while the engines were being tested. A de Havilland Progress Report recorded:

> Whilst running both engines at full speed, the pilot was inhaled into the port air intake, fortunately without extensive damage to pilot or intake. Collaborating firms are, however, warned of this danger.

On receipt of this report, Johnson wrote a rather dry comment in the margin — "We have been warning people for two years." Thereafter large-mesh wire screens were fitted across the intake orifice of each nacelle. At Power Jets these were naturally known as "Daunt Stoppers". (I hope Michael Daunt will forgive me if I mention that he was no featherweight, and the fact that *he* could be whipped off his feet into the intake was an indication of the very powerful "vacuum cleaner" effect if one got too close. Fortunately, he suffered nothing worse than shock. How fortunate he was has been tragically illustrated during the past few years when similar incidents have had fatal results.)

CHAPTER 46

Power Jets' hope that Rolls-Royce would produce the W.2/500 after completing 100 W.2.Bs. faded as time passed, because Rolls-Royce showed an increasing reluctance to do so. Their attitude was perhaps understandable in view of the rapid development of the W.2.B., and the fact that the tooling at Barnoldswick was planned for the W.2.B.

Formal terms of reference were received from the Director of Contracts in a letter dated 4th April, 1943. They were generally in accordance with the points agreed between Roxbee Cox, Hives and myself at the end of 1942. Power Jets accepted them, but Rolls-Royce did not.

I had a talk with Hives at Derby on the 19th April at which he hinted that they did not regard the terms of reference as satisfactory. Hives said he was very dissatisfied with the lack of clarity in M.A.P. policy. I, in turn, said I was dissatisfied with the way things were going in the engineering liaison between Rolls-Royce and Power Jets. For example, we had been told that they were going ahead with an engine known as the B.37, which was a "straight-through" engine generally similar to the B.26, but incorporating several features of the W.2/500 design. Power Jets were not being consulted in the matter. Hives agreed that the closest possible engineering collaboration was necessary, admitted that they had not kept us as well informed as they should have done, but stressed that this was not deliberate, and was largely due to their preoccupation in taking over at Barnoldswick. He said they had also been somewhat influenced by their belief that I was about to leave the job for some time. Hives said that in any case the B.37 was considered to be so small a step from the B.26 as not to justify any special fuss over it.

The B.37 was intended to give a thrust of 2,000 lb. and was thus competitive with the Power Jets W.2/700 (a development of the W.2/500) which was also designed to give a thrust of 2,000 lb.

Hives reminded me that they had always felt that the only way to get the close collaboration necessary was to have a definite link-up between the two firms. I replied that as a serving officer I did not think it was appropriate for me to discuss commercial matters. To my surprise, it then became apparent that Hives was under the impression that, when this subject had previously been discussed, it had been left with Power Jets to make the next move. I told him that, if my memory served me right, Power Jets had explained that they were not in a position to negotiate, but had given Rolls-Royce the option of a first refusal before any commercial alliance with any other firm was considered. Hives seemed very surprised to hear my version of the way things had been left. It thus seemed that a possible link-up had been delayed by mutual misunderstanding. This became even more obvious when Sidgreaves joined the discussions later. Both he and Hives thought that a letter had been written to Power Jets to which there had been no reply. I said I had no recollection of any such letter. Sidgreaves said they had been unable to pursue the matter further from their side without appearing overanxious, but they had been forced to conclude that Power Jets wished to maintain complete independence. I said that I felt most strongly that if commercial negotiations were reopened, it should be done in a way which would not hamper or spoil the engineering liaison.

These discussions were very amicable and Hives agreed that Power Jets had shown plenty of goodwill and willingness to co-operate. He said that he always told third parties that he got on well with myself and Power Jets, but he emphasised that Rolls-Royce would not be satisfied with a position in which they had to take their orders from Power Jets. I replied that I would like to see an organisation for engineering liaison set up of so intimate a nature that it would not be possible even to use such a phrase.

It then became evident that their attitude towards Power Jets was very much coloured by what was likely to happen to me. They questioned me closely about my position, and Sidgreaves commented that they regarded me as Power Jets' major asset.

The next day I spoke to Hives on the phone about the matter of the letter they were supposed to have written. Hives admitted that his memory had been at fault and that their proposals had been made verbally at a meeting. He added that the position was as before — they wanted a proposal from Power Jets. They wanted to know how far Power Jets were willing to "let them in" and how much it was going to cost them, particularly the latter.

A few days later a Rolls-Royce delegation, headed by Hives, visited Power Jets. Hives said that the Meteor was coming back on to the map once more, largely (he claimed) as a result of a Rolls-Royce brochure which showed that it would make a very good training aeroplane with 1,600 lb. thrust engines, would be a useful operational aeroplane with 1,800 lb. thrust, and would become outstanding with 2,000 lb. thrust. He was confident that the order for Meteors would be raised to 300 almost immediately, and said that the engine production programme would be dominated by this aircraft programme for the succeeding months.

Hives then went off with Williams, Tinling and Johnson for a separate talk while the engineering representatives of the two firms held a technical meeting at which, *inter alia*, Dr. S. G. Hooker confirmed that the B.37 combined what they regarded as the best features of the B.26 and the W.2/500.

The separate discussions with Hives were recorded by Johnson. In effect, there was no progress in the matter of a possible alliance. Power Jets' representatives explained that they were in a worse position to negotiate than they had been before, in that the contract position with the M.A.P., far from being cleared up, had become even more complex. Another important difficulty was that it was not possible to obtain the sanction of Power Jets' shareholders to any disposal of assets without violating the Official Secrets Act.

Johnson reported that Hives had said, very bluntly, that Rolls-Royce intended to be the centre of the whole orbit of jet propulsion, and that they were not accepting the M.A.P.s terms of reference because they could be interpreted as putting their activities subject to the authority of Power Jets — a position they would not tolerate. According to Johnson, Hives also claimed that the venture was, in effect, dead until Rolls-Royce came into the picture a few months earlier and that Rolls-Royce were the sole instruments of its revival, as demonstrated by the fact that they had engineered an increase of the Meteor programme. We felt that the successful demonstration of the E.28 to the Prime Minister at Hatfield and the success of the W.2/500 had probably had as much influence, if not more, on policy than any representations made by Rolls-Royce. (We were willing to concede that they had revivified the W.2.B., but felt that the claim to have "rescued" the whole project from extinction was a serious exaggeration.)

In fact, the proposals for a commercial link-up came to nothing and no terms of reference were mutually agreed, but fortunately, I am able to record that the technical collaboration between Power Jets and Rolls-Royce was unaffected, and the atmosphere was so cordial that it gave rise to firm and lasting friendships between the engineers of the two firms. The personalities of the individuals concerned contributed much to this happy situation. We were fortunate indeed in having to deal with such people as Elliott, Chief Engineer, and Stanley Hooker who was "in command" at Barnoldswick and Clitheroe. Their policy was not "to be different for the sake of being different", but to make the utmost use of any work of value shown up in the results of Power Jets. This policy bore valuable fruit.

It is probable that at least two factors contributed to the apparent reduction of enthusiasm on the part of Rolls-Royce for a commercial alliance with Power Jets, as compared with their attitude in 1942. In obtaining control of the factory at Barnoldswick they had become the largest firm in the jet-engine field, without the necessity of making a "deal" with Power Jets for the purpose. Also there was some foundation for their belief that I was becoming less active than hitherto, and indeed while negotiations were in progress I was almost entirely inactive so far as the turbo-jet development was concerned, because I was attending the R.A.F. Staff College at Gerrard's Cross and it was by no means certain that I would return to Power Jets. This may well have greatly weakened Power Jets' bargaining position in view of what Sidgreaves had said on the 19th April.

CHAPTER 47

By the beginning of 1943, the expansion of Power Jets had been considerable. The greater part of the Whetstone factory was in use. Unfortunately, output had not increased in proportion. Indeed, in my eyes, the output at Whetstone was very unsatisfactory in proportion to the manpower and equipment available, especially when compared with the output in proportion to our strength before the Whetstone factory was built. Relatively, both the quality and quantity of the work had fallen off, chiefly due to dilution by poor quality labour. Many of the more recent employees were not voluntary recruits, but had been "directed" under wartime regulations and without much regard to quality. The result was that the morale did not compare with that which had existed at the Ladywood works. Not only did this diluted labour lower the standard of workmanship, it also fomented an atmosphere of unrest. Part of the lowering of morale was undoubtedly a consequence of the Ministry's policy. The employees knew that such firms as Rolls-Royce were apparently reaping the benefits of Power Jets' work, and this gave rise to the belief that Power Jets as a firm was not likely to survive and that the management had been weak in allowing this state of affairs to come about. There was some justice for the first of these beliefs, and the second, though unfair to the management, was understandable because it was not possible to explain Ministry policy or to give an account of the attitude of the management towards this policy. The fact remains that the management received the blame for events over which they had no control.

Among the new recruits were one or two very active agitators who were ringleaders in unofficial strikes. This was a time when Communist agitation for a second front in Europe was becoming vociferous and I, for one, had no doubt that many of our labour troubles were due to Communist influence.

We did what we could to raise morale; without saying too much we tried to convince disaffected employees that their work was not being wasted, as some of them seemed to think, but was making a direct contribution to the war effort. We arranged for a demonstration flight over the works by a Meteor, and also, during a lunch break, gave an engine demonstration to all the employees with an engine mounted on a lorry. Incidentally, I suppose Power Jets can claim that they had the first gas-turbine-propelled road vehicle — for what such a claim is worth! (I would have given a lot to have seen the effects on the general public of a run of our jet-propelled lorry along a public highway.)

The low morale had a very depressing effect on me after the most unusual and satisfying degree of loyalty and enthusiasm of the great majority of the employees to which I had become accustomed when we were about 200–300 strong.

A little variety was introduced into my normal routine when, during March, 1943, I was called in by a section of the Intelligence to give technical advice in connection with the interrogation of prisoners of war. In the light of what we now know, the sketches and items of information which were presented to me were a mixture of fact and fancy; some of it related to work actually in progress in Germany, and some of it to projects which at the time were very little more than a twinkle in the designer's eye. Perhaps the most definite item of information was that experiments with very large rockets were being conducted at Peenemunde and elsewhere.

The total picture was distinctly alarming, and I reported to this effect to Roxbee Cox and to Sir Stafford Cripps, who had then become the Minister of Aircraft Production.

Though much of the information we received at this time proved subsequently to be greatly exaggerated, it nevertheless served as a powerful stimulus to work in the U.K. and the U.S.A.

One consequence of the Intelligence Reports and the proceedings of a special committee, of which D.S.R. (Lockspeiser) was chairman, was that it was decided to start or intensify work in Britain on such devices as ramjets and rockets. Power Jets was expected to make their contribution to the ramjet section of this work.

This general extension of the scope of jet propulsion activity led to certain changes of organisation in the M.A.P. Roxbee Cox's Deputy Directorate was made a full Directorate and he was given the title of Director of Special Projects. Wing Commander G. E. Watt was his Deputy Director.

I have always regretted that I never flew the E.28/39.

Until May, 1943, M.A.P. permission for me to do so had been refused, presumably because it was not desired to risk both the aeroplane and myself. When, eventually, permission was given, I was balked at the last minute. After spending a few days at the R.A.E. putting in flying practice on the Miles Master, Hurricane and Spitfire, I was cleared to fly the E.28, and was in the act of climbing into the cockpit when I was told that the aeroplane had been declared unserviceable, and was likely to remain so for several days because of an adverse report by the pilot who had flown it immediately before.

It has since been suggested to me that the real reason was that somebody at the M.A.P. had suddenly become nervous about my flying the aeroplane and had phoned through instructions that I was to be prevented. Possibly someone had reported that I had fallen asleep from exhaustion after flying a Miles Master for two hours.

During this visit to the R.A.E. I met Air Marshal R. S. Sorley (later Sir Ralph Sorley) for the first time. He had succeeded Air Marshal Linnell as Controller of Research and Development at the M.A.P. In the course of a short talk he said he understood I was quite happy with the Rolls-Royce situation. I replied that this was not entirely true. We had counted on them to produce the W.2/500 and they were not showing many signs of doing so.

The changes in policy at the end of 1942 did not come in time to arrest a deterioration in my health. Seven years of frustration and anxiety were taking an increasing toll. In order to provide the change which was "as good as a rest", it was decided that I should attend the three months' War Course at the Staff College at Bulstrode Park, Gerrard's Cross, beginning on May 24th, 1943. This period was certainly a change, but anything but a rest, especially as it was necessary to maintain some contact with my normal work. On a number of occasions I had to absent myself for a day or more at the request of the M.A.P. when certain special matters required my attention. The course was very intensive and was very much a full-time job for the normal student. It would not have been possible to have combined my studies with these other tasks if I had not been granted special privileges. Air Vice-Marshal Hill (later Air Chief Marshal Sir Roderick Hill) was the Commandant, and Air Commodore Fiddament ("Fido") was the Assistant Commandant, and both were very understanding about my special position. I was excused certain of the less important "exercises", and was allowed to have my secretary, Mary Phillips, to help me; she was quartered with the W.A.A.F. personnel during her visits.

Our time was divided mainly between lectures, visits and "exercises".

The expeditions which were organised for the students were usually very interesting — to aircraft firms, to the various Command Headquarters, and so on.

From my point of view, the most interesting of the visits was to the Photographic Interpretation Unit at Medmenham. This was a key unit in the Intelligence organisation, and its function was to glean information from photographs taken by reconnaissance aircraft. One of the staff engaged on this work was a young W.A.A.F. Officer, Flight Officer Constance Babington Smith, an attractive young lady who combined considerable personal charm with an intense interest in aircraft. It was she who spotted much of the evidence betraying the work the Germans were doing on jet- and rocket-propelled aircraft, work for which she was subsequently decorated.

As soon as she realised who I was, and my connection with jet propulsion, she virtually detached me from the rest of the Staff College party to get my views on some of her more interesting photographs, and so I spent most of the time with her poring over photographs of Peenemunde and other airfields with indications of German jet activity. I was particularly struck by the way scorch marks on the grass indicated that the Germans were flying twin-engined jet aircraft, though none of these aircraft actually appeared in the photographs. Other photographs, however, showed quite clearly the tailless rocket-propelled interceptor, Me. 163. While she and I had our heads together over the photographs, I noted that I received many envious glances from the other students and a very amused one from "Fido" Fiddament. On the return journey to the Staff College, "Fido" pulled my leg unmercifully. I had a little of my own back when he asked what perfume she used. I replied, "Judging from its effect on you, sir, it must have been 'Air Commodores' Ruin'," at which he roared with laughter.

At Power Jets we had for some time past been giving much thought to power plant for long-range bombers, but we were rather at sea as to what the design target should be. I succeeded in getting some guidance on this by persuading the Commandant to arrange for the course to hold a discussion on the subject. In effect, I invited the directing staff and my fellow students to give their views on the kind of performance required for a long-range bomber for operations in the Far East. This discussion was very valuable, and led to the broad conclusion that what was needed was a bomber capable of carrying a bombload of 12,000 lb. at a cruising speed of 450 m.p.h. and having a still air range of 4,000 miles. These figures[44] became the basis of subsequent project work at Power Jets.

While at the Staff College I was promoted to temporary Group Captain. This made me the most senior officer on the course; the ranks of the other students ranged from Flight Lieutenant to Wing Commander.

At the end of the course I was re-posted to the Special Duty List and returned to Power Jets.

It had not been intended to re-post me to Power Jets. When the Directorate of Special Projects was formed, Roxbee Cox wanted me to become a Deputy Director in parallel with Watt, but I made it clear that the idea of working at M.A.P. was unattractive to say the least of it. When it was agreed that I was to return to Power Jets, it was on the understanding that because of my state of health I would be less active than I had been before, and would mainly be concerned with future project work. A Special Projects Section was formed at Brownsover headed by L. J. Cheshire, who by now had been allowed to transfer from the B.T-H. to Power Jets.

During my time at the Staff College, the second E.28/39 (powered by a W.2.B. engine) was destroyed when the pilot — Squadron Leader Davey of the R.A.E. — was forced to "bale out" at a height of 30,000 feet because the aileron controls seized up.

CHAPTER 48

During the last six months of 1943 the development effort at Power Jets was largely transferred from the W.2/500 to the W.2/700. Whereas in August we had four W.2/500-type engines on test and only one W.2/700, by December we had five W.2/700S and only two W.2/500S. We failed to achieve the 2,000 lb. thrust target with the W.2/700 during 1943, but managed it early the following year. We did, however, succeed in getting over 2,000 lb. thrust under overspeed conditions with a W.2/500 which had an experimental compressor casing (with the "Type 16" diffuser). The superiority of this type of compressor casing had earlier been demonstrated on one of the W.2.Bs. This, of course, was a further inducement to provide a similar type of compressor casing for the W.2/700, and it was this modification which enabled us to achieve the 2,000 lb. thrust target.

During November, 1943, two W.2/500S were flight-tested in one of the prototype Meteors, but the amount of flying was very limited during that month because one of the engines was severely damaged by failure of the compressor impeller during a ground run.

Impeller failures represented another serious "disease" and gave us a great deal of anxiety. A particularly puzzling feature was that some impellers of that particular design had accumulated a large amount of running time without any sign of failure. Though I was less in touch with day-to-day engine development than I had been hitherto, I gave this problem much thought and wrote a paper on the subject, in which I came to the conclusion that failure was due to a resonant vibration which must be occurring at quite modest speeds. On investigation I found that the test-house personnel were in the habit of running quickly through the speed at which there was a pronounced "howl" from the engine, which probably accounted for the apparent safety of some impellers. After running an engine for an hour at "howling" speed to test this hypothesis we found every impeller blade cracked.

In addition to these fairly serious troubles, there were others, many of which, I am sorry to record, were attributable to a falling off in the quality of workmanship; for example, we had two bearing failures which were traced to faulty assembly.

In view of the intensive work on the W.2.B. at Barnoldswick, there was a reduced need for Power Jets to expend much of their effort on this type of engine and the amount of work on it gradually diminished.

Rolls-Royce's development drive at Barnoldswick continued with increasing intensity, and in addition to a large amount of bench running with the W.2.B. an increasing number of engines were provided for flight trials. They also were getting impeller failures — in one month there were three failures, one of them in flight in a Meteor prototype. The trouble was dealt with by stiffening up the impeller blades. However, their most significant development work was with the B.37 which, as I have already indicated, was an engine generally similar to the "straight-through" B.26, but having a number of features of the W.2/500. During October, 1943, a 100-hour development test was done at a rating of 1,800 lb. thrust. By then four B.37 engines had been completed. In November there was a further advance, when a 100-hour development test at a thrust rating of 2,000 lb. was done.

The work at Barnoldswick on the B.37 and the work at Power Jets on the W.2/700 were closely in parallel. This put the M.A.P. in something of a difficulty for a time — to decide which of the two engines should succeed the W.2.B. in production. Ultimately, in fact, the B.37 was selected and went into production as the Derwent 1. However, there was an interim period during which the decision hung in the balance, and Power Jets were requested to prepare plans for a possible "pilot line" production of the W. 2/700 in case the decision went in favour of that engine. Roxbee Cox suggested that this plan should be for production at the rate of ten per month.

The number of engines on test at de Havilland's increased from eight in July, 1943, to fourteen by the end of the year. Flight trials in the Meteor were continued, but by far the most significant event in the de Havilland programme was the completion, and first flights of, the D.H.100 — the prototype of the now famous Vampire. Another de Havilland engine was sent to the U.S.A. to power the Lockheed X.P.80 (the prototype of the "Shooting Star").

Metropolitan Vickers accumulated a fair amount of running on a total of six engines — their work included flight testing in the Lancaster "flying test bed"[45] at the R.A.E. Also two of their engines powered one of the Meteor prototypes which had been specially modified. These flight tests began in November. Unfortunately, early in January, 1944, the aircraft crashed and the pilot, Squadron Leader Davey, who had done much valuable work on the E.28 at the R.A.E., was killed. He tried to escape by parachute but was struck by the tailplane. The evidence indicated that the primary cause was the bursting of the compressor drum of one of the engines.

Shortly before the end of 1943, Roxbee Cox had told me that, under pressure from the U.S. Government, it had been decided that some official disclosure of Allied work on jet engines should be made; nevertheless, despite this prior warning, when it happened it was a shattering experience.

I received the C.B.E. in the New Year's Honours List, 1944, but this, in itself, caused no Press comment, because there was nothing unusual about the award of the C.B.E. to a serving officer of my rank. At the same time one other member of Power Jets received recognition — G. B. Bozzoni received the B.E.M. I must confess to a feeling of disappointment when the New Year's Honours List appeared, because I had hoped that several other members of the team would have been honoured, or rather, knowing that publication was imminent, I had also hoped that the nature of our achievements would justify a special list of awards, separate from the New Year's Honours List, and following publication. Apart from marking the special nature of our work, this would have had an important propaganda effect in underlining the British origin of the project.

On the evening of the 6th January, 1944, a joint statement was issued by the British and U.S. Governments for publication after 11 p.m. on that day. I did not receive a copy of the official statement before it was issued to the Press and, in fact, I had no knowledge of its contents until a copy was shown to me by Miss Iris Carpenter of the *Daily Herald* shortly before I heard it on the midnight news of the B.B.C.

The next morning the news was prominently featured in the national Press. I was by no means prepared for the astonishing consequences of publication. I had been too close to the job for too many years to see the situation from the point of view of the average citizen. Our failures were more prominent in my mind than our successes, and so the reaction of the Press and the public had a stunning effect.

It is a strange thing indeed to have worked for years in secret, and then to have the whole world told about it. I found it a very odd experience to open a newspaper and see my photograph displayed on the front page and my name splashed in the headlines.

Few people who have not had the experience can understand the consequences of sudden fame and publicity. I was besieged by reporters and snowed under with mail. Most of the letters were congratulatory, but many of them were not quite so pleasant; some were quite spiteful. These were usually either from individuals who claimed to be the real inventors of the jet engine, or from individuals who were opposed to scientific progress of any kind, on the ground that any advance in technology was another step towards the total destruction of civilisation. I received many requests to lecture; begging letters; requests for my autograph, letters from inventors proposing "improvements" to the jet engines or other devices, most of them wildly fantastic. I heard from many relatives, but the letters from genuine relatives were far outnumbered by those from people claiming to be relatives — these came from all over the world.

In my inexperience, I attempted to deal with most of this correspondence to the detriment of much more important tasks. Since then I have learned to make a generous use of the wastepaper basket.

This heavy correspondence was by no means the only embarrassment resulting from the publicity. I found it was virtually impossible to move about in public without being accosted by complete strangers who recognised me from the published photographs, and my movements therefore became greatly restricted. I no longer felt able to travel by train, because almost invariably either a stranger or a slight acquaintance would buttonhole me and pester me with questions. This was particularly distasteful in my then state of health. I was in no mood to be sociable with strangers.

No doubt many people envied the position into which I was thrust so suddenly, but few realised the penalties which went with it, not the least of which was having to answer the same old questions over and over again, *ad nauseam*. The same thing has been happening more or less ever since, and frequently for this reason official cocktail parties and the like are often a severe ordeal. On occasions like these, perhaps the thing I dread more than anything else is being cornered by an inventor.

I personally believe that all this publicity was premature, in that we let the cat out of the bag before we should have done, especially in the light of Intelligence reports received from Germany after the war. These suggested that there was a great intensification of German work on turbo-jet aircraft after the joint Anglo-American announcement.

CHAPTER 49

The British public, who had been told of the achievements of Power Jets and myself in the official announcements of January, 1944, must have been more than a little surprised when, only a few weeks later, they learned in further official announcements that Power Jets Limited was to be nationalised.

It is with regret that I have to record that I triggered off the train of events which led to this result. On the 29th April, 1943, I wrote to Sir Stafford Cripps, the Minister of Aircraft Production, about the future of the gas turbine industry in Britain and said, *inter alia*:

> As you know, many big commercial concerns are now entering into the gas turbine field, largely as a result of the stimulus provided by my efforts. There are a number of signs that a fierce commercial struggle is likely to develop. In my opinion this should never be allowed to happen. With the exception of Power Jets (which has not been allowed to contemplate quantity production in any case) not one of the firms involved has taken any speculative risk and is not therefore entitled even from the most capitalistic standpoint to benefit financially, other than from the profit allowed in Government contracts.
>
> In my view *there is a very strong case for complete nationalisation* viewed from any political standpoint. This case is based mainly on the following:
>
> (1) Public money expended on gas turbine development up to date must (I believe) be of the order of at least two million pounds, while the only private money expended (as far as I know) is about £23,000 subscribed by the shareholders of Power Jets, and which served to start the ball rolling. In other

words, 99% of the total expenditure to date has come from public funds as against 1% from private shareholders.

(2) Apart from the direct expenditure on gas turbine development, a great deal of the necessary information required for design has been provided by Government institutions, namely, the R.A.E. and the N.P.L. and has therefore also been paid for with public money.

(3) The three leading engineers in this field, namely Mr. Constant, Dr. Griffith and myself, are, or have been, State servants. Mr. Constant and myself are of course still in that position. Dr. Griffith is now an employee of Rolls-Royce, but he was a Government servant at the time that he did the greater part of his gas turbine work.

(4) In so far as gas turbines are likely to find their greatest applications in aircraft and ships, the State is likely to be the principal user, and the normal commercial field is therefore probably limited to the potential overseas market.

(5) The interchange of technical information, etc., which has taken place between the various firms on official instructions is such that it is going to be virtually impossible to sort out the patent rights, etc., when the time comes, particularly as most inventive ideas arise out of joint discussions, or through knowledge of the activities and difficulties of others.

The circumstances are therefore quite unprecedented and the case for nationalisation seems to me to be overwhelmingly strong, so much so that the public would be entitled to raise a vigorous outcry through Parliament if a few private firms are allowed to grasp for the benefit of their shareholders that which should properly be the property of the State...

This letter went on to suggest steps which should be taken, and included the suggestion that the private shareholders should be bought out.

This was, of course, by no means the first time that the suggestion that Power Jets should be taken over by the State, or at least be Government controlled, had been made. As I have already recorded, there were various suggestions to this end in 1941, which came to nothing on "broad grounds of public policy".

There have been many times when I have bitterly regretted writing this letter to Sir Stafford Cripps, but I console myself with the thought that the position of Power Jets was probably beyond saving in any case. Repeated efforts by the management of Power Jets and senior Civil Servants in the Directorate of Contracts of the M.A.P. had failed to sort out the extremely complex contract position of Power Jets. Apart from anything else, this made it virtually impossible to negotiate a commercial alliance with any other firm. Without such an alliance, the chances of Power Jets' survival seemed to me to be negligibly small.

What I was advocating was consistent with the political beliefs I had held for many years, though I hasten to add that my enthusiasm for public ownership *per se* was severely undermined by the subsequent history of Power Jets — nowadays I do not align myself either with those who advocate 100% public ownership or 100% private enterprise.

I further deluded myself into believing that, in a nationalised gas turbine industry, the Power Jets' team would naturally be at the apex of the pyramid.

Sir Stafford Cripps requested me to see him on the 11th May, 1943. He told me that he agreed in general with the points I had made in my letter, but that his problem was ways and means, because the Government was not a Socialist one, and the law only allowed him to take over firms if they were inefficient. At this point he gave me a rather penetrating look, and said, "Power Jets does not give me that excuse, does it?"

I replied, "No, sir!"

Nothing further happened for several months. Then, on the 25th October, 1943, at the Minister's request, I saw him again. He told me that he had decided that Power Jets was to be taken over by the State on the ground that it was essential to have a State-owned gas turbine experimental establishment, and that it would be wasteful to start building another while an organisation which had already absorbed a large amount of public money was already in existence.

At the time of the interview I didn't fully grasp what Sir Stafford Cripps had in mind. However, I had understood enough to make me feel extremely uneasy, and that the Minister intended the nationalisation of Power Jets only, which was a far cry from my original proposals.

I wrote to the Minister the following day and, *inter alia*, recorded my objection to the nationalisation of Power Jets alone. I pointed out that there was less justification for the nationalisation of Power Jets than for any other of the firms concerned, because Power Jets was the only firm which had taken the risks of private enterprise. I went on:

> Moreover, if Power Jets alone were nationalised, it would have the appearance of a punishment, and the inevitable consequence would be a general belief that Power Jets had been inefficient as compared with the other firms, whereas in fact I believe Power Jets to be the most efficient of all the firms engaged (though still leaving a lot to be desired). It is my view that many of the civil servants in the Ministry are quite ready to do ruthless things with the young and still small Power Jets, but are too much afraid of the old-established firms to be equally firm with them…

On the 2nd November, 1943, Sir Stafford Cripps and Sir Harold Scott had a meeting with Sir Maurice Bonham Carter, Williams and Tinling, and repeated to them much of what had already been said to me. The price to be paid for the assets of Power Jets was vaguely discussed, with an indication from Sir Stafford Cripps that he was thinking of a sum somewhere between £100,000 and £250,000, and that if there were no quick agreement on the sum to be paid, he would take the alternative course of taking over possession of all the plant operated by the Company and directing all the labour to a new Government Company, leaving Power Jets in possession of its paper assets, such as patents, etc., and nothing else. This threat to put the Company into "cold storage" took more definite shape in a letter from Sir Stafford Cripps to Sir Maurice Bonham Carter dated 26th November, 1943, in which the following appeared:

> I have now received a report from Mr. Sam Brown[46] as to his visit to Power Jets, and it is quite clear that there is no basis between us for acquiring the assets of the Company. I must therefore consider immediately the other alternative as we urgently need the plant for general experimental purposes.

There was another meeting between the Minister and the three Power Jets' directors on the 1st December, 1943, at which Sir Harold Scott and Mr. Sam Brown were also present. The Minister told Power Jets' directors that the Treasury would not support a sum in excess of £100,000 in payment for the Company's assets, and once more inferred that if some such sum were not acceptable to the shareholders, the Company would be dispossessed of its personnel and premises.

When I heard about the attitude of the Minister, I thought it grossly unfair and said so in a phone call to Roxbee Cox on the

2nd December. He gave me to understand that he sympathised with my point of view, and so did many other senior officials in the Ministry. He told me that Freeman, Sorley and he had discussed the matter with the Minister; the inference was that they had all indicated their opposition to the proposed plan. I gathered that amongst the reasons that the Minister had given for his action was that it was my wish. I told Roxbee Cox that the action being taken was not at all consistent with what I had recommended, and that I was most strongly opposed to the nationalisation of Power Jets alone. I made it quite clear that I was extremely indignant, and expressed myself in unusually strong terms.

In the middle of December the Minister saw Sir Maurice Bonham Carter, Williams and Johnson, and it appeared that he had relented to some extent, because he now said that he was prepared to offer approximately £130,000 for Power Jets' assets.

A letter dated 3rd January, 1944, from Tinling to Mr. Sam Brown made it clear that though the Board intended to accept the offer of the Minister, that offer was not considered to be fair, and that it was only being accepted under the threat that the Minister would use his powers to put the Company into cold storage if it were not accepted. This letter records that the Minister had even rejected the Company's proposal that the value of the assets should be submitted to arbitration.

I saw the Minister again on 3rd January, 1944. This time, as a result of my experience at previous interviews, when I had felt that I had been manoeuvred into saying things I didn't intend to say, I armed myself with a set of notes, a copy of which I handed to the Minister. These clearly recorded my disapproval of the nationalisation of Power Jets alone, for the purpose of establishing a national gas turbine establishment. It also recorded my disapproval of the manner in which it was proposed to acquire the Company.

> … It seems to me unsatisfactory and unnecessary to impose a price with the virtual threat of extinction as an alternative. I do not understand why arbitration cannot be tried…

The Minister read my notes and the discussion was more or less guided by them. Sir Stafford made it clear that he had given up hope of nationalisation of the gas turbine industry, giving as a reason that the political situation just did not permit it. He repeated that his purpose in acquiring Power Jets was to bring into being a national gas turbine experimental establishment. I pointed out that that was not at all what I had intended when I had first made my suggestions, and that I was very doubtful indeed as to whether the plant and personnel were suited to the purposes he had in mind.

An important letter dated 6th January, 1944, from Mr. Sam Brown to Tinling placed formally on the record the Minister's point of view:

> After due consideration, the Minister reached the definite opinion that the national interests demanded the setting up of a Government-owned centre of gas turbine technology. The present stringency of building labour and resources generally renders it quite impossible for the Government now to construct a suitable new establishment. In these circumstances the Minister was forced to the conclusion that he had no option but to exercise his rights, which are not, I think, in dispute, to re-take possession of the facilities occupied by the Company at Whetstone, but constructed wholly at the Government's expense, and which are now and always have been the property of the Crown.

> At the same time the Minister recognised that the adoption of this course would seriously prejudice the Company's future. He therefore considered it only fair to tell you and your colleagues quite frankly of his intentions, and to say that if you wish to do so, he was prepared to delay taking action while an attempt was made to see whether it was possible by negotiation to arrive at a mutually acceptable price at which the Government should buy out the Company.
>
> In the result a mutually acceptable price has been reached.[47] In the Minister's opinion — as indeed in my own — it is a very full one, and one which can be justified only because of the difficult position in which the Company is placed, and the very special relationship which has existed for some years now between it and the Department.

Correspondence of early February, 1944, shows that the impending transaction had got to the ears of Rolls-Royce, who had requested and received an assurance from the M.A.P. that the proposed Government Company would not be competitive with industry. This was exactly the kind of thing which I had foreseen and feared.

Faced with the grim alternative of dispossession of plant and personnel, a meeting of shareholders accepted the Ministry's offer on the 28th April, 1944. The total cost to the State for the outright purchase of Power Jets' assets was £135,563 10s.

The circular letter to the shareholders recorded that the plant and equipment operated by Power Jets had been provided at a cost of £350,000, and that a further £950,000[48] had been expended by the M.A.P. on development work at Power Jets.

So ended Power Jets Limited, the private Company which had founded an industry. Rarely, I imagine, have a Ministry's powers been used so ruthlessly, and I still do not understand why even arbitration was refused.

The Government Company was called Power Jets (Research and Development) Limited and so there was some continuity in name as well as in personnel and equipment with the old Company. Roxbee Cox was appointed Chairman and the Board included Williams and Tinling.

The terms of reference of the Government Company were set out in a letter from the Minister of Aircraft Production dated 27th April, 1944. This important document read as follows:

> Now that Power Jets (Research and Development) Limited, has been formed and is ready to operate, I think it would be useful to you and your colleagues on the Board if I were to set out shortly the primary objective which I would like the Board to pursue in managing this undertaking. This objective may be summarised as follows:
>
> To act as the recognised national establishment for furthering, in collaboration with industry and the Services, the advancement of knowledge on the subject of gas turbine engines and their use in aircraft, and for this purpose:
>
> (1) to conduct research on such engines and their components, accessories and materials of construction;
>
> (2) to design, construct and develop prototype engines, components and accessories, and to develop materials for their construction;
>
> (3) to devise methods of manufacture appropriate to such engines, and to manufacture small batches of such engines so as to carry development up to the production stage;
>
> (4) to test such engines, their components, accessories and materials of construction, on the test bed, in the laboratory and in the air, and to design, develop and construct apparatus for this purpose;
>
> (5) to make available to those concerned by reports and otherwise the knowledge obtained by such work;

(6) to train Service and civilian personnel for the various countries of the British Commonwealth in the technique of the gas turbine engine and the other work carried on at the Establishment; and

(7) to do such other work or things as the responsible Minister may direct on behalf of His Majesty's Government.

As you are aware, it is my wish that on questions of technical policy, you and your colleagues should seek the advice and assistance of, and work in the closest collaboration with, the Gas Turbine Technical Advisory and Co-Ordinating Committee, which I am establishing under your Chairmanship.

CHAPTER 50

The price paid for the assets of Power Jets did not include any payment to me, because I had offered to surrender my shares and rights to the M.A.P. some time earlier, and when Sir Stafford Cripps decided to take over the Company he also decided to accept my offer. This timing made it seem as though the two things were associated when, in fact, my offer had nothing to do with the act of nationalisation. Indeed, when Cripps had asked me if my offer still held good, I had confirmed that it did with considerable reluctance because of my strong objection to the nationalisation of the Company, and because Cripps had said, in effect, that it would make no difference to the price which would be paid for the assets of Power Jets — it would merely have the effect of giving the other shareholders more.

My reasons and feelings on the subject were recorded in a letter to the Minister dated 11th January, 1944:

> My main reasons for deciding to part with all financial interest in my shareholding were:
>
> (i) My belief that a serving officer should not be in a position to benefit from his employment in any commercial sense...
>
> (ii) In order that I could be held to be free of any taint of commercial motive, so that I should not be barred from the counsels of the Ministry especially on matters of policy...
>
> My second object has never in fact been achieved, partly no doubt because the offer of shares to the Ministry was not formally accepted, and the position therefore remained ambiguous, and partly because my actions were not

sufficiently known to individuals concerned. I say that I failed in this object because, in my opinion, I have not carried anything like the weight I should have done in matters of policy.

While it is quite true that I have no particular desire to 'make my fortune' I think my disinterest in money matters has been overrated. That may be my own fault. There is always a difference between what one would like to do and what one believes one ought to do. It may be that I have overstressed the latter. The truth is, as I told you in my first interview, that I am sufficiently interested in financial matters to desire sufficient for comfort and to be free from the need to worry about my bank balance and to ensure that my family would not suffer hardship in the event of anything happening to me. You are not therefore to think that this offer was a light-hearted one; on the contrary, I felt it to be a duty — and a painful one…

The letter then set out the reasons why I felt I was making a considerable sacrifice. The points I made were: that I thought that my Service career had been prejudiced by over-specialisation; that my health had suffered severely through overwork, frustration and worry; that I was very uneasy about the nationalisation of Power Jets alone and that my action might be taken to have contributed to this situation; that my sacrifice was proving, in effect, to be a gift to the other shareholders.

A series of discussions with Sir Harold Scott and Mr. Sam Brown ended in the signing of an agreement between myself and the Minister of Aircraft Production dated 28th March, 1944.

In the preamble of this agreement, the following occurs:

> The Inventor considers that as a serving officer engaged on full-time employment on such development, it is improper for him to have or to appear to have any commercial interest in the results of the Company's operations, and that accordingly it is his duty to divest himself absolutely of his financial interest in the Company and in the commercial development of his inventions, and to rely on official awards for his rewards, and the Minister, while being of opinion that there is no legal obligation on the Inventor to dispose of such financial interest, recognises the Inventor's conception of his duty...
>
> ...The Minister has agreed to accept such transfer, on the understanding that such transfer shall not prejudice or affect any application by, or on behalf of, the Inventor for the grant of an ex gratia award in respect of the inventions, and that he shall be entitled to retain for his own benefit any award so granted to him. Also SUBJECT to the requirements of the public interest, the Minister shall afford the Inventor such facilities as he may reasonably require for the purpose of presenting and supporting his application for the grant of an ex gratia award in respect of the inventions.

According to the absurdly low price fixed by the Minister for the purchase of the assets of Power Jets Limited, the value of the shares and rights I was surrendering was about £47,000. This was no light sacrifice to make, and I had serious arguments with my conscience before I made it. It was none the easier because certain senior officials implied that it was unnecessary, and that I was taking an over-conscientious view of my duty. Moreover, I had received a strong hint from Sir Wilfrid Freeman that I was unlikely to receive promotion if I did not broaden my Service experience, because it was against Service policy for senior officers to be over-specialised. (He rightly emphasised his point by remarking that I could scarcely expect to be an Air Chief Marshal attached to Power Jets. I countered certain of his arguments by pointing out that if things went the way I thought they would, I would be one of the very few officers thoroughly familiar with the type of equipment of the R.A.F. of the future.)

After the tremendous blaze of publicity which followed the official announcement on January 6th, I had begun to learn that one of the penalties of fame was an unavoidable increase of personal expenditure. In short, I had to make the sacrifice at a time when, for various reasons, I was feeling less secure financially than ever before.

I was so disturbed about suggestions which had been made that my action was both unnecessary and unwise, that I felt it very desirable to have some formal approval of my action in writing. As I told Sir Wilfrid Freeman in the conversation referred to above, I did not want to run the risk of going down in history as a fool, or to have my action used as evidence that I had gone out of my mind, and therefore I was making it a condition of the transaction that my interpretation of my duty should be officially endorsed. I commented that it would in any case be presumptuous on my part to insist on doing what I was doing as an act of duty, if my superiors did not uphold my view. I therefore wrote formally to the Air Council on the 27th March, 1944, and after briefly explaining the circumstances of the transaction, and stating the reasons for my actions, I invited an official endorsement of them.

I did not, after all, wait for a formal approval of my interpretation of my duty by the Air Council, before signing the agreement.

Sir Stafford Cripps then wrote (29th March, 1944) as follows:

I have just learnt that the formal agreements, under which you are transferring to the State without payment all your financial interest in Power Jets Ltd., have been signed.

Now that this transaction is complete I want to tell you how greatly I appreciate the high conception of your duty which has led you to make this gift to the State, and to tender you my sincere thanks for your generous action.

May I also take this opportunity of expressing my admiration of the inventive genius and hard work you have put into the development of your engine? It represents a valuable asset to the State, and the success already achieved must be as gratifying to you as it is to me.

I did not receive the Air Council's reply until the latter end of May. It said, *inter alia*:

...the Council accept the view, that as a general principle, a serving officer should not make a commercial profit out of his fulltime employment.

The Council are satisfied that, the principle is already stated adequately in the regulations ... the application of the principle is sometimes difficult, and the cases which arise shade imperceptibly from one class of case into another. The regulations accordingly provide that exceptions may be made with the special sanction of the Air Council. Thus, in your case, the award of a percentage of commercial profits was made to you with proper authority; and you were free to act on your own judgment either to retain your financial interest in the company or to surrender it. The Council, however, appreciate the high motives which have led you to adopt the second alternative, and consider that your action was in accordance with the best traditions of the Service.

...the Council have seen a copy of the letter addressed to you on March 29th, 1944, by the Minister of Aircraft Production, and they wish to associate themselves cordially with the tribute paid to you in the last paragraph of that letter.

This Air Council letter was sent with a personal letter from Air Marshal Sorley who said, *inter alia*:

> I feel sure that this letter, together with the one which the Minister sent you on the 29th March, should be sufficient to ensure your position when the time comes for you to go to the Royal Commission.

In a reply to Sir Ralph Sorley's letter I included:

> The Air Council letter is especially valuable to me in that it will no longer be possible for any person to suggest that my action was unnecessary and unwise, or to use it as an example of unsoundness of judgment (some people would be quite capable of suggesting that it implied lack of balance), or to accuse me of presuming to interpret my duty differently from my superiors.
>
> As for ensuring my position when the time comes for me to go to the Royal Commission, I hope that it may never be necessary for me to have to *ask*, though I may be driven to it for the sake of my family. It would be extremely distasteful to me to have to do so, and I feel that I should never need to do so — the State should look after its own…

The final phases of the nationalisation transaction and the surrender of my shares and rights to the Government occurred while I was a patient in the R.A.F. hospital at Halton.

I was admitted to hospital on the 20th March, 1944, after a sudden deterioration in the chronic eczema of the ears from which I had been suffering for many years. I had been repeatedly told that the basic cause of my troubles was nervous strain. The effects of the sudden and unwelcome publicity of a few weeks earlier, my resentment over the nationalisation transaction and my severe internal conflict about the surrender of my shares, undoubtedly played havoc with an already overstrained nervous system. However, while in hospital, I didn't drop my work entirely, and I received quite a number of official visitors.

Early in May I was transferred to the R.A.F. Officers' Convalescent Hospital at Cleveleys, near Blackpool, but my doctor there thought that X-ray treatment should be tried and this could be done much more conveniently at Halton, and so I was transferred back on June 11th a few days after D-Day.

(I remember being very surprised indeed to hear the news of the successful landing on the coast of Normandy on the 6th June, 1944, because that day had been particularly stormy at Cleveleys with high seas, and it seemed unlikely that the weather in the Channel could be sufficiently different for a successful amphibious operation to be possible.)

For a time my condition seemed to deteriorate, and for a few days in the middle of July my doctor placed a complete ban on visitors. I recovered sufficiently to be allowed out occasionally at the end of the month, and was discharged at the end of August.

Two days after leaving hospital, I learned that I had been promoted to temporary Air Commodore with effect from 1st July. This was very welcome news in view of the indications I had received that promotion was unlikely until my Service experience had covered a wider field.

CHAPTER 51

During 1944 the tempo of engine development greatly increased, and the volume of work done was far too extensive to be recorded in any detail here. Power Jets, the Rolls-Royce Barnoldswick factory and the de Havilland Engine Company continued to be the main contributors.

The nationalisation of Power Jets in April did not greatly affect the engine development programme during that year. The emphasis was on the development of the W.2/700, on which there was fairly satisfactory progress. One of these engines completed 100 hours' endurance running in January at a thrust rating of 1,800 lb. A thrust of 2,130 lb. was achieved with another, which was fitted with the improved type of compressor casing which had already given good results on a W.2.B. and the W.2/500. This engine also gave the lowest specific fuel consumption recorded up to that time, namely, 1.042 lb. per hour per pound of thrust. Thus, in the three years since the flight trials of the E.28, we had achieved a reduction of about 30% in specific fuel consumption.

Two W.2/700 engines were installed for flight test in one of the prototype Meteors during April, and flight testing was also done in the E.28 and in the tail of the Wellington flying test bed during the year.

One of the W.2/700 engines was fitted with lengthened turbine blades. It gave a thrust of 2,290 lb. (December, 1944).

There was a substantial amount of useful work on the W.2/500, but much of this was in the nature of secondary development. A speed of 476 m.p.h. was achieved with the E.28 powered by a W.2/500. At first the occurrence of compressor surging at high altitude limited the performance of the aeroplane, but after a slight modification the E.28 was able to reach heights of the order of 43,000 feet without any sign of surging. It still had a rate of climb of 1,000 feet per minute at that height, but could not go higher because the cockpit was not pressurised.

By the end of the year, work on the W.2/500 had virtually ceased. One of the two remaining engines was used for training purposes at the Gas Turbine School which Power Jets (R. & D.) had formed at Lutterworth.

Miscellaneous test work on the W.2.B. at Power Jets included running with petrol as fuel (early in the year)[49] and — during the latter half of 1944 — the development of thrust boosting by burning additional fuel in the exhaust after the turbine ("after burning").

At Barnoldswick the main development effort of Rolls-Royce was transferred from the W.2.B. and the B.26 to the B.37. There was still a very large amount of work on the W.2.B., some of it to supplement work on the B.37, but, as the W.2.B. was regarded as obsolescent, the chief aim was an increase of reliability at the 1,600 lb. thrust rating rather than attempts to increase the rating.

The first Meteor I's powered by Wellands (i.e. the production W.2.B.) were delivered to the R.A.F. in May, 1944. A unit known as the C.R.D. Flight had been formed at the Royal Aircraft Establishment under the command of Wing Commander Wilson. By June the C.R.D. Flight had received six Meteors and were putting in a considerable amount of flying time. A few weeks later these aircraft were transferred to 616 Squadron at Manston, for operation against the V.1 flying bomb.

(I subsequently heard that the first flying bomb to be "killed" by a Meteor was dealt with in most unorthodox fashion. The pilot, Flying Officer Dean, found that his guns had jammed and so he flew alongside the V.1 and tilted it over with his wing tip until it went out of control. The wing tip of this Meteor has been preserved as a souvenir by the Gloster Aircraft Company.)

Some idea of the volume of the work done by Rolls-Royce is given by the fact that by July the total flight and bench running of engines passed the 10,000 hour mark, and by November 10,000 hours of bench running alone had been completed. In the course of this, the reliability of the W.2.B. engines had been improved steadily, so that by August the time between overhauls for engines in operational aircraft was increased to 150 hours. During September one W.2.B. completed 500 hours, endurance running on the bench, with only minor component changes in the course of it.

The work on the B.37 at Barnoldswick and that on the W.2/700 at Whetstone was both co-operative and competitive. At Power Jets we still hoped that the W.2/700 would be selected for production, but the course of development on the two engines was so closely parallel that there was little to choose between them. Both were giving much the same thrust and had the same overall diameter. The W.2/700 was a little lighter, had a distinctly lower fuel consumption, and could be installed in the Meteor without modification to the aircraft, but against this the B.37 offered more scope for subsequent development and so eventually went into production as the Derwent 1.

The first production engine (as distinct from development engines) was produced in October, 1944. By that date Rolls-Royce had a new production factory in operation at Newcastle-under-Lyme, headed by Mr. J. P. Herriot, who, prior to this appointment, had been chiefly responsible for the development work on engines at Barnoldswick under Dr. Hooker. However, though the W.2/700 did not go into production, the work on it was by no means wasted, because many of its design features were incorporated in the Rolls-Royce engines.

During the year, de Havilland's put the Goblin (H.1) firmly on the map. With the D.H.100 (Vampire) aircraft powered by this engine a speed of over 500 m.p.h. was achieved. This engine also was used in the first flights of the Lockheed P.80 in the U.S.A. (January, 1944). During the year there was steady progress towards a 3,000 lb. thrust rating for the Goblin.

This intensive development was, of course, not all plain sailing, but the troubles which accompanied the steady increase of performance and of running were relatively fewer than would have been encountered at a corresponding stage in piston engine development.

One highlight of 1944 was the manufacture and first testing of the engine known as the R.B.41. This was the prototype of the Rolls-Royce Nene. It was a product of the Barnoldswick team. Drawings of this engine were sent to the workshops in June, 1944; it was on the bench a little over four months later, and in November, 1944, a thrust of 4,500 lb. was achieved. In the following month it did a 50-hour run at a rating of 4,000 lb. for take-off and combat.

Jet development in Great Britain involved a second fatal accident in April when Mr. Crosby Warren, one of the Gloster test pilots, was killed in a prototype Meteor. This accident was not a consequence of engine failure.

The year 1944 was one of great activity in the turbo-jet field in Germany also. The Germans were desperately in need of high-performance fighters. The Allied bombing offensive both by day and night had reached a devastating intensity, and the enemy was thrown more and more on to the defensive. This acted as a great spur to their production of both turbo-jet and rocket-propelled aircraft. Soon, the Me.262 powered by Junkers 004 turbo-jet engines, and the rocket-propelled Me. 163, began to be a serious menace especially to the daylight bombing operations of the U.S. Army Air Force. The effectiveness of the Me.262 was well illustrated on one occasion when the Americans lost 32 out of a formation of 36 Flying Fortresses. There were a number of other occasions when the casualty rate was very heavy. For this reason the British Meteors were temporarily withdrawn from combat operations (the V.1 attack had in any case almost ceased, because of the advance of the Allied Armies through France and the R.A.F's bombing attacks on the launching sites) and used in tactical trials with British-based American bomber and fighter formations in an effort to evolve defensive tactics against the Me.262 during daylight bombing operations. Lockheed P.80s and Bell P.59As were used for similar tactical trials in the U.S.A. In Wing Commander H. J. Wilson's report on trials in Britain he commented:

> Results of these trials must have proved very depressing to the Americans with their existing aircraft, as it would appear that the Meteors could sail in as and when they pleased, each destroying two or three Forts, and pull away without the escorting fighters (even Mustangs) being able to do very much about it.

He concluded that the only answer to the enemy jet aircraft was a long-range escort jet fighter.

CHAPTER 52

When Power Jets (R. & D.) Ltd., was formed, the personnel and plant of the old Power Jets and of the Gas Turbine Section of the R.A.E. at Pyestock were amalgamated. Constant, formerly the head of Pyestock, became the Chief of the Engineering Division of the whole organisation. I was Chief Technical Adviser to the Board. Because of poor health my contact with day-to-day development was much less close than hitherto, and I was chiefly concerned with future projects.

Since the terms of reference of Power Jets (R. & D.) covered the application of the gas turbine outside the aeronautical field, our design work included two marine gas turbine projects, one intended for a motor torpedo boat and the other for a frigate.

Work on sundry aircraft projects continued, but for reasons which I shall give later, none of them came to fruition.[50]

By the end of 1944 the course of the war was moving so obviously in favour of the Allies — Italy had capitulated some time before — that any project work then in progress was unlikely to contribute to the war effort. This partly accounted for a general reduction in the enthusiasm and drive which had formerly characterised the work of the Power Jets' team, but there was also little doubt that nationalisation resulted in a serious drop in morale. This was probably aggravated by a sharp cleavage between those like Constant and the Pyestock team of engineers, who were content to regard the organisation primarily as a research establishment, and others, like myself and the pioneer team which I had recruited, who still hoped that the Government Company would retain its dominant position as engine designers. It was a great pity that Constant and I, who had worked in harmony for so many years, should find ourselves at variance when we had to work together in the same organisation.

I personally felt that my usefulness within the organisation had virtually come to an end, but I took no steps to make a break at that time, because I was fairly sure that any such move would be followed by the resignation of a number of other engineers, and I did not wish to expose myself to the charge of breaking up the Government Company.

It was a depressing experience to see the pioneer team losing heart, and this at a time when the hesitation and doubt which had hampered the development in earlier years was rapidly being dissipated. Thus, during a four-day visit to the Rolls-Royce factories, Hooker told me that Hives had decided that Rolls-Royce quite definitely intended to switch over from piston engines to gas turbines, and that future development work on piston engines would be very limited, if not stopped altogether. I gathered that the Chief of the Air Staff had also indicated that the R.A.F. would be going over almost entirely to jet engine fighters. These things may not sound very dramatic in the light of present-day developments, but at the time they were of great significance and denoted a revolutionary change in outlook.

In January, 1945, I was invited to become a member of the Board of Power Jets (R. & D.) and, with the sanction of the Air Council, I accepted. I did so in the hope that I would regain some of my former influence on engineering policy. I believe that Roxbee Cox and other members of the Board also hoped for this and that it was the primary object underlying the invitation.

I had not been invited to be a member of the Board when the Government Company was first formed, partly because I was in hospital at the time and partly because there was then some doubt as to whether a serving officer would be allowed to act in such a capacity.

The Minister had appointed an Advisory Committee whose function was to advise the Board of Power Jets (R. & D.) and the Ministry on the activities of the Company, and to ensure the co-ordination of the Company's work with other gas turbine work in Britain. This committee was given the somewhat cumbersome title of The Gas Turbine Technical Advisory and Co-ordinating Committee. Roxbee Cox was the chairman and W. E. P. Johnson was secretary. The aircraft industry was represented by Hives of Rolls-Royce, Halford of de Havilland's and Rowbotham of Bristol's. The B.T-H. and Metropolitan Vickers were represented in the persons of H. N. Sporborg and K. Baumann. There were also a number of M.A.P. and Admiralty representatives. I also was a member, but I was not present at the first two meetings, again because I was in hospital.

Internally, a Technical Policy Committee was formed — I was a member of this also.

The meetings of the Technical Policy Committee were often the occasions of serious disagreement between those led by Constant, who believed that the organisation should concentrate primarily on feeding the industry with research information, and those who felt, as I did, that the emphasis should continue to be on the design and development of prototype engines up to, but not including, the production stage. For a time it seemed that I might have my way, even to the point of obtaining a substantial expansion of capacity to enable the Company to make sufficient numbers of engines to provide a "feed" for the development of production methods. Proposals along these lines were approved by the Technical

Policy Committee, and subsequently by the Board, and were then submitted to the M.A.P., and again for a time it seemed as though the Ministry would authorise the extension of capacity, because at a meeting in C.R.D's office on the 14th March, it was generally agreed that the Company needed the increase in capacity for which it was asking. But at this point certain members of the G.T.T.A.C.C. showed their hand, and brought pressure to bear on the M.A.P. to change the terms of reference in such a way as to prevent the Company from any activity which they regarded as competitive with industry.

In the view of Roxbee Cox, myself and others, an undertaking, given by a Government spokesman in the House of Lords that Power Jets (R. & D.) would not compete with industry, was meant to imply that the Company would not engage in quantity production and sell engines in competition with industry. However, the representatives of the Aircraft industry on the G.T.T.A.C.C. argued that if Power Jets were permitted to design and build prototype engines they would be competing with industry.

The third meeting of the G.T.T.A.C.C. was held on the 18th April, 1945, and it was at this meeting that Hives and others made it quite clear that in their view it should be no part of the Company's function to design and build even prototype engines. The representatives of the aircraft firms received support from one or two other members of the committee, notably Sporborg and Baumann. The way in which this discussion was brought up (under an item of the agenda concerned with test facilities) gave the Power Jets' representatives the very strong impression that several members of the committee had previously reached agreement to take concerted action. The degree to which these members wished to restrict the activities of Power Jets was most clearly shown when Halford asked if Power Jets, acting as consultants, would design an engine for a firm if requested to do so. Roxbee Cox replied that if the pressure of other work did not preclude it, the Company would be prepared to furnish a general arrangement drawing. Several members then indicated that in their view any such action would be competitive. Lockspeiser, the Chief Scientist of the M.A.P., put it to these members: "Your case is that if Power Jets make a complete engine they are in competition?" Halford replied "Yes".

When it became clear that M.A.P. officials were tending to side with the industry on this subject, and showed it by a reversal of attitude about the provision of capacity for batch manufacture, I resigned from the committee. The writing on the wall was painfully plain.

At this point I was so disgusted with the course of events that I had lost all desire to remain associated with the Government Company. I made this clear to Roxbee Cox and other members of the Board on a number of occasions. The only thing which restrained me from a complete break was that I was still unwilling to risk exposing myself to the charge of being responsible for the disintegration of the pioneer team, though I knew that unless there was a reversal of policy it was only a matter of time before the team broke up in any case. It was obvious to me that, like myself, such people as Walker, Cheshire, McLeod, Fielden, Ogston, Voysey, Bone and many other members of the original pioneer company would not tolerate a situation in which *those who had founded an industry were deprived of the right to design and make experimental engines.*

As time passed and proposals for new and more restrictive terms of reference passed back and forth, it became increasingly clear that the view of M.A.P. officials was that, if the Company were to undertake engine design at all, then the engines concerned must incorporate bigger steps into the unknown than those normally undertaken by industry, and that batch production (for development of production methods) was out of the question. These vague and woolly suggestions, that Power Jets should confine themselves to pipe dreams which might possibly lead to practical engines around the year A.D. 2000, left me quite cold. I could see that if we became engaged in long and probably unsuccessful struggles with very long-term gambles, while the rest of industry was grinding out successful engines, we would soon lose our engineering reputations, probably be accused of wasting public money, and risk having our earlier work discredited. Perhaps that was what was desired by some. Others just didn't know what they were talking about.

The unconditional surrender of Germany on May 8th, 1945, did not have any immediate effect on the Company's work, nor did the General Election of July 26th, which resulted in a large Labour majority.

One would have expected that a Government Company which was fighting a losing battle with industry would have found its position greatly strengthened by the advent of a Labour Government. At first there seemed to be some hope of this for, when Roxbee Cox had a talk with the new Minister of Supply and Aircraft Production, Mr. John Wilmot, on the 22nd August, he reported that the Minister had agreed that it was undesirable to take any step which might prejudice the possibility of the Company's engines being made use of later by the R.A.F. or by civil airlines. The Minister had also said that industry would have to accustom itself in future to a certain degree of State competition. Nevertheless, if these were the views of the Minister he was not successful in making them effective, and the permanent officials of the Ministry continued their opposition to the Company's designing and making new engines.

CHAPTER 53

Despite the decline of Power Jets as a development organisation, 1945 was an important year of progress in the history of British aircraft gas turbine development.

Even at Power Jets, in spite of the discouraging trend of policy, there were some noteworthy achievements. By March, 1945, the manufacture of W.2/700 engines was running at the rate of 30 complete engines per year, with additional parts equivalent to about another 15 engines per year. I very much doubt whether any other firm could have shown an output in proportion to manpower as favourable as ours. Moreover, we were not relying on sub-contractors to the same degree as Rolls-Royce and the other firms. We were making all our own sheet-metal components and most of the fuel-system components, whereas the other firms were relying on Messrs. Joseph Lucas and other sub-contractors for such work. We depended on sub-contractors only for such things as castings, forgings, and other raw material supplies, and such proprietary auxiliaries as fuel pumps, governors and so on.

Much valuable development work was done on the W.2/700 both on the bench and in the air. During April, 1945, one W.2/700 completed a 100-hour test at a rating of 2,200 lb. Also during the year a modified version of it achieved a thrust of 2,500 lb. This really represented the peak of the main line of engine development at Power Jets. *In the four years which had elapsed since the W.1 did its flight trials, we had nearly trebled the thrust without any increase in size and only about 70% increase in weight, and all this was accompanied by a very great improvement in the specific fuel consumption.*

Another important item of Power Jets' work was the continued development of exhaust re-heat for temporary thrust boosting. This work, which had been initiated by the Pyestock team, was carried out both on the bench and in the air with the W.2/700 and Rolls-Royce Derwent 1.

At Power Jets the year was marred by tragedy. Our Chief Test Pilot, Squadron Leader Moffat, was killed while demonstrating a Meteor, powered by Derwent 1's, to the employees and their families during a Gala Day held near Whetstone. We never knew what caused the accident, because the aircraft struck the ground at extremely high speed and was disintegrated to an extent which made it impossible to deduce the cause from examination of the wreckage. According to eyewitnesses, the aeroplane was doing a normal upward roll when it suddenly started to flick round in a most unusual manner and then went into an inverted dive from which it never recovered.

Throughout the year de Havilland's continued their intensive development of the Goblin (i.e. the H.1) and of the Vampire. With this aircraft they achieved a speed of 547 m.p.h. at a height of 20,000 feet during April, 1945. During July, with the Goblin, they were the first to complete a Service Type Test. This was done at a rating of 3,000 lb. thrust. They were also in the early stages of development of the more powerful Ghost engine, for which the target was 5,000 lb. thrust.

But it was Rolls-Royce who made the most striking contributions to progress during 1945. In January, a 100-hour test at 4,000 lb. rating was completed with the Nene; the following month a thrust of 5,000 lb. was achieved with this engine,[51] and before the year ended a 100-hour test was completed with the Nene at the 5,000 lb. rating.

At Rolls-Royce, 1945 also saw the early phases of the Clyde and the start of the design of the Avon. The Clyde was a propeller turbine which had a number of novel features, while the Avon was a turbo-jet engine with an axial flow compressor with 6,500 lb. thrust as the target. The Clyde was subsequently abandoned. This, I think, was rather a pity because, in my view, it had a number of features which offered great scope for development.[52]

But of the many achievements of Rolls-Royce during 1945, by far the most outstanding was the intensive development of the Derwent V, which ultimately became the standard power plant of the Meteor IV, and which enabled Britain to establish a new world speed record of 606 m.p.h. with a Meteor IV on November 7th — less than one year after the design of the engine began. For the air-speed record the engine was rated at 3,600 lb. thrust.

During October, 1945, I flew a jet aeroplane for the first time myself — this was a Meteor I powered by two Power Jets' W.2/700 engines. Strictly speaking, I should not have done so without C.R.D.'s permission and, in fact, I did not intend to do so when I climbed into the cockpit — or at least I don't think I did! On the morning of the 19th October I went to our airfield at Bruntingthorpe to make one of my periodic visits of inspection. I felt a sudden urge to do some taxying tests in the Meteor. After some twenty minutes of this I returned to Whetstone, but returned to Bruntingthorpe again after lunch. After two flights in a Tiger Moth, I decided to do some more taxying tests. By this time I had acquired a familiarity with the cockpit layout and with the feel of the aeroplane up to take-off speed, and so yielded to an irresistible impulse to take off. I landed after a few minutes at very modest speeds.

I derived intense satisfaction from the experience, partly because, having had only about two hours' flying practice on elementary training types during the preceding twelve months, I had found myself much more at home in the aeroplane than I had expected, and partly because this particular Meteor was powered by W.2/700 engines designed and made by Power Jets. The occasions when an engine designer has piloted an aeroplane powered by his own engines must have been very few since the Wright Brothers' first flights in 1903.

Three days later I flew the Meteor again. This time the duration of the flight was 45 minutes and I essayed much greater speeds and heights than on the first occasion. I was very much impressed with the simplicity of the controls, the complete absence of vibration, and the excellent visibility from the cockpit, in which respect it was far superior to anything I had previously flown.

I had an even more exhilarating experience while I was at Herne Bay in connection with the attempt on the High Speed Record. At the request of a public relations officer of the Ministry of Supply, I flew a Meteor III up and down the High Speed Course. At the time this request was made, I was still suffering from the effects of a Rolls-Royce party at Margate the evening before, so I agreed with some misgiving and with the mental reservation that I might cancel at the last moment, but by the time I reached the airfield at Manston I felt completely recovered and so took off.

The High Speed Course was clearly marked by a line of buoys spaced a few hundred yards from the low cliffs which border the Thames estuary east of Herne Bay. Herne Bay Pier marked the western end of the course.

Approaching from the eastern end, I dived down to the beginning of the course from a height of about 1,500 feet, pushing the throttles wide open as I did so. I levelled out at a height of about fifty feet and covered the three kilometres in about fifteen seconds. I then climbed, did a wide turn and repeated the procedure from the opposite direction. Visibility was extremely good and I felt only slight bumps as I made my two runs, and I was therefore rather puzzled as to why a decision had been made not to attempt the record on that day. I never knew what my speed was, because at that height I deemed it unwise to do other than use my eyes to see where I was going, but I assume that it must have been about 450 m.p.h., as this was the maximum speed of the Meteor III with Derwent 1 engines.

When I returned home a few days later I failed to impress my younger son, then nearly eleven. When he asked me "What speed did you do, Daddy?" and I replied "About 450 m.p.h. I should think", his disappointed comment was "What! only 450!" The day following he told a friend of the family: "He only did 450 you know, and they will do 600 — he must be out of practice!"

I missed the successful High Speed Record attempt itself, because of a lecture engagement in Swansea. Two Meteor IV's were used, flown by Wing Commander Wilson and Mr. Eric Greenwood; the former beating the latter by a small margin.

CHAPTER 54

After the collapse of Germany many British and American technicians were sent to Germany to investigate and report on German work in the gas turbine field. Amongst these were several engineers from Power Jets. The Ministry had wished me to go, but as I was unwell at the time I was excused.

The reports of these visits revealed that the Germans had indeed made great progress in many forms of jet propulsion, but while they had extended their efforts into a much broader field than ours, their numerous lines of research and development had suffered from lack of co-ordination — not to mention interference by Allied bombing.

According to the records, the first jet aircraft to fly in Germany or any other country was the Heinkel He.178. This little single seater flew on August 27th, 1939 — nearly two years before the Gloster Whittle E.28/39. This fact is often emphasised by those who derive pleasure from decrying British achievement, but there was a difference of great significance between the flights of the He.178 and the E.28. The German aircraft made one flight of ten minutes only and never flew again. What happened on that one flight — whether the aircraft landed safely or crashed — I have never been able to find out. No other German jet aircraft flew before the E.28, so far as I know.

I cannot, of course, make the definite claim that the German work stemmed from my first patent which was published throughout the world in 1932, but it is a fact that German technical journals published several of my patent drawings in the pre-war years.

The type of turbo-jet engine used in the He.178, similar in many ways to Power Jets' engines, was not further developed, and thereafter the Germans concentrated entirely on the type of engine using an axial flow compressor. They put two types into production, namely, the Junkers 004 and the B.M.W.003 — both in the 2,000 lb. thrust class.

A Junkers 004 engine was shipped to Power Jets for test, and we were able to verify what we had long suspected — that the quality and performance of the German engines was far inferior to our own. For example, the specific fuel consumption of the Junkers 004 was nearly 40% greater than that of the W.2/700. Its life between overhauls was about 25 hours as compared with upwards of 125 hours with British engines in service, but, speaking as a pilot, its most serious drawback was its poor response to a rapid opening of the throttle. Indeed, any attempt at a rapid opening resulted in stalling of the compressor and serious overheating of the turbine. There is good reason to believe that this dangerous characteristic, plus the poor reliability of the engine, was responsible for many fatal accidents with the Me.262. If a pilot is balked in an attempt to land, and his engine fails to respond to a rapid opening of the throttle control, the consequences are often disastrous. It is said that one unit lost twenty-three pilots in three months in accidents.

The Germans were, of course, handicapped by a shortage of the metals necessary for the manufacture of alloys with high creep resisting properties for turbine blades. This, in turn, was largely due to the success of the Allied economic blockade. It was in the quality of high temperature materials that the difference between the German and British engines was most marked. They attempted to compensate for their compulsory use of inferior materials by such devices as air cooling of the turbine blades.

There is no doubt that, of necessity, the Germans had embarked on quantity production long before they had reached a state of development which would have been considered satisfactory in Britain.

Though the German engines were undoubtedly greatly inferior to ours, very high speeds were achieved with the aircraft powered by them — again, because they had cut down on safety factors. They used far higher wing loadings than we were using at that time, and in consequence they had a high take-off and landing speed. A few months after the end of the war in Europe, one or two of the German aircraft were flown by R.A.E. test pilots at Farnborough. I was present on the occasion of a demonstration. Wing Commander A. E. Louks, whom I had known for many years and who a few months before had been appointed Ministry Overseer at Power Jets, was standing with me. When the Me.262 took off — taking almost the whole length of the runway and seeming to clear the trees in the far distance by only a few feet — Louks turned to me with a shudder and said "Now we know why Hitler wanted to extend the Third Reich!" A day or two later one of the R.A.E. test pilots was killed when flying a German type known as the Volksjaeger — the tail unit broke away through structural weakness.

CHAPTER 55

During 1945 I was called upon to give many lectures and attend a large number of public functions, at many of which I had to make speeches. Of the many lectures by far the most important were the First James Clayton Lecture of the Institution of Mechanical Engineers entitled "The Early History of the Whittle Jet Propulsion Gas Turbine" and an address to the Royal Institution. I spent a fair proportion of my time during many months on the preparation of the Clayton Lecture, but my trouble was well repaid because when I delivered the lecture on October 5th, 1945, the lecture hall of the Institution of Mechanical Engineers was packed and many had to be turned away. A repeat lecture was arranged in the larger hall of the Institution of Civil Engineers, and once again I had a packed audience. I was called upon to repeat the lecture at most of the regional branches of the Institution of Mechanical Engineers, and in nearly every case the demand for seats was far greater than the supply. I was subsequently awarded the Clayton Prize of the Institution of £1,000 in recognition of the pioneer work described in the paper.

On April 5th, 1945, I received the following letter from Sir Harold Scott who was then Secretary of the Ministry of Supply:

> I am directed by the Minister of Aircraft Production to inform you that consideration has been given to the granting of an ex gratia award to you for your inventive services in connection with internal combustion turbines and jet propulsion...
>
> It is appropriate that this question should be referred to the Royal Commission on Awards to Inventors, but as it will be

some time before the Commission is set up, and it is not possible to say when any particular claim will be dealt with, it has been thought fitting that an interim award should be offered to you.

As you will appreciate, it is necessary that nothing should be done which will limit the freedom of the Royal Commission to take their own view as to a proper award in the light of all the circumstances. An interim payment, also, should be assessed on a conservative judgment as to the view which the Commission may take, since there can be no question of reducing an interim award once it had been made, but particular difficulty is felt in forecasting the view which the Royal Commission may take in your case as the circumstances present unusual features.

Having such considerations in mind, it has been decided that an interim award of £10,000 may be made, and I enclose a cheque for this amount on the assumption that it will be agreeable to you to receive this sum now. Its acceptance will not prejudice your eventual claim in any way.

You will see from the enclosed copy of a letter from the Inland Revenue Department that this payment is not liable to tax. A similar exception would apply to any award which might be made to you by the Royal Commission.

The Minister desires me to take this opportunity of expressing his appreciation of the valuable services you have rendered to the Air Forces, and to aviation and engineering generally, and of the sense of public duty which has marked all the steps you have taken.

This letter has been written after consultation with the Air Council who wish to be associated with the Minister's expression of appreciation.

Naturally, this was very welcome, especially as, owing to my then state of health, I had a strong feeling of insecurity about the future.

CHAPTER 56

Ultimately, when I lost all hope that the Company would retain the right to design and develop engines and to continue development of production methods, I decided to resign from the Board.

My earlier fear that my resignation would precipitate general disintegration no longer deterred me. By the time I did resign there were clear signs that this break up was inevitable in any case. Indeed, it had already begun. Two key members of the original team had left the organisation the preceding October and they had been followed by three others a short time after. Throughout 1945 the unrest had been increasing, with a consequent serious deterioration of morale and reduction of output. The situation had become so bad by January 1946, that there was a virtual "revolt" on the 14th of that month when forty-five engineers refused to conform to a requirement that they should account for their time. As in most such situations, the reason given was really a symptom of much deeper causes of dissatisfaction. It was at this point that I felt there was nothing I could do to save the situation.

My letter of resignation, addressed to Roxbee Cox, dated 22nd January, 1946, read as follows:

> It is with much regret that I have to ask you to accept my resignation from the Board of Power Jets (R. & D.) Ltd.
>
> I am very sorry indeed to have to take this step, but I have come to the conclusion that I can no longer share the responsibility for the affairs of the company in circumstances so unfavourable to constructive effort, however able the members of the Board may be.

At the time I agreed to become a director of the company, I believed that in the then circumstances the directors had an impossible task to perform, but hoped for changes of a kind which would make success possible. However, the opposite has happened and the position is far worse now than it was then. One consequence is that the morale of the engineers has deteriorated to such a point that there seems little or no hope of keeping the pioneer team together within the present company. The enthusiasm vital to constructive work has evaporated, and the atmosphere of frustration which pervades the organisation has lowered efficiency to such a level that in no sense is the output commensurate with the expenditure.

I have been on the verge of taking this step for some time but have refrained hitherto, because it was represented to me that it would have extremely serious effects and that I would expose myself to the charge of wrecking the company. I now believe that my action will make little difference to the fate of the organisation.

The primary factor in the whole unfortunate situation is that the Power Jets' engineering team is largely built up of engineers who have an intense interest in doing a practical job of work, who desire to see their products used, who are only interested in research as a necessary ancillary to development and not as an end in itself, and who require the stimulus of a succession of fruitful short-term objectives. In short, the team is not suited to the present functions of the company. It is the right crew in the wrong ship. They feel that things have gone from bad to worse since 1940. Before the company was nationalised, there was strong resentment against the restriction of the functions of the old Power Jets to research and development. The team — the pioneers who had launched the aircraft gas turbine — regarded this as a grave injustice. Not only did they feel that their pioneer status entitled them to be provided with all the necessary facilities to carry the job through, but they also felt, rightly, that they were the most competent designers, which also entitled them to those facilities. Instead they were restricted to research and development, were compelled to hand over their technique to other firms, and had the mortification of seeing those other firms given a licence in design for which they were not qualified, and provided with facilities far greater than themselves.

Despite the handicaps under which the old company laboured, it preserved the technical lead until 1944 (though Rolls-Royce were becoming close challengers) and they were buoyed up by the hope that this fact would eventually receive appropriate recognition, but this hope was killed by the nationalisation of Power Jets — and Power Jets alone (the only company which had risked private money in the aircraft gas turbine). One faint hope lingered on in some, namely, that the structure and functions of a private company would be preserved, and that facilities would now be provided for the carrying out of functions from which the company had been hitherto restricted, and that the company would be allowed to operate on a self-supporting basis. This hope also died as it became clear that the company's initiative was to be further stifled and that the emphasis was to be placed more and more on the new company's functions as a research organisation. Moreover, there have been no compensating signs, despite the passage of nearly two years, that the company was really to be used as a central gas turbine establishment in the sense of being regarded as the principal authority in the United Kingdom in the gas turbine field. The company is never called into consultation by the Ministry of Aircraft Production in matters of engine specifications, etc., and when there are signs that (say) the Admiralty desires to make use of the organisation there is every indication that this will be resisted by M.A.P. officials.

The company has lost all real initiative. It does not own the capital equipment it uses, nor any funds with which work can be initiated at the sole discretion of the Board. It may not start an engine project without first receiving a contract from the

M.A.P., and these contracts are rarely forthcoming. When, after much labour, a carefully considered proposal is submitted it gets a lukewarm reception. We are told that it is the wrong size, or that it is not ambitious. That it is our duty to be 'two jumps ahead' of anybody else. In other words: 'We are expected to make an immense detour into desert regions where there is no practical stimulation to refresh the traveller.' Moreover, certain Ministry officials who have never been responsible for the design of a gas turbine, and for whose technical competence our engineers have very little respect, show a strong tendency to dictate the programme of work in the company. In short, the team finds itself with far less scope for initiative than it possessed many years ago, when the available facilities were very meagre. It is dominated both technically and financially by the M.A.P. It is in a position analogous to that of a very competent architect with only one customer who not only fails to specify his requirements but insists on telling the expert he employs how to do the job.

If the organisation is to carry out its function as a National gas turbine establishment many drastic changes will be required. Above all it would need to be freed from the dominance of one government department. I do not propose to enlarge on the other changes required, but, as I have indicated, above, a new team more suited to such an establishment would need to be built up. I personally doubt whether there are a sufficient number of individuals of the right type for this to be done.

I find myself in sympathy with the views of the majority of the engineers, and therefore do not regard myself as suited to head the engineering team of a research and development organisation of the type Power Jets is supposed to be. My forte is to direct a few large-scale projects towards a near and worth-while objective. I cannot arouse much interest in a myriad of small-scale and relatively unrelated experiments which end merely in a mass of reports.

Air Marshal Sir Alec Coryton had succeeded Air Marshal Sir Ralph Sorley as Controller of Research and Development a few weeks earlier. I wrote to Coryton on the 24th January, 1946, enclosing a copy of my letter of resignation and said:

> …for some time I have been very dissatisfied with the way things have been going. Despite my reputation and my qualifications (which I dare to claim are unequalled by anybody in the field of the aircraft gas turbine) it has never been more difficult than it is now for me to initiate and carry through a gas turbine project.
>
> When I wrote my letter of resignation I was aware that the Lord President's Council[53] had decided upon the conversion of the Company into a Government establishment, but I should explain that my action was not connected with that fact (though I should have regarded that as the culminating disaster in any event, in the sense that had things been otherwise going smoothly it would itself have meant the break-up of the old pioneer team).
>
> …my resignation from the Board of Power Jets does not necessarily entail that I cease to be attached to the organisation, and it would be possible for me to revert to the position I held before I joined the Board, i.e. Technical Adviser, but I do not think that this would be satisfactory from any point of view, and in any case, I feel that it is time to move on to a broader stage. I have already endured a subordinate role in this field for too long…

At the time of my resignation the argument about the revised terms of reference for the Government company had not been settled. Several members of the Board still felt much the same way as I did, and were still resisting the efforts of the industry and the Ministry to restrict the organisation's activities in the manner I have indicated, and this, I believe, was why the Government decided to solve the problem by converting the organisation into a research establishment generally similar to the R.A.E. This meant that the Board would be dissolved and those who remained in the organisation would become Civil Servants.

In a further letter to Coryton (dated 30th January, 1946), I said:

> What I have to say below is based on the assumption that the decision to have a central gas turbine organisation in the form of a government establishment is irrevocable.
>
> The purpose of this letter is to try and put more clearly the views I expressed to you orally at our talk on 25th January.
>
> Firstly, I believe that the administrative difficulties attached to converting Power Jets (R. & D.) Ltd. into a government establishment would be very great, and secondly, I am convinced that the majority of the engineers who constituted the old Power Jets team would not agree to stay with the new organisation. I therefore strongly recommend that the central gas turbine establishment be formed as a separate entity from Power Jets (R. & D.) Ltd., and that it should, as a start, take over from the latter the plant, equipment and personnel centred on Pyestock. (This could be done almost immediately.) If it were decided that Power Jets (R. & D.) Ltd., were to cease to exist eventually, the new establishment could take over such extra plant and equipment as it required by stages.
>
> I also strongly recommend that something should be done which will have the effect of keeping the old Power Jets' team together and engaged on gas turbine design and manufacture. That team is already breaking up (for reasons indicated in my letter dated 24th January, 1946, and enclosures) and if the process is to be arrested something drastic will have to be done. The cardinal requirement is that it must be made possible for them to design and make gas turbines for useful purposes, with the assurance that they will receive the credit

for their products. I suggest that the remnant of Power Jets (R. & D.) Ltd., after the central gas turbine establishment has been split off, should operate as a normal design and manufacturing company on a self-supporting basis. The self-supporting condition is one most essential for efficiency.

It does not seem to me to matter very greatly as to whether the company I propose is State owned or privately owned, as long as it is allowed to operate as a normal self-supporting competitive company, but I do think that an essential condition for such a company to hold its own, despite the fact that its competitive position has been severely prejudiced by the handing over of its design and technique in the past under Government compulsion, is that it should possess at least those patents which were owned by the old Power Jets before it was taken over. In other words, if it were to be a State company it would need to retain most of the assets of Power Jets (R. & D.) Ltd. If it were to be a privately owned company money would have to be raised to purchase back from the State the assets taken over from the old Power Jets.

I believe there is a strong tendency in many quarters to believe that it would not matter very much if the old Power Jets' team did break up. In my opinion it would be a disaster. With an engineering team the whole is far greater than the sum of its parts, and the Power Jets' team is a national asset which must not be allowed to go to waste. There seems to be a quite unjustified belief that there are a number of competent gas turbine design teams in the United Kingdom, but in fact only three teams have produced successful aircraft gas turbines so far, namely: Power Jets, Rolls-Royce and de Havilland. The others are floundering in development difficulties. I am willing to concede that the Rolls-Royce team led by Dr. Hooker is at least as good as the Power Jets' team, but even their achievements are based on a very considerable contribution from Power Jets. The latter did more than initiate the aircraft gas turbine. I do not think it would be an exaggeration to claim that 80% of the design features of the

Derwent V are of Power Jets' origin. Much of the manufacturing technique derives from Power Jets, and so on. Very much the same is true of the most successful American developments.

I would not guarantee that any action of the kind indicated above would now suffice to hold the team together, but at least the attempt ought to be made.

Sir Alec Coryton replied in a letter dated 27th February and said my suggestions had received most careful and sympathetic consideration, and then went on:

...we share fully your desire that the team of workers should remain as a team on gas turbine work, and we hope that, despite your fears to the contrary, they will in fact remain. But the suggestion that Power Jets (R. & D.) Ltd. should remain as a normal design and manufacturing Company is, we feel, hardly practicable.

As you yourself say, such a Company would have to be self-supporting, and it is perhaps not for me to express an opinion as to whether the necessary capital would be forthcoming. Even, however, if it were, the requirements of the Government establishment in the way of capital facilities would have to take precedence and this would mean that, *inter alia*, the Whetstone premises would not be available for the new Company. Moreover, as you are doubtless aware, the Department and the Board of the Company have both reached the conclusion, independently of each other, that it is desirable to keep the present Company in existence for the purpose of holding and exploiting patents.

In these circumstances the position as we see it is that your suggestion could be carried into effect only by the formation of an entirely new Company, backed by sufficient resources to enable it to set up in fresh premises and to acquire afresh the necessary plant and equipment.

In the event, Power Jets (R. & D.) remained in being as a small patent holding Company, while the manufacturing and experimental resources of Whetstone and Pyestock and the Flight Testing Unit at Bruntingthorpe were taken over by the National Gas Turbine Establishment.

While these exchanges were going on, I made one or two unsuccessful attempts to obtain financial support for the formation of a new private Company, but a draft of a letter to Coryton, which was not sent, indicates that by 5th March, 1946, I had given up hope of this. In this same draft I recorded a further expression of my feelings as follows:

> To me what has happened is little short of a tragedy, and it would be difficult to find words to express my feelings on the subject. The engineering team which launched the aircraft gas turbine has been progressively bludgeoned into ineffectiveness. By virtue of their achievements and quality, no team in this field had a greater right to carry on doing the work for which it was most fitted, yet their reward is bitterness and resentment. The situation is particularly painful for me, because the individuals concerned put such faith in me that they believed that I had sufficient prestige to arrest the deterioration in their status which has been imposed upon them during the past few years.
>
> Even if the team did stay together under the new arrangement, they would have only a fraction of their one-time effectiveness because they are depressed and uninspired by their new functions. However, I would not myself regard it as important that they should remain together once the spirit has gone out of them…

CHAPTER 57

The break up I had foreseen occurred a week or two later.

Some sixteen key members of the original pioneer team resigned *en bloc*, leaving only Wing Commander Lees and one or two others of those who had formed the backbone of Power Jets since 1940. Those who resigned were quickly snapped up by other firms, but only one or two went to the aircraft industry. The majority joined heavy engineering firms such as the English Electric, Messrs. John Brown, Parsons, Ruston Hornsby and other firms who were beginning work on industrial and marine gas turbine projects.

Some argued that there was no real loss to the nation in the break up because what Power Jets lost, other firms gained, but I have always felt that a very valuable thing was lost when the team dispersed. I think there are very few former members of that team who would not agree with me. I believe it is true to say that very few of them indeed have found themselves in surroundings as congenial to creative work as those they knew in Power Jets in spite of all the frustration.

Since the break up I have had remarkable proof of the strength of the team spirit, and of the nostalgia which the majority of my former colleagues feel for the old Power Jets' days. When the break up occurred the members of the old pioneer team formed an association known as "The Reactionaries"[54] to meet annually at a dinner held on the Saturday nearest to April 12th — the anniversary of the first run of the first experimental engine in 1937. It is a source of great satisfaction to me to be able to record that, up to the time of writing, there has always been a remarkably large attendance, usually of the order of 50 to 60, some making long journeys for the purpose.

The reasons for the downfall of Power Jets were many and complex. A great deal of what lay behind it all was not known to me. A careful inquiry would be necessary to establish the whole truth. Some have suggested that I was responsible for the break up of the team, but I hope the foregoing record will prove that, on the contrary, I sought every means of delaying that break up. Again, in one official document it was suggested that my refusal to compromise on the matter of manufacture precipitated the crisis. This I also deny. I had never at any time desired that Power Jets should include within its functions quantity production, in the sense that this is carried out by a normal manufacturing firm. What I had tried to do was to restore Power Jets' former lead in all branches of gas turbine technology including the development of manufacturing technique. For this latter purpose I had wished that the Company should manufacture sufficient numbers of development engines to put new production methods to the test of practice. There was nothing unreasonable in this, and indeed, in my view, Power Jets had clearly established a moral right to include this as one of its functions because, as the technical history shows, not only had Power Jets pioneered engine development itself, but had also contributed more to the evolution of special production methods than all the rest of the firms put together.

Powerful forces had operated against the Power Jets' team from 1940 onwards, and it would have gone under many years earlier if it had not, despite severe handicaps, proved its technical excellence. Many individuals contributed to what happened — they included Government officials and influential individuals in industry — and for many different motives. There were those who definitely desired the suppression of Power Jets for commercial reasons; there were those who wanted to ensure the survival of Power Jets, but in the form of a research organisation; there were those who wished to discredit the principle of a Government Company for political reasons, but their actions, whether for good or bad motives, all contributed to the same end.

At the time of the break up, it was a striking and significant fact that, though the Company's functions had always been restricted to research and development, only Rolls-Royce and de Havilland's had put more jet engines into the air than Power Jets. Indeed, no other firm had yet equalled Power Jets' record for the number of *types* of engine which had powered experimental aircraft (W.1, W.1.A., W.2.B., W.2/500 and W.2/700).

Another striking paradox is that a Government Company was virtually smothered to death while a Labour Government was in office.

Of the many causes which contributed to the break up of the team, I believe that the most important was the attempt to force its members into a type of work, namely, pure research, for which they were temperamentally unsuited. Their reactions to the research "straitjacket" were very aptly summarised by one of the leading members in a document from which the quotation in my letter of resignation was taken. This document contained other pithy comments which are well worth repeating:

> Productive development was to be deprecated and neurasthenic intensive research to be the key to heaven… The best research is not very amenable to organisation. The Faradays, Maxwells and Einsteins do that which they must do or burn internally. The best researchers are best because of

their utter absorption. In contrast, the inventors — the Edisons, Stevensons and Parsons — are more realistic and live close to, if a trifle in front of, their generation … the sanest, healthiest and most productive method, in the short or long run, is to start a vigorous intensive *development* programme with an overlapping series of short-term programmes, so that whilst there is a decent amount of foresight, there is stimulation by virtue of the nearness of the next objective in line… An organisation which claims to do development *must* do research; an organisation which claims to do research (only) is merely a harbour for cranks, inefficient people, people who are afraid of life, and misfits… A Government institution which does not control *the whole and all-related fields* finds itself in competition with other companies, whether or not it wishes such a state of affairs, and a trawl net for sifting personnel is established… The combination of research minds and civil servants' minds then can have various results. Near, desirable, motivating ideals are amputated and distant targets too far off to cause worry about Reckoning Day are substituted… There is no production, little testing, no enthusiasm; ability is measured in length and abstruseness of reports … airy fairy schemes grow like toadstools on decaying matter… The good old Governmental rule of 'never sack an inefficient man' is being applied. Personnel must be moved round or promoted if inefficient in their jobs… The saddest thing about the policies of this emasculated Company is not the things which it has done but the things which it has not done — the engines which might have been… Meanwhile, others drive on piling up a vast mass of experience and new ideas. For us, necessity is no longer the mother of invention — we must research with no other stimulation than very long-range dreams, which are a poor substitute for healthy foresight. There are too many dreams for an organisation ten times our size, and it is the writer's opinion that time will see most of our projects melt quietly away. This will not stop more projects for the still further

> future, and they, in turn, will melt away as Reckoning Day draws near.

Though I was not in entire agreement with all the views expressed in this document, there was not much I would have wished to have toned down.

EPILOGUE

After my resignation from the Board of Power Jets I remained nominally attached to the organisation for a few weeks, but on my return to England from a short lecture tour in Holland and Belgium I was informed that my post had been disestablished on the 25th May, 1946 — this was, of course, a consequence of the formation of the National Gas Turbine Establishment (though Power Jets (R. & D.) Limited remained in being, it was shorn of all its manufacturing facilities and all but a very small nucleus of personnel). I was thus temporarily without official employment.

I was not the only one to find myself without a job. Williams and Tinling ceased to have any further connection with either the N.G.T.E. or Power Jets (Research and Development) Limited. (Johnson, by virtue of his extensive patent knowledge, became the Managing Director of what was left of Power Jets (R. & D.) Ltd.)

The break up of the old team was a tragedy for most of us, but particularly for Williams and Tinling, who, though they had taken a leading part in building up the plant and personnel of Power Jets over the preceding ten years, suddenly found themselves deprived of their chief interest in life. There is no shadow of doubt that but for their initiative in 1935 my work would never have taken practical shape. There is equally no doubt that they were primarily responsible for bringing into being the Whetstone Factory. They also carried the greater part of the administrative load throughout the time during which Power Jets expanded from nothing to an organisation of about 1,300 strong. I sincerely hope that if this record does nothing else, it will make clear the magnitude of the debt which the nation owes to these two men.

When the N.G.T.E. was formed, Roxbee Cox was appointed Director and Wing Commander Lees and Constant were appointed Deputy Directors.

For a time the Air Ministry did not know what to do with me, and I was in danger of reverting to the rank of Group Captain and being placed on the supernumerary list. On the day (3rd June) that I was warned of this possibility, I had a talk with Mr. R. B. Williams Thompson, Chief Information Officer of the Ministry of Supply and Aircraft Production.[55] When I told him that I was likely to be an unemployed Group Captain, he was horrified and said he would take the matter up at once with the Minister, Mr. John Wilmot. He acted so swiftly that later the same day the Minister spoke to me on the telephone and offered me the post of Technical Adviser on Engine Design and Production to the Controller of Supplies (Air). I accepted.

During the remainder of 1946 I did two lecture tours in the U.S.A. and paid a short visit to Paris, also in connection with lectures. The first of the tours in the U.S.A. was very long, and in the course of it I covered eighteen major cities and included a large number of factory visits and technical conferences.

I was rather unwise in agreeing to a second visit to the U.S.A. before I had recovered from the strain of the earlier one, and my health broke down before I had completed the programme of the second tour. In consequence, Air Chief Marshal Sir Guy Garrod, head of the R.A.F. Delegation in the U.S.A., arranged for me to have a month's sick leave in Bermuda. Unfortunately, this did not prove sufficient and I became a patient in the U.S. Naval Hospital at Bethesda (near Washington) for over two months.

After my discharge from hospital in March, 1947, and a further short period of leave, I paid a short lecture visit to Canada. Shortly after my return to England, my health deteriorated again and I had to go to hospital once more, and remained there until shortly before Christmas, 1947.

Early in 1948 the question of my retirement became the subject of much discussion. In a friendly talk with the Chief of the Air Staff, Lord Tedder, on the 13th April, we agreed that retirement was the best course in the circumstances.

Throughout these discussions I received the utmost consideration both from the Ministry of Supply officials concerned and from the Air Council. The Air Council in particular were most anxious to avoid any impression that I had been "dropped" by my Service.

The Ministry of Supply proposed that on my retirement I should take a post as a temporary civil servant in the Ministry at a salary which, with my R.A.F. pension, would leave my financial position substantially unchanged. This was quite a generous gesture, because the purpose of it was purely to provide a "cushion" between my retirement and the taking up of a post in industry suitable to my qualifications, and thus free me from the need to feel rushed into taking another post for financial reasons.

Fortunately, I was relieved from all immediate need to worry about my financial position when, in May, 1948, the Ministry of Supply and the Treasury accepted a recommendation of the Royal Commission on Awards to Inventors that I should receive an ex gratia award of £100,000 free of tax.

In view of the misunderstanding there has been on the subject from time to time, I wish to emphasise that I was not a claimant before the Royal Commission. What happened was that the Ministry of Supply, having decided that a further award was to be made, formally requested the Royal Commission to go outside their terms of reference as such, examine my case, and make a recommendation. Lord Justice Cohen, the Chairman, agreed. The case was prepared on my behalf by the late E. L. Pickles and other Ministry officials.

During my absences on lecture tours in U.S.A., Canada and in hospital, I heard little or nothing of what was going on, and so the sudden turn of events in May, 1948, came as a very welcome surprise. It was not until after I had received the award that I learned of some of the steps which led up to it. One of these was a letter written by Roxbee Cox, dated 2nd October, 1947, at the request of Mr. P. H. Goffey of the Patents Branch of the Ministry of Supply.

This letter, which no doubt had a very considerable influence on the course of events, read as follows:

> You have asked me for an appraisal of the work of Frank Whittle. It seems to me a little strange that in this year of Grace after so many people, including myself, have defined the major contribution to progress which Whittle has made, and after so many learned and professional bodies have given him their major awards, any appraisal is necessary. However, I will do my best to sum up the Whittle achievement once again.
>
> I think you are aware that jet propulsion is one of the most direct illustrations of a fundamental law of nature — Newton's Third Law — and has been recognised by man since at least 150 B.C., when an engineer with the somewhat flamboyant name of Hero made proposals for its employment in an engine.
>
> The gas turbine also is not new. The first design recognisable as a gas turbine was patented by John Barber in 1791. Thereafter there was only very slow progress in gas turbine technology until the present century. It is generally

accepted that progress was delayed by the lack of material suitable for continuous operation at high temperatures with appreciable stress.

Whittle's contribution was the association of jet propulsion and the gas turbine. Before him the gas turbine had been regarded, like other turbines, as a machine for supplying shaft power. Whittle recognised it as the ideal means of providing jet propulsion for aircraft.

His patent embodying this idea is dated January, 1930. His subsequent difficulties in getting his idea taken up and exploited are too well known for recapitulation here. Finally, with the aid of two men whose contribution has been too often overlooked, J. C. B. Tinling and R. D. Williams, a jet propulsion gas turbine engine to Whittle's ideas was designed, constructed and, in 1937, tested.

It is one thing to have an idea. It is another to have the technical and executive ability to give it flesh. It is still another to have the tenacity of purpose to drive through to success unshaken in confidence, in the face of discouraging opposition. Whittle, whose name in the annals of engineering comes after those of Watt, Stephenson and Parsons only for reasons of chronology or alphabetical order, had these things.

It is, I think, generally admitted that without Whittle's determination to turn his idea into reality we should not have begun to think about the jet-propelled aeroplane (whatever thoughts we might have slowly developed about the propeller gas turbine aeroplane) until the idea had been forced upon us by the exploits of the enemy with their jet-propelled machines. In the closing stages of the war, however, we had in fact developed, on the basis of Whittle's efforts, a new fighting weapon in the form of the Meteor aircraft; now we are well on the way towards a jet-propelled air force, and the gas turbine engined civil air fleet is being developed.

It may be said that without Whittle the jet propulsion engine and the other applications of the gas turbine would have come just the same. They would. But they would have come much later. Whittle's work gave this country a technical lead in aircraft gas turbines of at least two years. Properly exploited and maintained, this lead should mean that this country can sell its aircraft gas turbines abroad for years to come. You know better than I do the extent to which Rolls-Royce and de Havilland's are producing income for the country. The first of these firms is achieving this with engines which are the direct descendants of the Whittle engine. The second is achieving its contribution with an engine which would not have been designed but for the stimulus and information provided by the early Whittle successes.

The success which Whittle achieved reacted rapidly upon the work of others in the gas turbine field, notably the R.A.E. team working in association with Metropolitan Vickers Ltd. They had been concentrating on a propeller engine with an axial compressor, in contrast to Whittle's jet propulsion engine with a centrifugal compressor. Whittle's work inspired them to swing over to axial compressor jet propulsion, and to that extent he is the stepfather, so to speak, of that class of engine, the first example of which in this country was the Metropolitan Vickers F.2.

The notable success scored by the British aircraft engine industry in the aircraft gas turbine field, a success due in part directly to Whittle, and as for the rest, directly stimulated by him, naturally attracted attention in other fields. The successful application of the gas turbine in the difficult aeronautical field begat endeavour in the land and sea applications of the gas turbine. The knowledge gained through research and development for the aircraft application was largely applicable in these other directions. Here again, if the chance is grasped, there is a wonderful opportunity to build a great industry and, if our technical lead is properly exploited, one which will provide us with considerable national income. If and when this comes to pass, some of the credit will be Whittle's.

> So far the gas turbine in Great Britain has been generally regarded as a means of propulsion of fighting aircraft. I think posterity, looking at its achievements on land and sea as well as in the air, will see it rather as a great commercial asset — presuming that we today do our duty in exploiting it. They will see too that the initiative in its development came from aeronautical technologists, and at the head of these they will see Whittle.

The members of the Royal Commission paid a visit to the Whetstone Factory on the 25th May, 1948, and the formal public hearing took place at Somerset House on the following morning, and lasted only one and a half hours. The Chairman opened by addressing Mr. E. L. Pickles, who represented the Ministry of Supply, and outlined the purpose of the proceedings, namely, that though I was not a claimant, the Commission had met to consider my case at the request of the Ministry, that he understood that I had agreed to the procedure, and that the Treasury would accept the recommendation of the Commission.

Pickles was then called upon to make the statement he had prepared. In this he gave a brief summary of my career and of the early history of my turbo-jet proposals. After referring to the successful flight trials of the E.28 at Cranwell, and my continued work on jet engines, the statement continued: The Department has received, as will be shown, great benefits and generous treatment from Air Commodore Whittle. Freely, he gave to the Department all his commercial rights in Power Jets, in his designs and his patents, relying only on such ex gratia award as the Crown might give. It has been thought that the Department should reciprocate, and it has not required him, in his present state of health, that he should have the anxiety of preparing his case for presentation by him to the Commission.

Indeed, it would have been distasteful to him to present a claim. As Shakespeare has it, 'We wound our modesty and make foul the clearness of our deservings, when of ourselves we publish them.'

"The Department in the circumstances has undertaken the preparation and submission of the case. It is only concerned to place before the Commission the relevant facts, leaving the Commission to assess the award."

He detailed the list of honours and awards by which my work had been recognised and ended by quoting from Roxbee Cox's letter.

Roxbee Cox was then asked to take the witness stand and was asked if he had anything to add to his letter or any further comment to make. He amplified certain of his written remarks, emphasising the effort needed to carry the job through to maturity, and pointed out that some ideas were of importance because of their fundamental quality, that other ideas were important because of their consequences (though in themselves they might be trivial), but that the turbo-jet idea was of the highest order because not only was it important in its quality, but it was important in its consequences as well.

I was then asked if I wished to question him about his evidence and I replied "No". I was next to take the witness stand. The Chairman asked me to describe briefly how the idea had first occurred to me. He then asked whether I considered my training at Cambridge had been an important factor. I replied that it would be very difficult to overestimate the value of the engineering training I had received from the R.A.F., particularly at Cambridge. Finally, he asked me whether I agreed that the development chiefly owed its success to support from the Government. I replied that it was almost certain that it would never have started but for private money, but that if we had been compelled to depend on private money only, it would probably have died at an early stage.

After one or two further questions addressed to myself and to Pickles by other members of the Commission, the Chairman brought the proceedings to quite an abrupt close by telling Pickles that the Commission would write to him.

I supposed that it would be several weeks before I heard anything further, and I was therefore extremely surprised the day following to receive a phone call from the Permanent Secretary to the Ministry of Supply, Sir Archibald Rowlands, telling me that an express letter would reach me by hand later that day and that an official announcement would be made the following morning. At 4.45 that afternoon a Ministry of Supply courier arrived at Brownsover Hall on a motorcycle, and handed me a letter from Sir Archibald Rowlands reading as follows:

> In the absence of the Minister, who is on tour, I am writing on his behalf to let you know that the Royal Commission on Awards to Inventors have recommended a total award to be paid to you of £100,000.
>
> The Minister has accepted this recommendation, which is also acceptable to the Treasury.
>
> May I say, in the name of myself and all your other old colleagues at the Ministry, how pleased we are with this further recognition of your outstanding contribution to aeronautical engineering.

I was naturally well satisfied with the way *my* case had been dealt with, but I was not wholly content. I felt that some award should also be made to many members of the team who had worked with me. When I mentioned this to certain of the officials who had handled my own case, I was told that the matter would be considered, but that it was unlikely that anything would be done, because it could be argued that they had only done what they had been paid to do, whereas, as the record clearly showed, my own early work had been extra to my normal Service duties and the first engine was in being before Power Jets had recruited a team. I tried to counter these arguments by pointing out that though it was true that the members of the team I had in mind had been paid employees of Power Jets, or officers on loan, nevertheless, their zeal and sense of duty had well exceeded that which might reasonably be demanded of them. Moreover, it could be argued that because of the difficult financial circumstances of the Company in the early days, they had been seriously underpaid in proportion to their ability; and that, further, their inventive contribution to all phases of the development after the first engine was in being was considerable. I told the Ministry officials concerned that with such a closely knit team it would be very difficult indeed to assess awards on the basis of individual contributions, and I therefore suggested that a lump sum should be allocated and divided in the proportions which I indicated in a list of names which I handed to Mr. P. H. Goffey. I had gone to some trouble to assess these proportions, and in weighing the figures I had taken into account the scale of responsibility, the enthusiasm, ability and inventive contribution of each of the individuals named. However, nothing happened. A series of overseas tours prevented me from following it up personally, but I still hope the matter has not been forgotten and that this history will do something to revive it, especially as, since then, large payments have been received from the U.S.A. for patents and technology, mostly of Power Jets' origin, and British jet aircraft and engines have come to form a very important part of British export trade.

The award to me, of course, removed a number of problems associated with my retirement. Accordingly, after a Medical Board, I received a formal letter from the Air Ministry dated 30th June, 1948, telling me that in the light of the findings of the Medical Board, the Air Council had reluctantly reached the conclusion that it was necessary to place me on the retired list. This letter went on to say that the effective date of retirement would be the 26th August, 1948, and that I would retire with the rank of Air Commodore.

A few days before I received this letter I was awarded the K.B.E. in the Birthday Honours List, and was subsequently knighted by King George VI at an investiture during July.

As the King touched me on each shoulder with the sword, I became the first Old Cranwellian to receive the honour of Knighthood. The satisfaction which this gave me was overshadowed by my regret that I was leaving the Service in which I had served since the age of sixteen, and which had given me the training which made possible the jet engine.

A NOTE TO THE READER

If you have enjoyed this book enough to leave a review on **Amazon** and **Goodreads**, then we would be truly grateful.

The Estate of Sir Frank Whittle

SAPERE
BOOKS

[1] *Journal of the Institution of Mechanical Engineers*. Vol. 152, p. 419.
[2] 1926–28.
[3] Later Air Marshal Sir Philip Joubert.
[4] In those days one had to be at least thirty years of age or of the rank of Squadron Leader to qualify for marriage allowance.
[5] Renamed *Pegasus* when the name *Ark Royal* was transferred to an aircraft carrier under construction.
[6] In the person of Air Marshal Sir Frederick Bowhill, Air Member for Personnel — who was also responsible for approving my posting to Cambridge.
[7] A product of High Duty Alloys Ltd.
[8] Later Sir David Pye.
[9] In a sense it would have been too good to be true because, with the available fuel supply it would have meant an efficiency far beyond our most optimistic expectations.
[10] These pitiful sums were of course absurdly low by comparison with what is normally spent on engine development.
[11] W. A. Randles was the engineer immediately responsible to Collingham for work on the Power Jets' contract.
[12] Later Sir William Farren.
[13] These three fitters had virtually built the engine.
[14] The first impeller had 30 blades; the new one had 29 to avoid resonant "coupling" with the 10 blade diffuser system.
[15] i.e. as the conditions for which it had been designed were approached.
[16] Because all patents taken out in my name were subject to "Agreements for User" between the Air Ministry and myself.
[17] The W.1 and W.2.
[18] The birth of the Meteor.
[19] This remark, which pleased me very much, held a wealth of meaning. It implied that as members of the same Service we shared a tradition and a concept of duty and integrity which set us a little apart from many of those — Civil Servants and others — with whom we had to deal. (And a long way apart from some.)
[20] 1940.
[21] Hitherto our testing had been done in a walled-off section of the main foundry which had formerly been a core store.
[22] Who had returned to the Air Ministry as Vice Chief of Air Staff.
[23] To replace an Air Marshal who had been captured on his way to North Africa.

[24] The B.T-H. reverted to the de Laval type fixing at one point but were compelled to return to the "fir tree" design.
[25] Mr. A. H. Hall, formerly Director of the R.A.E. was given the somewhat nebulous task of co-ordinating the work on the W.2.B., but without executive authority.
[26] From the B.T-H.
[27] Which eventually became known as the W.2. Mark IV.
[28] An engine to the design of A. A. Griffith.
[29] i.e. Compressor.
[30] These temperatures were very moderate by today's standards but with the materials then available 600°C. was regarded as a limit.
[31] This was an understatement to say the least of it. Had the discrepancy not come to light there and then, the consequences might have been very far reaching. Certainly Power Jets' position would have been further, and seriously, weakened.
[32] It had been decided that, for security reasons, jet engines were to be referred to as "superchargers" in correspondence, etc.
[33] i.e. an increase of 60 m.p.h. in top speed compared with the first flight trials ten months earlier.
[34] Major A. A. Ross.
[35] At this time the R.A.E. was building up its own gas turbine section. Amongst other things, this had involved the recall of Dr. W. R. Hawthorne. His place as head of the combustion engineers at Power Jets was taken by D. G. Shepherd.
[36] The main workshops were about 80,000 square feet in area.
[37] Regular commercial trans-Atlantic flights were still a thing of the future.
[38] Whittle Unit.
[39] The B.T-H work continued at much the same modest tempo for another year or two but eventually died out. No further reference to it is made in this record.
[40] One of which had been used as spares for the others.
[41] Chief Engineer of Rolls-Royce.
[42] In "exchange" Rover took over tank engine production from Rolls-Royce.
[43] i.e. Meteor prototype.
[44] Which seems very modest in the light of modern developments, but were then very ambitious indeed.
[45] In which the engine was mounted below the fuselage.
[46] Later Sir Sam Brown.

[47] The implication that Power Jets had willingly accepted the price was, of course, quite wrong. Having had the "pistol" of the threat of extinction pointed at them, they regarded it as something akin to "armed robbery".

[48] We had revolutionised aeronautics for the cost of two Comet jet airliners spread over eight years.

[49] Except for the earliest runs of the first experimental engine — when Diesel oil was used — we had always used various grades of kerosene.

[50] They included two "ducted fan" projects. One — the L.R.1., intended for a long-range bomber or transport — drove the fan through reduction gearing. The other — known as the "No. 4 Augmentor" — was intended to power the Miles M.52 supersonic aeroplane project. In this scheme the fan blades were extensions of turbine blades mounted on rotors in the exhaust stream of a W.2/700 engine.

[51] By restoring certain features of Power Jets' compressor design which had been discarded. (Intake guide vanes — as Dr. S. G. Hooker frankly and amusingly admitted not long after, Rolls-Royce got a medal for throwing away all the "gubbins" that Power Jets had put into the intakes, and then got another medal for putting it all back again.)

[52] Before this Rolls-Royce had experimented with a propeller turbine engine known as the Trent. The Trent was a modified Derwent 1 fitted with a reduction gear and a propeller. A Meteor prototype powered by Trents made a few flights. The Trent was thus the first propeller turbine to fly.

[53] This should have read "Lord President of the Council".

[54] This name has no political significance. It was derived, of course, from the fact that the jet engine is based on Newton's Third Law: "Action and Reaction are equal and opposite."

[55] About my then impending lecture tour in the U.S.A.

Printed in Great Britain
by Amazon